G000167672

DAVID MEATON

THE RICHES OF MORGAN'S ORCHARD

The Book Guild Ltd

First published in Great Britain in 2021 by
The Book Guild Ltd
9 Priory Business Park
Wistow Road, Kibworth
Leicestershire, LE8 0RX
Freephone: 0800 999 2982
www.bookguild.co.uk
Email: info@bookguild.co.uk
Twitter: @bookguild

Typeset in 11pt Minion Pro

Printed and bound in the UK by TJ Books LTD, Padstow, Cornwall

ISBN 978 1913913 465

British Library Cataloguing in Publication Data.
A catalogue record for this book is available from the British Library.

To Christine
for all her patience and support

PART ONE:

ONE

Bedwas to Lidsing 1914–1916

When the village boys started dropping out of school at twelve or thirteen years of age to start in the pit or as farmhands, I was reading Shakespeare, Wordsworth, Keats, and Dickens and following the history of England with a passion that was nurtured by Yanto Richards, the headteacher at the village school. Mr Richards introduced me to the world of innovation and mechanics as well so that I might acquire an understanding and knowledge of how motors and machines worked which, Mr Richards was certain, represented the future. He was sure that no pit village boy, however good, would be admitted to the scholarly world of literature and history, but could succeed as an engineer or artificer. Mr Richards was born with a club foot, which barred him from all kinds of manual work but was, thankfully, blessed with the sharpest mind and active brain enabling him to train as an elementary school teacher. The vast majority in his classes had no desire to acquire more than a basic education and get out to work as soon as they could but there were a few boys in every year who were destined to go much further and to these he dedicated his special attention.

At fourteen, I won a scholarship for poor boys at the grammar school in Newport largely through Mr Richards' coaching and there I was able to study for the School Certificate. At 16 I passed my examinations with flying colours but the scholarship money to go on to the higher level was no longer available so reluctantly I left the school and started work as an office boy with the gas company the following week. Work was monotonous and repetitive, comprising mostly of mindlessly following processes that I did not understand very well and offered no opportunity to innovate or rethink how they could be done better. Although accuracy, punctuality and obedience

1

were the golden rules in the office, I found my mind shutting down and hated the gas company office wholeheartedly from the very first day. Things were made worse with the outbreak of war, and some of the men from the office volunteered to serve in the South Wales Volunteers who were recruiting a battalion from the pit villages.

I was desperate to go and tried to sign up at the Drill Hall twice, but each time was rejected because I was not yet seventeen. The trouble with recruiting for a local regiment is that everyone knew each other which made it difficult for keen but under-aged boys to sneak into the ranks undiscovered. I would just have to wait. My two older brothers, Clifford and Dylan, were now serving in the Brecon Company, South Wales Borderers and they promised they would put in a good word for me when I was nearer to my eighteenth birthday. I would have to be patient and continue at the gas company office for the time being.

However, the departure of some of the senior men in the office to the war brought in some young women as their replacements for the duration and the atmosphere of the office became less stuffy and more friendly. The routine remained, but the women and girls were more light-hearted and laughed at a lot more whilst they were working. Mr Evans, the senior clerk, seemed to approve however as the productivity of the office went up and he was seen to smile a little when he received praise from the directors. I began to find the office at least a tolerable place to work and as I was now a junior clerk with more responsibility than the office boy, I did not find the job quite as boring as before. The yearning to join up did not diminish and I could not wait for my eighteenth birthday to come.

In early March 1916, my eighteenth birthday finally arrived. I had planned secretly that I would report to the Drill Hall as soon as I could on my actual birthday. I would go during the lunch hour from work, keeping it a secret so that no one would try to stop me. It was difficult for me to contain my excitement through the long morning at work. At 12:30 my lunch hour arrived, and I could not wait to escape. Checking that my birth and school certificates were still in my pocket; I ran down the stairs to the front door in a mighty rush of exuberance and out into the street almost running. Striding down High Street towards the Drill Hall, with my chest stuck out, I was certain that everyone would recognise that I was going to volunteer before my call-up papers came through. But the closer I got to the Drill Hall the more my confidence began to diminish, and then completely vanished when I saw the length of the queue of men and boys waiting for admittance in a long snake in front of the main doors. Two burly soldiers stood guard at the door and the recruiting sergeant with a clip board was taking the names and details of those waiting to be let in.

The war had been going badly and the casualty lists were getting longer each week. Wounded soldiers were becoming an almost familiar sight in towns and cities all over Britain. Many people were still largely ignorant of the carnage and terrible impact of the war on the young generation of citizen soldiers fighting for their lives for a victory for the Empire. There was a great deal of apathy towards the war felt by many who, unless they were touched by tragedy themselves, carried on complacently so that after the first patriotic zeal of the early years when there was a ready supply of volunteers, the government was now forced to call up able-bodied men and boys to replace the widening gaps in the ranks caused by the increasing numbers of dead and wounded. I could see many in the line before me were clutching their call-up papers and brought with them small bags of personal possessions and shaving and washing kit. I had no call-up papers and wondered whether as a volunteer, I would be turned away, but when my turn came the sergeant spoke to me kindly and asked why I wanted to volunteer. I told him that if I volunteered instead of waiting to be called up, I would be allowed to join my brothers in their regiment at the front and how I desperately wanted to be with them. The sergeant asked me about the job I had done since leaving school and what schooling I had received. When I showed him my School Certificate and report from the grammar school in Newport, he said I should have to speak to the captain when I got inside and made a note on his board.

Very slowly the snake moved forward, until I was finally at the door and I could see from the clock on the Drill Hall wall that it was already well after 14:00 so I was already more than half an hour late for the afternoon at work. I just had to be successful because I may not have a job to go back to tomorrow. Inside the door there were four shorter queues before tables where army clerks wrote down the personal details of the conscripted soldiers on sheets of paper and filed them in a thin cardboard folder, which was handed to the recruit to take into the doctor for the medical check-up.

The clerk took down all my details and filled in the record sheets but filed them in a different file cover which had a large "V" printed on the front and I was sent to see the doctor. I asked why my folder was different; he replied that it was because I was a volunteer and to remind the doctor to check for insanity during the medical check-up. He laughed as he handed me the folder. The doctor, of course, spent little more than a few minutes on a cursory check of my fitness, but then told me to get dressed and report to the captain's office in the left-hand corridor. Most of the conscripts were queued up again in front of desks where three lieutenants were sat administering the swearing in of the new recruits who were now no longer civilians but had become soldiers of the King that very afternoon. I was the only one directed to the captain; as I knocked and waited outside of his door, I could feel a strange tingling sensation in my stomach and a wondering why I had been singled out from the rest, who seemed so happy to have joined up and would soon be on their way to basic infantry training. Perhaps I was not good enough or had some unknown physical weakness that made me unsuitable. My spirits plummeted but a muffled voice from inside the door called me to enter and I gulped down my fear and entered the office. The captain was middle-aged and hunched over a file, signing his name.

He put the file to one side and looked up and said to me, "Morgan, what on earth are you doing here?" I realised that I was looking at Mr Willoughby-Jones, my former schoolmaster at Newport Grammar, now dressed in the uniform of a captain of the South Wales Militia Regiment. He sighed, then admitted how deeply despondent he was seeing so many bright boys pass through this recruiting office destined for the infantry and what a tragic waste it was to see them broken and bloodied in mind or body by the experience of war. Just occasionally he had a chance to steer someone with talent away from the hell of the infantry. He told me I was lucky to volunteer today whilst the were inducting conscripts.

"Sergeant Thomas knew you were different when you said you were a volunteer and when he spotted your school certificates from Newport Grammar School, he knew that I would want to speak to you personally. I am glad to have the chance to do so and to write a recommendation for you to go somewhere more suitable for a boy as clever as you. I will arrange for you to be admitted to the Royal Engineers Technical School where you can learn an engineering trade that will exercise that excellent brain you have and give you a chance to contribute your skills towards winning this war."

I had mixed feelings but said thank you. Captain Willoughby-Jones pushed his chair back to shake my hand and wish me the best of luck, and I left the room. I was, of course, interested, and excited to train as an engineer and to contribute to the war effort but felt a deep disappointment that I wasn't marching away to war behind the band playing with the other boys today, with people cheering and girls blowing kisses. I could hear the band playing all the way down the hill to the station and the train whistle shrieking as the locomotive pulled away from the platform on the journey to the barracks at Cardiff. I wondered how many of these boys would come back to this village and valley as heroes when the war was over. I sauntered back along High Street and went into the gas company office to give in my notice to my boss, Mr Evans, and apologise to him for taking time off without permission. When I had blurted out what I had done that afternoon and the result of my chance meeting with my old school master, he was remarkably understanding and congratulated me on my courage in joining up. He said I could work until I received my joining papers, and he would pay my wages until the day I left and keep my job open for when I returned after the war.

I now had to face Mum and Dad. I knew they would miss me at home and the little extra I paid into the family budget from my wages would be sorely missed. When I walked through the back door, Mum was in the kitchen getting our tea ready and Dad was sat in the parlour reading the war news in front of the fire. He looked tired after his twelve-hour shift underground and I knew he had already scrubbed away the coal dust and grime in the small tin bath in the outhouse before entering the house. Mum would not let him into the parlour until he had washed and changed his clothes. As I came into the parlour he looked up and smiled as he put the match to the tobacco in his pipe bowl and after a couple of draws to get the tobacco properly going, he blew out a great billow of pipe smoke, tamping the top of the bowl with his thumb. He was proud that I came home from work still clean and neat in a business suit and clean shirt, collar, and tie. I usually went straight upstairs to my small room to hang my jacket and take off my collar and tie before joining Dad in the parlour to wait for tea. Tonight, I was humming with excitement because of the news I could hardly contain in myself. Dad thought I was just excited for my birthday, even though there were no presents and truly little else special to celebrate it.

I hesitated and then just let it all come out, what I had done and why I had done it and the outcome. I was surprised that he took it so calmly and he called Mum in from the back kitchen to share the news with him. He was pragmatic and thought that enlisting in the Royal Engineers would be a good thing for me and my future. He asked me, several times, if I was certain that this was the right thing to do for me; I think I must have reassured him sufficiently because he smiled and said he agreed with me. I am not so sure that Mum concurred for although she said nothing, I could hear some sighs and sobs when she returned to the back kitchen.

My enlistment papers for the Royal Engineers arrived about ten days later giving me the orders and travel warrant to report for basic training at Lidsing Camp in Kent on the following Monday by 15:00. The warrant was for a journey by train to Rochester, via Cardiff and London. Army transport would be waiting at the station to the camp. In my eighteen years, I had scarcely left the valley very much except for my schooling in Newport and a couple of family outings to Cardiff and Porthcawl. I had heard of Rochester before because it dated from Roman times and figured in the story of the Norman Invasion in 1066, when the victorious progress of William was halted by the yeoman of Kent, who blocked the bridge at Rochester and would not let him pass. I knew that there was a Norman castle and cathedral built there subsequently. I spent some hours in the library searching out any snippets of information about the area and the Engineers in particular. I learned that the Engineers had originally been formed as sappers and miners, tunnelling under enemy fortifications to undermine them with explosives but were also interested in mechanical transport, tanks, and aviation. Lidsing Camp was adjacent to what had been the Royal Engineers Balloon Park where they had pioneered early military use of balloons. The technical college was some five miles away, close to the Royal Navy dockyard at Brompton, and specialised in training specialist mechanicians to support the army in the field.

The two weeks before leaving whizzed by so quickly in a round of visiting and saying farewell to all my friends and relatives. Mum worked hard to get my small wardrobe clean and pressed and ready for me to travel whilst Dad concentrated on issuing pithy advice for how a young man should conduct himself in the wider world, which seemed to revolve around, not missing chapel, avoiding strong drink, fast women, and slow horses. They both, insisted that I write every week to let them know how I was getting on and not to let them down by my behaviour away from the guiding influence of home. Mr Evans remained true to his word, paid me right up to my last day and two weeks' holiday pay extra I had accrued during the time in their employ. This was good because I could leave money to help with the household expenses for some time after I was gone. Dad surprised me, the night before I was due to leave, by giving me twenty-five shillings that had been saved for family emergencies, stressing that it was not to spend but only to be used when it became necessary.

At six the next morning, Mum and Dad walked with me to the station to see me off as I was to catch the 06:20 to Cardiff Central and then join the London train at 07:40. Dad was a bit stiff and formal as he shook my hand for one last time, anxious to be away to the colliery for his shift, but Mum cried and clung to me until the porter took out his whistle and I climbed aboard the last carriage before he blew to signal departure. I pulled down the window strap and hung out as far as I could until the train entered the bend, and I could not see their small figures waving any more. The compartment was empty: I settled comfortably into the seat and watched the familiar valley roll by, which calmed my thoughts and boosted my confidence until the countryside gave way to the outer suburbs of Cardiff, which made me feel small and unsure again. The bustling noise, station announcements and hundreds of soldiers with full kit and rifles all trying to board the Red Dragon Express to London. Railway transport officers were rounding up groups of troops to get them to board the various trains and I just felt lost.

In the sea of khaki figures, I saw a face I thought I knew; he seemed to recognise me too and pushed through the crowd towards me shouting, "Derfal, boy what are you doing here?" I shouted back that I was joining the Engineers in Kent and by now I could see that this friendly face was Billy Matthews from our street, who had joined up two years ago. He had two stripes on his arm and oversaw a section of South Wales Volunteers on their way back to the front after some leave at home. Billy smiled and said I could travel with his boys as they were boarding the Red Dragon and taking the train to the Kent coast from Charing Cross too. He said I was to follow him, and I soon found myself on the train in the company of Billy's small section. They were friendly boys and but seemed so much more mature than me, even though they were probably not much older. They seemed happy to be going back to France and were full of jokes and banter, accepting me as easily as if we had grown up together. Billy Matthews was probably only twenty years old but seemed to be like a father or older brother to the boys in his section, and he was certainly kind to me. The journey passed so quickly and in three hours we were approaching Paddington Station through the sprawling, crowded west London suburbs. The speed of the train slowed to a walking pace and we stopped several times at red signals waiting for our turn to enter the station. Eventually we entered the vast station, many times bigger than Cardiff Central we had left behind a short time before.

The atmosphere was frenetic with steam, the noise of the engines and thousands of people disgorging from trains that seemed to be arriving at dozens of platforms at the same time. Most of the passengers were in uniform and carried their kitbags on their backs heading for the exit barriers. There were military police and railway transport officers trying to bring some order and direct us where to go. Billy stepped forward and flashed his orders in front of the RTO who waved us through, pointing to the steps leading down to the Underground that would take us to Charing Cross station. It was no less crowded at the bottom of several deep flights of stairs, which took us to the right platform going east. We were eight-deep back from the platform edge; we had to let two trains pass before we were at the front and all boarded together through the middle sliding doors of the carriage. It was crowded and uncomfortable but thankfully the journey only lasted fifteen minutes, and the frequent stops and the stations on the way brought some temporary relief with a blast of recycled air from the fans on the station platforms. As we climbed out of the Underground to the ground level, we emerged in front the magnificent façade of Charing Cross Station and I caught a glimpse of the Strand and Trafalgar Square, crowded with motor and horse-drawn vehicles of all kinds. The station itself was smaller than Paddington although no less crowded with soldiers, but our trusted corporal led us to the correct barrier to board the Dover train. There was a short time to wait because the train had not yet arrived from Dover, so we were able to get a welcome cup of tea and cheese sandwich from the soldiers' tea stall. The Dover train pulled in and scores of rather scruffy and tired-looking soldiers dismounted, then came the walking wounded, followed by more serious cases carried by stretcher bearers, and accompanied by military nurses and medical officers making their way to the row of ambulances parked by the barrier, waiting to take them to hospital. I was somewhat shocked by my first sight of casualties of the fighting, but my new-found compatriots were not fazed at all, calling out cheery greetings and some ribald comments to their wounded comrades, which made me realise how powerful the spirit of soldierly comradeship and loyalty really was.

Billy led us to the train, and we boarded together; I sat by him and he explained that when the train reached the river Medway the next station would be Rochester. I shook hands with all the boys in the section and wished them luck in France, and they all cheered and shouted rude comments about the Royal Engineers when I got down from the train at Rochester station. It was a long, bleak platform, open on one side direct to the wharfs and warehouses of a commercial dockside. I could see tugs and grey-painted auxiliary craft chugging about the river frontage and giving attention to frigates and sloops moored in flotillas in the middle of the river. I could only see as far as the bend in the river but the upper works of bigger naval vessels visible in the dockyard hidden just out of sight. I began to feel that I was getting closer to the war and although excited, I felt some anxiety about what might lie ahead at Lidsing Camp. I crossed over the footbridge over all three platforms, which took me to the land side of the station and climbed down the long staircase to the ground floor. On entering the booking hall, I was approached by a middle-aged soldier who asked me for my name and checked me off his list. He told me to put my bag into the horse-drawn cart on the station frontage and to climb up into the back of the motor lorry behind it. I heaved my bag up into the cart and was surprised to find it was almost full of baggage, so when I climbed up into the back of the lorry, I could see that there were only a couple of seats left to be taken. I heard the middle-aged soldier shout to the driver that there were only two more to come and we would be off promptly at 15:00. Every one of us was quiet, nervous, and uncertain what lay ahead, but names were exchanged by a few of the more friendly recruits. The last two arrived on the next train and we set off for Lidsing Camp on time.

TWO

Basic Training 1916

Lidsing Camp was not exactly a large military establishment, but merely a closely connected number of fields on what had once been a small farm. The farmhouse was where the officers were billeted, the barns had been turned into storage and parking for the vehicles and there was a stable block for the horses. NCOs lived in a collection of wooden huts and everyone else lived in four-man tents. The largest barn had been taken over by the field kitchen unit, who would feed us during our stay at the camp.

As we climbed down from the lorry in the farmyard the corporal drill instructor who was waiting for us tried to get us into some semblance of military order. He finally managed to get us into two ranks and made us stand at ease, waiting for the sergeant major instructor to address us. He told us he was Corporal Macloud and he would be with us throughout our time in basic training. After ten minutes or so an elderly barrel-chested man who was at least fifty years of age, sporting a collection of medal ribbons on his chest, attesting to his credentials as a soldier, came out of the front door of the farmhouse and we were called to attention. The SMI looked a formidable figure and he appeared to inspect us before ordering us to stand at ease to listen to his introductory briefing. He told us we were now under military discipline and although we had not yet received our kit and uniforms, we were to consider ourselves as soldiers and members of the Royal Engineers from this moment on. He explained that training would begin at 06:00 in the morning with physical exercise before breakfast at 07:00, and then the issuing of kit would begin immediately after that. He said that our entry number was 16/2016 RE and we would be given our service numbers in the morning. He told us we would undergo basic training in discipline, drill, shooting and rifle drill, military writing and physical fitness and this programme would last for eight weeks. If we were successful, we would pass-out and be sent for specialist training to the technical school at Chatham or the workshops at Lodge Hill on the other side of the river. There would be no free time except for Sunday afternoon after Church Parade, when trainees could walk out of the camp to the nearest villages of Lidsing or Bredhurst. He stressed that the Hook and Hatchet and the Bluebell Inn public houses were strictly out of bounds to all recruits, who were not permitted to partake of alcohol. He said, however, we could smoke if we wished to during stand easy. He told us that the CO was Major Arthur Armstrong MC RE who was decorated for gallantry and severely wounded in action in France in 1915, and he would address us in the morning.

We were dismissed and the drill corporal directed us to our tents, which were all together in one corner of the second field. There were just sixteen of us in our entry so we could be billeted in four tents in a line together. Each of us had a camp bed with two sheets, pillowcase, and pillow, plus a thick blanket to keep us warm. By the side of each bed was a small locker and a rough wooden wardrobe. The latrines and wash basins were about a hundred yards beyond the tents, and we were about 250 yards from the cookhouse. The corporal indicated that the main hot meal of the day was usually at 12:00 but as we had just arrived at the camp, the cookhouse would have a hot meal for us at 17:00 today only. He told us to be ready at 06:00 to go for a run and PT before breakfast in the morning and bid us good night. The four of us in my tent slowly began to open to each other as the evening went on, and although we came from differing backgrounds and geographical parts of the country, I felt we would become friends during this training. I found I was sharing the tent with Charlie Palmer from Streatham, Albert Sykes, a tall ginger boy from Scotland, and George Smithers from Birmingham. We were all of roughly the same age except for George, who was twenty-four and a time-served engine fitter. The cookhouse served a hot beef stew with dumplings for our supper and after we had eaten our fill, we made up our beds and fell asleep by the time it got dark. I was tired out after the long journey and was fast asleep within minutes of my head hitting the pillow.

Basic training was hard work, but never boring because we were learning new things every day as the army tried to turn us from civilians into soldiers with a rudimentary knowledge of how to survive military life. We were on the go all the time from six every morning until five in the evening and sometimes there were extra classes after our evening meal, which meant that when we finally got to bed, we slept easy and deep until the reveille bugle called us the following morning. We learnt to regulate our life and actions by the bugle calls and military clock. We never walked unless we were alone but always marched everywhere, mostly at the double, and we ate our fill of the wholesome but somewhat large portions of food served up in the cookhouse. We complained amongst ourselves about the lack of choice and the limited range of dishes that the army cooks prepared but wolfed it down as if each meal were to be our last. It must have been good for us because in that eight weeks we all seemed to grow a bit taller and stronger and began to look more like men than the boys who first arrived for training.

There were very few spare moments to be had in the busy day, but we did get time to scratch a few lines in our letters home on Sunday afternoon for collection by the post clerk every Monday morning. Failure to write the weekly letter home always brought awkward questions from Corporal Macloud or a referral to the sergeant major for a second offence. Discipline was tight and even minor infringements of one's uniform dress or boots, late on parade or shirking were punished with extra duties or a stoppage from your pay. Cyril Garner in the third tent was late on parade three times and was made to clean the latrines for a week; I was fined two and six pence for not shining my buttons for church one Sunday morning and Charlie had to stand two extra guard duties for answering back. We did not resent the punishments too much because every one of us incurred some sort of penalty however hard we tried to avoid them, but we accepted that they were not particularly harsh, were generally fair and meant to teach us the vital quality of discipline.

I did not find basic training too difficult as I was easygoing with my tent mates and learned that supporting each other made us stronger as a group rather than trying to achieve solo success. I had always enjoyed physical activity, particularly on the rugby field, so did not mind the exercise too much and, surprisingly, found that I enjoyed foot drill, especially when the section began to come together and take pride from our smartness and swagger. Corporal Macloud constantly chided us for being over-confident, but I think he was secretly pleased with our performance although he tried to hide it from us as best he could. I also found that I had a good eye for rifle shooting and qualified for the marksman badge on the Lee Enfield .303. The long afternoons on the ranges firing at different distances up to 600 yards was always a source of great satisfaction to me. We were all given an opportunity to fire the service revolver at the twenty-five-yard indoor range, but I found this far more difficult than shooting the rifle.

The weeks rushed by and our training was coming to an end; we were beginning to talk about where we would be sent after passing out. By now we knew that those who showed the most potential for application and further study would be offered places at the technical college, whilst the others would be assigned to the workshops where they would learn more basic skills on the job. I felt that I had tried hard to make the grade and apart from one disciplinary infringement, had always seemed well placed in every test we faced. I hoped for a place at the technical college, but I could see that there were others who had done as well or maybe a little better who might win a place before me. We did not know yet how many places were available at the college and how many for the workshops.

As we came into our last week at Lidsing, daily routine orders published a list of names and times for some members of our entry to report to Major Armstrong later that day. There were six names on the list and mine was the last name to be included. We were each allowed a little time to ensure our turnout was up to scratch before we reported to the CO's office. My head was a whirl with all the many reasons we had been summoned, but I hoped that I had done enough to get to the technical college. Standing at ease outside the CO's office, I waited with a quiver of anticipation until the sergeant major came out, called me up to attention and marched me left, right, left, right in front of the CO. I halted, saluted, and remained at attention, looking straight ahead, waiting for the major behind his desk to speak. This was the first time that I had seen him face to face but could see that although he was not yet thirty, his face was haggard and lined like a much older man. The SMI barked, "State your name, rank and number." I responded, "Morgan, Trainee Sapper 0209616, sir."

Major Armstrong smiled and said, "' Stand at ease, Morgan." He said that I had done well, and they were impressed with my performance during the basic training, which he was glad to say suggested that I should be granted one of the four places available for entry to the School of Military Engineering at Chatham. I would study for a mechanician trade at a higher level and if I successfully passed the diploma, could go into the field as a junior NCO. I was elated but all I said was, "Thank you, sir," and then saluted, about turned and marched out of the office with the sergeant major behind me. The SMI called us to halt and then his stern face broke into smiles as he shook my hand in congratulations. He went on to say that after passing out on Friday morning we would be granted a weekend pass to go home, share the good news with our parents and report to Brompton Barracks by next Monday at 07:00. As I came out of headquarters, Corporal Macloud was waiting to add his good wishes too and said he was proud that four from his entry had been successful this time. He said he would prepare my leave pass and railway warrant for Friday, 12 noon. I was glad to hear that George from my tent had also been selected so I was pleased that he would be at Brompton next Monday too.

The week rushed past until our passing out on Friday morning. We paraded as smartly as we could and Corporal Macloud, the SMI and Major Armstrong all wore their best uniforms with their medals in honour of the passing out. The CO spoke some kind words about the quality of the entry, how hard we had all worked to achieve the standard and hoped that he would have the honour of serving with us later in our careers when we were qualified Engineers. He wished us luck and then presented us with our passing-out certificates and pay books stamped to show we had passed basic training. We were then dismissed to our duties and to strip down and clean our bed spaces ready for the next entry joining in the following week. Corporal Macloud threatened us that anyone whose bed space did not pass muster would not receive a leave pass at 12:00 and would be confined to camp all weekend. He didn't have to threaten us in this way as the forty-eight-hour pass was worth more than gold dust to us. I think he was only bluffing because we all passed his inspection easily and he handed out the passes with a big grin on his face. Some of us were lucky that we could snatch a brief weekend at home to see our family but some comrades, like Albert Sykes from Paisley, had no chance of reaching Scotland and back in time so had to choose local leave. We packed our kitbags and were ready to depart to the station at 12:00 noon on the dot, but this time we carried our kit with us in the back of the lorry. I was lucky that there was a fast train to Charing Cross at 14:15, which meant that I should be able to catch the Red Dragon from Paddington at 17:00 and probably make it home before midnight. There was no way to tell my parents I was coming unless I could send a telegram, but there was no post office telegraph to send one at Lidsing and no time on the journey itself.

We were a more boisterous bunch on this return journey to the station and what a difference eight weeks together had made to our spirits, as we were now loud and full of banter, singing songs and laughing like old veterans instead of basic recruits. The transport made it to Rochester station with five minutes to spare for my train, and I hopped over the tailgate, shouted farewell to my friends and ran to catch the fast train to London with several others chasing after me. Four of us piled into one compartment and continued laughing and joking in a high state of excitement all the way to Charing Cross. We separated at the Underground, making our way to our respective London stations for our onward journeys and I found myself alone on the Tube to Paddington. The rest of my journey went without a hitch and I only waited forty-five minutes for the valley connection in Cardiff. I was trudging up the hill from the station and knocked on our door sometime after ten pm. The door was not locked, so I went right in, dropped my kitbag in the parlour and called up the stairs that it was me, home on leave. Mum and Dad came racing down the staircase with much excited chatter and burst into the parlour almost together. I think Mum was first by a short whisker, but Dad was awfully close behind. They were both beaming to see me looking so well in my uniform. They bombarded me with so many questions that I did not know which to answer first. Mum could see my confusion and went to brew a pot of tea, and Dad stoked up the coals on the fire again and we sat and chatted for an hour before bed. My weekend went quickly because Mum wanted to parade me around the village to show off to all her friends and the neighbours of course. She wanted me to attend chapel on Sunday morning, but I explained that I had to travel back to Kent and check in to the guardroom at the School of Military Engineering by 23:59 so I could begin classes on Monday morning. She was disappointed but enjoyed her day on Saturday very much. Dad was on day shift but after supper he put on his best suit and took me to the Miner's Welfare Club for a pint with his workmates to show me off too, just like Mum earlier in the day. Dad was not much of a drinker but would enjoy a pint of beer on special occasions, and he figured that this qualified as special. My leave was soon over, and I was on the train back to Kent the following morning.

All the first week at the college was taken up with examinations and practical tests. I was in awe of the facilities, workshops, and machinery for us to learn on. The library was first-class, and the staff were a mixture of experienced military engineers and civilian schoolmasters who taught mechanics, physics, and mathematics to a very high standard. We were assessed and selected for the most appropriate course of training, which would begin the following Monday. Although the school was a military establishment and all the routines of a soldiers' life were the same as in an active unit, it had a scholarly atmosphere, and the library was packed with students at most times of the day. They worked on a principle of 60 per cent theoretical study backed up by 40 per cent hands-on practical experience, and we quickly understood that it was not enough just to know how to do it, but you must be competent at doing it too. When the results were posted we discovered that some of our number, were selected to study civil engineering, road building, construction, and surveying whilst another group were to specialise in ordnance and explosives and a third in electrical and mechanical. Within each cadre there were numerous specialisations determined by the requirements of the army for technical support in the field. In addition, to our chosen specialisms, all students had to study combat engineering. I was pleasantly surprised to have been selected to study electrical and mechanical systems and had selected motorised transport and aero engines as my specialist subject.

I was thankful for the excellent training I had received at the hands of Yanto Richards at the village school, who had taught me so well how to study and ask the right questions rather than always be obsessed with knowing the right answer. He showed me that the ability to solve a problem by working out the theory in your head and then proving it to be true by practical experiments was the only way to acquire real knowledge. The solid grounding in physics, general science, and maths that I had acquired at the grammar school also built constructively on foundations laid down by Mr Richards and his introduction to all kinds of machines, particularly engines. My enquiring mind enabled me to thrive in my first weeks and I quickly understood that my two years at Newport had given me the academic ability to cope with the standard required by the army and more. The alternating between the classroom and the workshop suited me fine, and I enjoyed the opportunity to put into practice what I had learned in the classroom. My teachers and army instructors seemed pleased and after the first month I was selected with four or five other promising students to be fast-tracked to a more advanced course. I soon discovered that we were all boys who had passed the School Certificate and were to be advanced at a faster pace because our academic knowledge was already above what was required by the army for the Army Mechanician Diploma Class 3. We were all excited because this diploma was equivalent to the Higher School Certificate and we would be taking our exams in October.

The enormity of this task dawned on me after the first glow of self-satisfaction passed, and I realised that I would have to put in extra work to ensure I lived up to the confidence that had been placed in me. I was disappointed that George Smithers from my tent in basic training was not selected for accelerated training alongside me but when I met him in the student' mess a couple of days later, he was not resentful at all but rather glad he had not been chosen. He said that he served his time at the motor works and could pull engines apart and put them together again with his eyes shut but did not have the book learning that we had and admitted that he struggled to remember the maths and formulas in the tests and exams. "You do your best, Derfal," he said, " and you will pass out a corporal in six months whilst I will still be trying to come to terms with the theory of mechanics and engines next year. I know I will make the grade in time, but I need that time to pass the diploma examination in April next year."

Being advanced to the faster-paced course gave me some trepidation, not least that I would have to move into the barrack block with my new training cadre and would have to start making new friends again. My fears were soon allayed when I realised that my new quarters were more comfortable than my old accommodation. I was assigned to a four-man room where in addition to our bed, locker and wardrobe, there were four large desks pushed together in the middle of the room for our private study. Previously, I shared a twelve-man room where there was no privacy or facility for quiet study at all. I was now a member of the senior class and we were entitled to more privileges than junior classes as we were near to graduation. My new barrack block formed part of the square around which the magnificent Brompton Barracks was built in 1812 with a view over the parade square from the front and over the naval dockyard to the river from the rear. The course leader gave us a red flash to sow on to our left sleeves, to indicate that we were now senior class students.

For the first time since joining the college I found myself challenged, not only by the subject matter we were learning but also by the quality of my fellow students and their ability to solve every problem. Luckily, I was able to rise to the challenge after the first couple of weeks and come to terms with the level of knowledge that I needed to put in some additional efforts to emulate them. I found that I liked working on all kinds of motors, but my absolute favourite were aircraft engines, probably because I was besotted with the whole idea of powered flight and flying. My three new roommates had accepted me in a fairly friendly manner and were supportive in getting me settled in, but had their own well-defined study routines which they did not want to interrupt too much to help a newcomer. I wondered why there was a spare bed in their room, but they didn't say too much except that those who failed the term 2 exams had been backcoursed into a lower class to be given a second chance. That explained why we were able to move up into the fast track to fill the gaps that they left.

By now it was approaching mid-summer and all the junior classes were granted four weeks' leave, but the senior class was retained to study for the diploma exams in October. The barracks were much quieter now and we had more time to study in the library and revise in our rooms for the final exams. The senior class would get leave on completion of the exams and the junior NCO training immediately after it. The exams were sat in the large junior ranks' mess during the first week of October, when we wrote the specialist papers we had studied for. In the second week of October, the whole class went under canvas in the training ground at Mereworth Castle for an intensive week of junior NCO leadership training and initiative exercises. This was considered a vital addition to the diploma because it determined whether we qualified as a lance corporal or corporal on passing out as qualified mechanicians at the end of October. The last two weeks of the month were spent in training for and rehearsing the final passing-out parade on the main square, with the corps band and in the presence of the Commandant of the College and the General Officer Commanding Royal Engineers from the War Office. We were issued with a new and better quality uniform, but not ceremonial blues as this was wartime. Much of our time was spent on the parade square perfecting our march past. The whole college would parade but only the senior class would be inspected by the reviewing officer and then march past to the stirring tunes and marches played by the corps band. It was expected to be a grand affair and we were all excited to hear the diploma results and our JNCO assessment.

Finally, the day before the passing-out parade, routine orders contained the results lists. I was staggered to see alongside my name and service number that I had passed the Army Diploma Class 3 with Merit, just one grade down from Distinction and was to be promoted to the rank of Corporal (acting, paid) in accordance with army regulations and satisfactory probation for six months. The promotion was effective from the morning of the passing-out parade. I was delighted and knew that everyone at home would be so pleased for me. I looked forward to seeing the surprise on their faces when I broke the news and they saw me resplendent in my new corporal's uniform when I returned on leave. I rushed to join the queue at the clothing store to draw out a pair of corporal stripes and the lanyard of a trained soldier to attach to my uniform jacket, then hurried to the pay office so that our pay books could be stamped effective with our new ranks by the following morning. Although we spent most of the evening in spit and polishing of our boots with a candle and teaspoon, shining our buttons and buckles before sewing on our new rank tapes, we were in party mood. The only information we were yet to receive was which unit we were to be posted to and when the joining date was to be. We all speculated about where we were going to be sent but none of us had any real idea of what was destined for us. We knew that if we were posted to an active service unit, serving overseas, we would get fourteen days embarkation leave but if we were joining a unit serving at home, our leave might be much shorter.

At 08:00 the following morning our postings were promulgated in routine orders and we flocked around the notice boards to find out our fate. I was pleased to see that I was posted to the South Monmouthshire Regiment RE, part of the Territorial Army, and I was to report to their headquarters near Chepstow where I was to learn that I was going to be detached as corporal in charge of transport for the Monmouthshire Siege Company RE who were serving in Northern France as tunnellers and miners. The 'moles' were not well liked by the infantry who fought above ground because they were wary of the tunnelling and explosives being laid beneath their feet by tunnellers from both sides. I was to report to the Regiment HQ in Chepstow in ten days for induction, which gave me some time at home before joining. The South Monmouthshire RE were formed as part of the Territorial Army, recruited mostly in the border regions of South Wales, and consisting of six battalions and four specialist companies. I was to join a company who specialised in siege technology – building trenches and fortifications and tunnelling and mining underneath the enemy positions to lay mines and explosives. The siege company was initially formed by transferring trained soldiers with a colliery background from other local regiments, as the work underground was both dangerous and highly skilled.

My leave was to begin immediately after the passing-out parade, and I decided to catch the earliest train from Chatham that I could. Trains through Chatham ran from Ramsgate to London Victoria and were much faster than the Dover to Charing Cross service. The total journey time was forty-five minutes with a single stop at Bromley South, so any train before 15:30 would get me to Paddington for the 17:00 Red Dragon Express. I managed to send a short telegram from the Brompton Post Office to say I would be home that night and set off on my journey about an hour later. Wartime trains were always crowded with soldiers going on leave or returning from leave with their kitbags on their backs. Trains from Chatham had many sailors on board departing from their ships for leave or to join another ship's company in another port. Their darkblue uniforms stood out against the khaki of the army; there was little animosity between the services but plenty of friendly banter and all seemed to muck in together.

I did notice, however, that now that I had two stripes on my arm some private soldiers kept a respectful distance and I found myself sitting in a compartment with some other corporals and lance corporals and a ship's petty officer. This was quite uncomfortable for me as they were all veterans and talked easily of their service in the war so far and wore the medal ribbons to show for it. Having come directly from training, awarded my rank by merit in the classroom rather than by soldiering in the field, I felt self-conscious and kept my mouth shut. Nobody bothered me except for a few questions about where I had come from and where I was going that morning. I told them I had just passed out of RE School of Military Engineering that morning and been promoted to corporal but was to be posted to join the Monmouthshire Siege Company in France in a few weeks. On hearing that I was destined to serve in France and would be in a front-line, cutting-edge unit they became more friendly, and all wanted to give me the benefit of their experience with tips of how to survive on the Western Front. They all agreed that life at the front line would be better in a specialist tunnelling unit than in the infantry, standing to at dawn and dusk, ready to repel any enemy advance or go over the top to push our front lines forward by a few feet. They joked that when all that was happening, I would be tucked up below ground or behind the lines bringing in the essential materials needed to shore up the tunnels and maintain vehicles. I was reassured a little bit, although I still felt inwardly that the siege company would be in the thick of the action wherever it was and would not be the cushy number they seemed to suggest. However, I thought that this was a good story to tell Mum and Dad and it would placate their fears for the safety of their youngest when I went to France.

Eight days at home before reporting for duty at Chepstow was an absolute delight as Mum and Dad did not make too many demands on my time, so I was able to meet with the friends I had left in the village and call on Mr

Richards at the village school, the gas company office where I used to work and generally enjoy myself. I had hoped to take off my uniform and wear civvies so I could be anonymous and relax, but the overwhelming feeling of pride felt by the community in their sons as soldiers made us keep our uniforms on when we went out. I changed indoors but had to spend some effort in brushing and pressing my trousers and uniform jacket to keep them looking fresh and clean for the following Monday. Mum did insist that I went to chapel on Sunday morning, where I sat through the service and a long and dreary sermon from Reverend Llewellyn Lewis in a congregation made up of two-thirds women and girls. The able-bodied husbands and sons of the village were not in chapel because they were on active service or working an additional Sunday shift underground. The few men present were older and retired, so I was the oddity being young and fit and this attracted the attention of the chapel goers as we filed out at the end of the service. Many women came and congratulated my mother but did not actually speak to me. Reverend Lewis said he would pray for me every Sunday for my safe return to the village, but as I turned away from the chapel steps trying to make an escape and looking around for my mother, I noticed a young and pretty face that caught my attention. Although she looked vaguely familiar, I could not remember from where I had seen her before, but she was certainly a cut above the average village girls from my recollection. I could not ask my mother who she was as this would be too embarrassing and risk gossip amongst the chapel mothers; if my interest became known before I was ready then I would be at the mercy of the middle-aged respectable women of the village to make the running. I was a fully trained soldier but only a mere novice when it came to women. The only girls I had ever known were at the village school and working in the gas company. The schoolgirls were too young and the office girls too experienced for me as I was just a boy with only a rudimentary notion of how one would talk in a romantic way to a real live girl yet the boys in training often talked about the girls they knew and the conquests they had already had when I had none.

As I collected my mother and we turned away to walk home, I noticed that this mystery girl gave me a fleeting look and the slightest impression of a smile crossed her lips. I was exhilarated and I could feel the heat in my cheeks as I was colouring up and hoped that no one would see my embarrassment. I could not get her face out of my mind all the way home but was in for another surprise for when we got home, my elder brother, Wesley, had come up from Cardiff by train to have dinner with us. Mum had managed to get a small piece of Welsh lamb at the butchers and was roasting it with potatoes and vegetables from Dad's allotment and plenty of her special gravy. Wesley was a policeman at the Tiger Bay Police Station, which served the docks and wharf area of the city. He said it was an area rife with all sorts of crime, involving violence, smuggling and espionage as foreign spies had been caught trying to track the movements of ships in and out of the premier Welsh port. He had just finished a night shift and after a few hours' sleep, had caught the valley line at 12:30 and would be able to enjoy the afternoon with us before returning to the section house to get ready for another night shift tonight. He regaled Mum and I with lots of funny stories about the goings-on in the docks until Dad and Gwyn came home from their shift. Mum told them to get a move on with their washing and changing their clothes, as dinner would be on the table in twenty minutes. The afternoon passed in good company with lots of laughter and a little prayer to remember my brothers killed in action and down the pit, and I clean forgot about the girl at the chapel. After Wesley had left for the station, I helped Mum wash and dry the dishes and then managed to get Gwyn alone in the backyard to try to draw out some information from him about who this girl at the chapel might be.

When I told him about her, he immediately made fun of me implying that I was right to seek the advice of an older and more experienced man and that I was far too young to be getting involved with women. He said that he would take over these duties for me, but I would not be put off and began to describe how beautiful she looked, well dressed, respectable and demure she was and how she had averted her eyes with a fleeting smile when I looked at her. Gwyn warned me not to take such looks too seriously as many girls will flirt this way and it does not mean anything. He scratched his head and said that there were no girls in the village that he knew of who fitted my description. He laughed that I would have to go to chapel next week just to find out who she is, but then he had a thought that she could be a girl from outside the village. He went silent for a moment and then his face became serious.

"I think she is the station master's daughter, Ruby, she certainly fits the description but Derfal, boy, I don't think you want to have anything to do with her. Her father, Geraint Thomas, took over the station master post at our station, from Mountain Ash a little further up the line, about two years ago and he and his family live in the Station House."

"But why is she not right for me, Gwyn? I think she is the most desirable woman I have ever seen."

"He dropped his voice and explained quietly that Ruby was engaged to a lad who was the booking clerk at Mountain Ash station until he joined up last year. He had been a good scrum half so was appointed as a runner carrying messages from the company headquarters to the platoon commanders, often under fire. He was blown up in one of the German counterattacks on their trenches during the battle on the Somme earlier this year."

"She is probably still in grief and it is not yet four months since it happened. I expect it is far too early for her to be thinking of another young man and she probably will want to steer clear of soldiers anyway."

I said I understood what he had said and thought he was probably right, but inwardly I knew that I had to meet this girl before my leave was over.

Monday morning was fine and cold with no sign of any rain clouds in the sky, so I decided to take a walk down to the village school and say hello to Yanto Richards, the headmaster. I chose to arrive just as the boys and girls ran out shouting and screaming for joy as they escaped lessons into the playground for their morning playtime. I knew this should give me at least twenty minutes to chat to Mr Richards. I knocked on the door of his classroom, which did not look any different from the days when I sat inside. Yanto was laying out the materials for the next set of lessons after break when he looked up and saw me standing there.

He smiled and said, "Ah, Derfal Morgan, Corporal of Engineers," and he ushered me in, shaking my hand and grinning with excitement. He had not changed much in the time since I had been his pupil except for a little bit of grey in his moustache and at his temples, and he excitedly began to close question me about the training at the military college and everything that had happened to me since joining the army. He asked so many questions that Miss Horsley, the assistant teacher, interrupted us to say the children had been outside fifteen minutes longer than usual and with a humph, she grabbed the handbell on the desk to call them back in for lessons. Yanto shook my hand again and I withdrew to let him get on with teaching the next generation of village boys.

I still had half an hour to kill before I could go into the gas office and meet up with my old colleagues when they went for the midday break at 12:30. At a loss what to do I found myself sauntering down the hill towards the station, perhaps in a vain hope that I might catch a glimpse of this mystery woman who had already captured my heart. Even though I passed by the house three times in slow time I didn't even see a curtain flicker, and nobody seemed to take any interest in me, even though I was highly self-conscious and expecting any minute to be moved on for loitering with intent by the village bobby. So, I began a slow climb back up High Street where a few housewives called out a greeting to me as they went about their daily shopping and two grizzled old colliers nodded to me as they waited outside the Railways Arms for opening time. Eventually it was near enough to the midday break for me to chance showing my face in the office.

I opened the double doors at the base of the steps and climbed up slowly with much more decorum than the way I had flung myself down them on my eighteenth birthday. When I reached the frosted glass door to the account's office, I opened it slowly, stepped inside and immediately recognised the working hum of people huddled over the monthly account ledgers just as I used to do. Nobody lifted their heads or turned to see who had entered and although I did not expect a great clamour, I felt a little deflated that nobody seemed to recognise me. I stood for maybe thirty seconds before there was a commotion erupting from the glass sided office on the mezzanine looking down over the main room. It was Mr Evans the chief clerk who rushed down the stairs shouting that it was Derfal come to see us. He shook my hand vehemently, patted my back and now the others were looking up and shouting greetings. I told Mr Evans that I did not want to disrupt work too much but would be at Mog Edwards' café a few doors up High Street when the break occurred if anyone wished to join me. I ordered tea and some Welsh cakes as I waited for them to arrive, and in a few minutes they all began to stream in with a hubbub of excited noise. The older married women were like my mother or favourite aunts, hugging and kissing me and saying they were so glad to see me alive and well. The younger girls were less voluble but smiled shyly and appeared reticent, anxious to protect their reputations by not appearing to be too forward. However, my world was shattered when the last small group of younger women came into the café and one of them was the girl from the chapel. It was explained to me that these three girls had joined the company after I had left, which is why I did not know them. I shook their hands politely and learnt that they were Freda Watkins, Lily Williams, and Ruby Thomas. I just managed to have a few seconds of light conversation with them until they moved to another table and sat down together. I knew who she was now, which was a major step forward, but I now faced the massive challenge of how to talk to her alone without her two companions in tow. I vowed that I would contrive to be passing by the office doors at closing time today with the optimistic hope of accidently meeting up with her by chance in High Street as she made her way home. It took me three further days of lurking around High Street before I managed to engineer a chance meeting and get to speak to Ruby Thomas alone.

THREE

Ruby

was going out of my mind with frustration for even though I had ensured that I was accidently on the same street where she was likely to be each morning and evening going on her way to and from the office, I had not even caught a glimpse of Ruby once. My mind could not think of anything else but the imperative to meet and talk with her. I needed to know if she was in any small way interested in me before I went away again to join the regiment next Monday, because I had no idea of when I might be home again. On Wednesday evening, I sat in the Railway Tavern drinking beer with one or two of the local lads and playing darts with them, but I felt quite miserable and was not good company. I left early and walked home; as I sauntered down the dark street, I decided that I would try once more in the morning so I positioned myself outside Mog Edwards' café, just twenty yards from the door to the gas office, where I had a good view down High Street towards the station. I was unable to see the station from this vantage-point, but I knew I stood a good chance of observing who was approaching from that direction. I had been loitering outside the café for ten minutes or so when I thought I saw her about 150 yards down the hill. I was devastated because she was in company and I thought all my efforts were in vain, but nevertheless I decided to try my luck. I crossed the road and strode determinedly down the hill trying to look like a man with a purpose and with a place to go.

As I got nearer, I could see that it was her and she was walking and chatting to another woman who I did not know, but as they got to Williams, the bakers, this woman broke off and went into the shop to get her bread and Ruby continued alone. I quickened my step and pretended that I didn't see her until I had almost passed her by, but then I checked my step and turned to face her, smiled and apologised for not greeting her, "'Miss… er … Ruby." She smiled a warm hello and said, 'Good morning Corporal Morgan." My knees went weak, and I could feel my heart quicken as I smiled back.

She must have thought that I was an immature and a blithering idiot as I stumbled over my words and tried to develop a conversation with her that was beyond the banal. I finally managed to blurt out that my name was Derfal and she patted my hand and said that she knew that, of course, and that it had been so much fun this week watching me hanging round in the morning and evening trying to catch up with her. I was totally deflated and ashamed that I was so transparent that she had seen through my subterfuge so easily. She said that she must continue to the office or she would be late, but if I wished I could walk with her the rest of the way. My heart leapt with joy and I fell into step alongside her back up the direction I had come from. Before she went into the office, she said that at the midday break she would walk in the churchyard and I could meet her if I wished to talk with her again, but she warned that she would be chaperoned by Freda Watkins as a guard to her modesty. I was ecstatic and became that blithering idiot again as I agreed to meet her just after half-past twelve. She smiled, slipped through the front doors, and was gone up the stairs just one minute before eight o'clock.

I was a different man as I made my way home for some breakfast and knew that I might have to endure some interrogation from Mum about my daily morning and early evening expeditions each day. As I breezed into the back-kitchen, Mum looked up from the stove, smiled and laughingly commented that I had cheered up, as the hangdog expression and air of gloom that had been hanging over my head all week seemed to have evaporated ever so suddenly. She smiled again and said that she was sure that the war was not over yet, so guessed that it must be something to do with a girl. "Your daily antics and secretive creeping about seemed to make it certain." I could not contain myself and spilled it all out to Mum, including that I was going to meet her in the churchyard at lunchtime. Mum was happy for me but said I must be careful and go gently with this young woman, who must still be very fragile after her recent loss. She said that Ruby was a decent girl and been a regular member of the chapel since moving from Mountain Ash two years ago. Her father had a good job as station master and was highly thought of, and her mother was hard-working and was in high demand as a seamstress and dressmaker. Mum was kindly but she warned me to behave courteously and honourably as befits a boy from a chapel household. "Remember not to sport with her feelings as you will be gone to the war next week or shortly after and she is still recovering from the loss of her last young man going to the war." I tried to press Mum for some details of Ruby's fiancé, but all she would say was that he was a decent young man, well thought of in Mountain Ash and that he was killed in the same great battle at the Somme which took Dylan and Cliff earlier this year. Your brothers went over the top on that first attack on the first morning of the Somme and were both killed in the first action of that great battle. I enjoyed a lazy morning chatting with Mum and then pressing my uniform and polishing my boots to look my best for my lunchtime assignation in the churchyard.

I entered the churchyard through the lychgate and wandered down the main path towards the church entrance. Looking idly at the familiar names on the gravestones indicating the history of some of the leading members of our village community – the merchants, teachers, bank manager and shopkeepers were all here. I wondered why there were no colliers in this graveyard but, of course, it dawned on me that they were all in the little cemetery behind the chapel as most of them were not Anglicans. I heard some female voices giggling behind me and as I turned, I saw Ruby and Freda scuttling along the path at the top edge of the gravestones leading to a bench at the corner by a large yew tree. I tried to be nonchalant and to walk calmly towards them hoping that I did not appear too eager. I remembered Mum's words to behave with dignity and decorum and to take heed that Ruby might still be suffering with grief, but I have to say that her smiling and laughing face as she shared some secret snippets with Freda did not suggest so.

Ruby had sat at one end of the bench resting against the arm and Freda sat on the inside of her, which meant that I had no choice but sit next to Freda and I sat down leaving a polite space between us. I would much rather have sat next to Ruby, but I reconciled myself to talking through or over Freda in this first instance. We engaged in polite but rather inane questions about ourselves, but it seemed everything I said caused great bursts of laughter and giggling from Ruby and Freda together. I told them about going to the grammar school, working in the same office that they were now working in and being in the Royal Engineers, all of which caused great comic effect. I was not aware that any of these experiences were remotely amusing, but I was not well acquainted with the ways of young women. However, I avowed to attempt to prise these two apart somehow, if I were to have any chance of a sensible conversation with Ruby any time soon. At twenty past the hour, the girls bade my goodbye and made their way back to the office, but Ruby shouted back to me to be here at the same time tomorrow. I sat for another twenty minutes or so trying to make sense of what had just transpired. I wrestled with whether she liked me or not because both girls seemed to find every single word, I said extremely comic. Were they taking me seriously or were they just having some fun with an innocent young man at his expense? I was totally confused but my interest in Ruby Thomas had not diminished, and she did tell me to meet her again tomorrow at the same time and place, which encouraged me greatly.

The next twenty-four hours inched by until finally it was time to report to the churchyard again. I entered as before but this time made my way directly to the same bench as yesterday. I sat in the middle of the bench so that there was only room for the girls to sit one either side of me; hopefully this would avoid the problem of talking to Ruby face to face rather than through her giggly friend. When I looked up, I was surprised to see Ruby approaching down the path but today she was alone. My heart jumped; I stood immediately to greet her, then she sat down close to me and whispered that we did not have much time because Freda would be along in a few minutes. She had only gone to run an errand for her mother and would be along directly. She took hold of my hand and said that when she saw me smart and erect in my uniform at the chapel last Sunday she was strangely attracted. She had vowed that she would not choose a soldier again but at this time, two years into the war, there was not much choice of good men who were not soldiers except for the wounded, disabled or middle-aged. She said she was interested to know me more before I went away. She was going to watch the rugby match between the village team and Maesteg on Saturday afternoon at two and would be delighted if I would be there too. She managed to get this invite out before we heard the giggly voice of Freda coming down the path. For the next thirty minutes, the conversation reverted to the same as yesterday and I was almost glad when it was time for them to go back to work.

I was more than happy that she wanted to see more of me before I went to join my regiment. I vowed that I would not waste a moment of our time together tomorrow at the rugby ground and I hoped that I would get a chance to talk to her without the interruption of Freda or her other friends. Even though finding younger and fitter players was much more difficult during wartime, most rugby clubs in South Wales managed to put out a reasonably good side most Saturday afternoons, especially in the pit villages where many young, strong miners could be available to play dependent on their shift patterns. Maesteg seemed to have arrived with a strong team and according to the gossip around the ground, they were a side on form and likely to win. Our village club, however, was a couple of players short because they were on Saturday day shifts today and could not turn out, so it looked like a couple of older players would have to turn out to make up the numbers. One of those missing his place today was my brother Gwyn, who usually played at scrum half. He was short and wiry and could turn a great lick of speed with the ball in hand. I was however a little taller and thicker set than Gwyn and without his deft handling and fast running skill, otherwise I might have volunteered to play in his stead. I was a reasonable rugby player but because of my stature, I had always played in the front row of the scrum and usually as the hooker.

Joshua Andrews was a deputy at the pit, he knew my father and Gwyn well and he was the chairman of the village rugby club. He waved to me when I entered the ground by the changing pavilion and beckoned me over to him. After a bit of small talk, he came to the point and asked would I be prepared to turn out for the team that afternoon. He said that he remembered seeing me play for Newport Grammar in the County Schools Cup a few years ago and he thought I played well. I countered that was a while ago and had not played much since school. Joshua would not be put off and said that he needed two players, a prop forward and a scrum half. I protested that I wasn't bulky enough to prop and not fast enough to be a scrum half, but he smiled again, and said,"But you were a good hooker, I recall, and if I switch Matt Williams from hooker to tighthead you could play hooker." I could see that I had been cleverly boxed in by Joshua so I said I would play, hoping as a last chance to escape that having no kit would save me. It turned out, of course, that the kit was no problem as there was always fresh kit available every Saturday because substituting players was a weekly occurrence. I was now resigned to playing and he directed me into the changing pavilion to get ready for the game. My spirits had dropped to the floor, I had come to spend the afternoon with Ruby, not to play in the match, but in the changing room I found I knew most of the boys in the team and they were happy to have someone young and strong to add to the front row. There was a lot of the usual rugby banter and a brief team talk from the captain about our tactics to contain the much stronger opponents that afternoon.

Kickoff was set for half past two, but I just managed to squeeze out of the pavilion at twenty-past to look for Ruby and explain what had happened.

At first, I could not see her but after a few moments' panic I saw her by the touchline, near the halfway line. I could see her standing with a group of people I did not know, although I could see Freda Watkins on the edge of the group and my heart sank. Ruby did not expect to see me in the hooped red and white jersey of the village club and almost took a double take when she saw me, but then smiled and said she thought she had been stood up. She was standing next to a taller man with grey sideburns and rather smartly dressed in a dark suit who she introduced as her father, Geraint Thomas, the local station master. Mr Thomas shook my hand and said, "I see that Joshua has grabbed you for the team, what position are you playing?"

" He wanted me to stand in for my brother, Gwyn Morgan, as scrum half, but I convinced him that would be a disaster as I am a front row forward so I shall be hooking this afternoon" I replied. He smiled and wished me good luck and looked forward to talking about the game after the match was over.

At two-thirty, we went on to the field, the referee tossed the coin, we lost the toss and Maesteg kicked off from the colliery end. Right from the first kick, we could see and feel the strength of our opponents who were fast and tackled hard; we were run ragged defending our try line. After twenty-five minutes, we conceded a scrum just outside the twenty-five-yard line in the middle of the pitch. For the first time we felt the extra pressure that comes from a pack that is used to working hard together and although I struck well, they pushed us off the ball and heeled it fast to their scrum half who placed it straight through the middle of the posts to score a drop goal. We were deflated because we had been gaining confidence from not conceding any points so far in the game and knew that for the next fifteen minutes, it would be crucial to not give away any more points. At the restart, we kicked long and charged forward to try to put pressure on their defence but the Maesteg full back caught the ball cleanly and hoofed it with a mighty kick seventy yards down the touchline to find touch. We ran slowly back and took up our positions for the lineout. The ball flew over the two lines and was taken by the Maesteg wing forward right at the back of the line who put his head down, side-stepped to clear the melee of players around him and set off for our line. Our back row came up too quickly to challenge him, leaving gaps in our defensive line and an overlap on the right wing which he was quick to spot and passed the ball high over his head into the hands of the centre just before he was brought down in the tackle. The Maesteg line swiftly passed the ball down the line and capitalised on the overlap by scoring a try in the corner. Our hearts went down even further when their full back converted it cleanly.

We hung on grimly until half-time and went in with our spirits low. Joshua Andrews gave us a pep talk while we ate our oranges and said that although we were behind on the scoreboard, we were still in contention and there was everything to play for. Ten minutes later we were kicking off to start the second half. This time we chose to kick short, just over the ten-yard line and be up on them quickly and this tactic seemed to take them by surprise as our scrummagers were on them before they had taken the ball and despatched it cleanly. A loose scrum was formed, the forward momentum was with us, and we pushed with all our might. I heard our scrum captain shout "lost" as the ball shot backwards out of the rear of their scrum and they started to recycle it along the line. I leapt up and without consciously thinking where the ball was, I seemed drawn towards it and as their scrum half passed to his left, the ball seemed to hang in mid-air and float into my hands as I intercepted the pass. Many thoughts went racing through my head; I knew I did not have the speed to run clear to the line myself, but I knew if I could burst the six or eight yards necessary our backs would have a chance at the line. I managed to sprint enough space clear to pass the ball to our centre, Dai Rees, who did have the legs to score right between the posts. The try was easily converted, and we were back on terms. We were elated but knew that we had to play at this pace for another thirty-eight minutes if we wanted to win the game. The next twenty minutes or so we played constantly in our own half but although were under extreme pressure, we held our discipline and did not concede any more points.

I knew that I, for one, would feel the physical effects of this hard match for several days afterwards but like the rest in our team was motivated by keeping them out whilst they were becoming increasingly frustrated that whatever tactic they employed, they had failed to score. The frustration began to show as they were penalised a few times by the referee for infringements at the scrummage and offside; slowly we began to hope that the tide was turning in our favour. Each penalty kick drove them back until we had the chance to escape from our half of the field and mount some pressure on their defence. They became so unsettled that having been penalised on the twenty-five-yard line for an offside, they did not retire the full ten yards and the referee ordered the penalty to be taken again, ten yards further forward this time. This silly mistake put them under real pressure from our forwards. Our full back took a quick tap kick then passed the ball to the nearest forward, and all the forwards charged together with enough momentum to get close to the line. There was no way through, so we recycled the ball and tried the pushover again but this time I was on the bottom of the scrum; as there was no way to ground the ball over the line, we recycled again.

This time the attack was led by the two prop forwards with great bravery,with me in support. There was now a great wedge in their defensive line, and I felt the ball spring up and into my hands as I dived over the top of the defenders to ground the ball on the other side of the try line. There was a cheer from the touchline and all the forwards were patting each other on the back for a great combined effort. The kick was a difficult one being almost on the touchline, but our full back took his time and coolly slotted the ball cleanly between the posts. There was only five minutes left to play and we were now determined not to let up on our opponents, who seemed to have become even more disheartened by this latest score. They were slow to take the kick-off; it was too long and went straight into touch, the referee called us back for a scrum on the centre spot. Our scrummage was gaining confidence and as it was our put-in, we were sure we could push them back and win the ball cleanly to give our backs a chance to run at their line.

We won the scrum without a hitch and Dai Rees saw the opportunity to kick deep for touch towards the corner flag. His kick was almost perfect and placed us just ten yards from their line. The tension was mounting as we knew we had to win this lineout and try to drive the ball over the line with an eight-man shove. We won the ball through an excellent jump by one of the second rowers and he drew the ball down so that the rolling maul could be formed and with a renewed vigour we set off for their line. Maesteg tried to skew us towards the touchline but in doing so opened a gap in their defence which our number eight was able to capitalise on when he peeled infield and dived through the hole that they had created, to score our third try. This time the angle was impossible for the full back to convert but we were certain that the victory was ours. The Maesteg boys were disappointed with their performance but acknowledged that we had played a better game,we all applauded both teams off the field and the spectators crowded round adding their congratulations to the celebrations. I was happy to have played a part in the win but was now anxious to make up for lost time with Ruby.

A couple of times I had glimpsed her stood on the touchline, excitedly absorbed in the game. She was animated and cheering our team on. I noticed that her hair had a reddish tinge and although she was only about five foot three inches or so tall, she did not seem to be small but nicely proportioned compared to some of the other girls around. I bathed and changed into my uniform as quickly as I could and hoped that she would still be there when I came out of the pavilion changing room into the club room. A small bar had been set up in the corner and players and members were drinking beer and chatting together. When the Maesteg players emerged from the visitors' changing room, we cheered them and sat down to eat a simple meal of lamb stew and bread together and passed around the jugs of beer for their refreshment. I was looking through the crowded room for Ruby when I felt my arm grabbed quite firmly from behind. It did not feel much like a feminine hand and when I turned, I was surprised to see Mr Thomas beckoning me. He said some kind words about my game and the pushover try I scored. I replied modestly that it was a group effort and that I was only the hand that put the downward pressure on the ball to score but all the forwards played their part. He waved my objections aside and said it was well done anyway. He told me that although he would like to stay and enjoy the club celebrations he had to leave soon because Mrs Thomas was feeling under the weather, but he would be incredibly grateful to me if I would escort his daughter home a little later. Perhaps I could ensure that she was home by nine-thirty. I was taken aback but quickly agreed and thanked him, perhaps a little too profusely. He smiled and pointed over towards a table at the other end of the room where Ruby was sat among the gaggle of girls from the office, and some I did not know. He said, " I wish you the best of luck in prising Ruby away from that bevy of beauties, but you have proved yourself a man with some mettle this afternoon. He wished me luck." we shook hands, and he was off. I was held back a little longer by Joshua Andrews, who wanted to thank me for playing and for scoring the pushover try. He enquired how long my leave was and was disappointed when I told him I was to report on Monday morning, but he made me promise I would turn out again if they were short when I was next on leave and I said I would.

Ruby made it easy for me when I finally was able to move across the room towards her group because she detached herself and came towards me. She clutched me hard and planted kisses on my cheeks and said how she was so proud of me on the field today. She seemed confident, excited, and perfectly at ease in my company, and was happy to spend the rest of the evening with me singing along with the great Welsh songs and favourite hymns when the piano was rolled out. Both sides sang together with harmonies that were great and got even better as the jugs of beer were flowing. At eight-thirty, the Maesteg team gathered their kit together, boarded the motor bus to take them back home and the numbers in the club began to drift away. I told Ruby that her dad had asked me to escort her home by nine-thirty, so we said our goodbyes. We decided to walk the longer way home avoiding the village centre and High Street so that we could draw out the walk home together for as long as possible. We took the lane behind the slag heaps and climbed over the stile into the meadow behind the churchyard, skirted the church and walked slowly down the footpath leading to the village school and Station Road. We talked all the way but when we were behind the school building, we stopped in the shelter of the boundary wall, I leant my face towards her, and we kissed on the lips for the first time. She caught her breath and leaned in closer to me and I felt as I was in paradise as I had never kissed a woman passionately before. Those few intimate minutes made everything worthwhile, and I knew that I had found the right girl for me. I could have stayed much longer cocooned in the warmth of Ruby's arms, but I was conscious that the time must be pressing. A quick look at my watch showed there was still a few minutes to make it to the Station House on time if we ran. We scuttled across the road, laughing like children reluctant to let go of each other and then stopped ten yards from the house to brush ourselves down and present ourselves modestly to Ruby's parents.

I lifted the doorknocker and knocked once, a voice from within called out then Mr Thomas opened the door and smiled at us. "Well done," he said to me, "I knew you could be trusted to bring her home safely and on time. Please step inside as I wish to introduce you to Mrs Thomas before you go." He ushered me in to the sitting room where his wife was sitting in a large armchair by the fire, hand-sewing some embroidery. She eyed me carefully and then remarked that I was the young man who beat Maesteg today, well done… She thought I looked very presentable, and my mother was a well-respected member of the chapel. 'I hope I will see you at Sunday service tomorrow morning as I know Ruby will want to see you again before you go" she said. I gave my farewells and was back into the cold night again within five minutes, feeling happy inside and tingly all over. I had a strange feeling that I had been put to some sort of test this afternoon and evening, and that I might have passed. I ran up High Street in a whirl of excitement and although I had already drunk quite a lot of beer in the club, dived into the packed taproom of the Railway Tavern to drink some more.

Next morning, I stumbled out of bed with a fuzzy head and a foul taste in my mouth and regretted those couple of extra pints at the Railway. I have not a clue who paid for the drinks, but I think they must have been supporters of the rugby team. I do not remember how many pints I had or how I got home but my mind was filled with the need to get myself into some better shape for chapel later this morning. Luckily, Mum had pressed my uniform and I had enough time to give my boots a polish before sitting down to breakfast. I did not feel like eating too much but knew that the sermons were an endurance test in themselves and if I did not eat something, I would be ravenous by midday. Dad had a day off, but Gwyn had already left for the day shift, and I was surprised when Dad appeared at the breakfast table newly shaved and dressed in his Sunday suit as it had not occurred to me that he would want to accompany us to chapel. Normally, Sundays were a good opportunity for him to spend some quiet time at his allotment for a few hours and to dig up some fresh vegetables for Sunday dinner. I guess Mum had told him about Ruby and his curiosity had got the better of him. I could see from the satisfied look on Mum's face that she was glad of his company in chapel, especially as I was joining my regiment in the morning.

The service was as long and tedious as it had been the week previously. The regular congregation did not seem to mind but rather enjoyed singing the rousing Welsh hymns with some gusto and then put up with the long address that was a kind of penance for their guilt at enjoying singing together, or so it seemed to me. I noticed that Dad had dropped his eyelids and was snoozing quietly through the rousing sermon while I contented myself on looking round at the congregation secretively. I could see the back of Ruby's head with her black Sunday hat sitting upright and appearing attentive to the words of the minister next to her mother, but there was no sign of her father this morning. I counted the panes in the chapel windows and the bricks in the wall but found I lost count before I reached the final total. I then tried to count the number of times the preacher said the word, "sin" which seemed to come up regularly in every other sentence, and then I found that I too was dropping off like my father. The copious amounts of beer I had consumed last night were catching up with me and perhaps I would have been better to have had another hour in bed to clear my head.

At last, the sermon ended, and we stood together to sing the closing hymn, 'Cwm Rhondda" but before the blessing the Reverend Lewis asked the congregation to pray for a young soldier who is a member of our community and joining his regiment tomorrow morning. He asked us all to pray for him and wish safe return to this valley. I went red with embarrassment when I realised, he was talking about me. He then gave the blessing and we all stood to leave. As we made our way slowly down the main aisle, I felt several hands press my shoulder or grab my arm and wish me luck. This was the best part of the Sunday service, when the congregation got to mix and chat together in front of the chapel for ten minutes or so and exchange all the gossip of the week. I was convinced that this was why the village ladies turned out in such large numbers to Sunday service and the snippets they picked up kept them going throughout the ensuing week. I guessed that Ruby and I might well be the centre of the gossip for the following week, when they realised what was happening between us and I was sure that not all the gossip would be well intentioned or favourable towards Ruby or me.

When we cleared the church steps, I steered my parents away from the main crowd towards Ruby and Mrs Thomas and introduced my father and mother properly without a great gang of spectators gathered around. Mum knew of Mrs Thomas already because of the sewing work that she did in the village and by sight from the chapel but Dad, of course, had no idea of who they were. After the first embarrassed seconds, Dad smiled and engaged Ruby in some pleasant conversation; I could see that he was as enamoured by this pretty woman as I was and approved of my choice. Mum and Mrs Thomas seemed to find that they had interests in common and were chatting amicably. I managed to prise Ruby away from the attention of my father and drew her a few paces aside so I could have a quiet word with her with some urgency, because I was leaving early in the morning and anxious to spend time with her before I went. Mum had already told me that our dinner would be at 3pm today so I suggested that perhaps her father might consent to us taking a stroll together before dinnertime. I knew that this was perhaps a long shot, but as he had been willing to trust me to bring her home on time the previous night then he might agree to my request this afternoon. Ruby smiled and said to leave it to her to persuade her mother, so they would ask him together as soon as they got back from chapel and we agreed I would call at her house at one-thirty. After a few more minutes, Mum and Dad broke off to head home; Dad was anxious to get the stiff collar off and Mum to get the dinner in the oven. I reluctantly said farewell to Ruby and her mother and set off for home after Mum and Dad. I had an hour to kill before I needed to set off to the Station House for our afternoon walk. I was hoping that it would stay fine as there were heavy clouds brewing up over the mountain, which usually meant heavy and persistent rain coming in. It was quite cold but not enough for snow, so I was optimistic that we would be able to get a short walk in before the weather broke. I filled my hour by packing my kitbag ready for leaving in the morning. I had already checked the railway timetable and knew that there was an early train at 05:40 to Newport where I could get a connection to Chepstow, giving me enough time to walk to the barracks for 07:00.

At one o'clock I made my excuses to Mum for not helping her set the table today and rushed out of the house to make my way to the station. I felt so exhilarated and buoyant that I was almost singing at the top of my voice as I hurried along High Street. Luckily, it being Sunday, there were no shops open and the doors to the Railway Tavern were bolted shut so there were no witnesses to my derangement. I was a few minutes early when I arrived at the Station House, opened the front gate, and walked up the path. I stretched out my arm to grab the brass knocker and the door was opened suddenly by Mr Thomas, dressed in his station master's uniform, before I had even touched the knocker. I thought he had been waiting for me deliberately to refuse my request but after my initial surprise, but I realised from his smiling face and welcoming posture that he was just returning to work after a lunch break and far from saying no to the walk, wished us a pleasant stroll. He said that I should go in and call out as Ruby has been dressed and ready to go since one o'clock. I stepped into the hallway, called out and Ruby came hurrying through from the kitchen with hat, coat and boots already on and her gloves in her hand. I went through to the kitchen to say hello to her mother, who said to keep watch on the weather and if it looks like it will come on to rain, to come back here and have a cup of tea with her rather than get soaking wet. I thought I would rather get wet through with Ruby than stay dry, drinking tea with her mum, but I thanked her for her kind offer. We were both anxious to get away and hurried out into the cold afternoon, retracing our steps from the previous evening with the intention of walking passed the rugby ground to the woods beyond.

However, as we reached the rugby ground the weather was getting worse, drizzly rain had started and it had got noticeably darker. We ran and took shelter under the canopy over the veranda on the front of the changing pavilion where there was a bench against the wall. We snuggled in together on the bench relatively dry and sheltered from the wind. We just talked and talked, silly stuff at first and then more serious as she wanted to know all about my posting and where I was going. I could not tell her much as I didn't have much information to tell her. I told her what I did know about the South Monmouthshire Engineers and that I did not know how long I would be away for, but I knew the siege company I was joining would be deployed in France in January for a new secret mission and I would certainly get some embarkation leave before leaving for France so could be home for Christmas or the New year, or perhaps both. I promised that I would write to her as soon as I had any real understanding of what was going to be happening and we kissed and cuddled together until it was time to walk back to her parents' house. We had one last embrace and a kiss on the doorstep, then she broke away suddenly with tears streaming down her face and ran indoors sobbing.

I ran home to keep as dry as possible and apologised to Mum for being a few minutes late for dinner. She told me to get that coat off and put on the airer by the fire quickly or I would catch my death of cold. I dried my hair, changed my boots, and put newspaper inside to help them keep shape and draw the damp out. This week, Mum had cooked a chicken and I enjoyed what could be my last Sunday dinner at home for what maybe sometime. I was up early in the morning and set off with my stuff for the station in plenty of time for the Newport train, which departed from the other platform from the Cardiff line. As I stood on the platform, my thoughts were all over the place as I thought about Ruby so close in the Station House, just to the side of the level crossing and yet so far away. My reverie was broken into by the sound of the train whistle as it rounded the bend. My eye was caught by a commotion by the Station House; when I looked up, I could see Ruby leaning out of an upstairs window and shouting good luck and blowing kisses. I responded and shouted back but my voice was drowned out as the engine clattered into the station. In half a minute we were off.

FOUR

The Regiment

I changed trains at Newport Station to catch the local train to Chepstow and found the platform already crowded with soldiers and naval personnel. A few minutes later I found out that the sailors got off at Caerwent where there was an Admiralty Stores Depot, which solved the mystery in my head of why there were so many sailors in rural Monmouthshire. Five minutes further on the train arrived at Chepstow Barracks Station. I got off and followed the khaki-clad crowd towards the station exit. The main gate of the General Gordon Barracks was just across the road, opposite the station and I could see a queue of soldiers had already formed at the guard room window, signing in on their return from weekend leave. I hitched my kitbag on my shoulder and crossed the road to join the end of the queue. The line moved forward quickly and when I got to the window, I presented my joining instructions to the duty sergeant who called me into the main guard room itself. As I waited in front of the counter, I could see the sergeant in a glass office at the back of the main room talking to a sergeant major.

In a few minutes, the sergeant major came out of his office to greet me. He was midheight and quite stocky, probably about forty years old. He stood upright and carried himself with a military bearing accentuated by the large royal warrant badge on his sleeve, the campaign ribbons on his left breast and the silvertopped cane he carried as his badge of office. He shook my hand and introduced himself as Mr. Ramsden, the regimental sergeant major and told me I was to leave my kitbag with the guard room staff and he would take me to the regimental headquarters to report to the adjutant, who is to take charge of the itinerary for my induction into the regiment. As we marched across the main parade square, he pointed out that he was the only person who by privilege of his rank could cross the main square when not on parade, as this was his domain. I was, however, this day privileged to be able to accompany him, but he warned that in future I would have to walk around the perimeter like everyone else. He gave me a brief history of the regiment and welcomed me into the ranks of its non-commissioned officers, who he informed me were the mainstay of this and all regiments. "The officers command but the NCOs make it happen, and when you are in the field and you find that your officer is inexperienced and poorly trained to exercise that command, you will still have to make it happen and protect your men from the failings of that officer." These words struck me greatly for, hitherto I had been conditioned to look up to commissioned officers as almost godlike. The words of the RSM made me realise that he wanted me to understand that they were only human beings too and that as an NCO I would have my work cut out to support them in the field.

The RSM also allowed me to share one further privilege that morning by allowing me to enter the main door of Regimental HQ, which is normally reserved for officers and the RSM only. All other ranks had to enter via the rear door. On entering the bright entrance hall with the regimental crest on the wall, the RSM turned left into a corridor with offices on each side. The first door on the right-hand side had a large, neatly painted sign which read, "Captain M. C. T. Edwards B.Sc. RE, Adjutant". The RSM knocked and waited, a voice from within replied and he called me to attention, opened the door and we marched into a surprisingly spacious office where the adjutant sat behind a large wooden desk in front of the window. We halted, saluted Captain Edwards, and stood at ease. The adjutant exchanged some pleasantries with the RSM and then invited him to sit. The RSM handed over my joining papers and introduced me. There was some conversation between them about my joining arrangements and induction before the RSM rose, came to attention, saluted, said he must return to his duties and that he would leave Corporal Morgan in his capable hands, then left the room. The captain seemed to relax after the RSM had gone, he smiled at me and invited me to sit where the RSM had recently been seated. I took off my cap and sat down, realising that the adjutant was only about twenty-three years old and was quite in awe of the presence of the RSM in his office. However, he had prepared a well-organised plan for my induction that day, taking care of my training needs as well as domestic. He said that in twenty minutes he would take me to meet the commanding officer, Colonel Sir Idris Llewellyn Hughes

Bart. MC RE and not to worry about this as it was only a formality, it would
be unlikely that you would come across the old boy again as this regiment had
six battalions and four specialist companies. He outlined what the regiment
had in line for me for the next couple of weeks before deployment to France
with the Monmouthshire Siege Company. There would be a chance to meet
the CO of the siege company, Major Wyn Rees-Evans, who I may remember
playing outside half for Wales in the 1913/14 season, who will be in HQ on
Wednesday morning.

I was to be temporarily attached to the Transport Section where I would
receive further training to fit me better for my role when I get to France.
After a very brief meeting with the regimental commander, we returned to
the adjutant's office where a tall and wiry corporal from the MT section was
waiting to start my induction. He was Charlie Staithe, about a year older than
me and easy to get along with, but what marked him out most was that he
was an Englishman in a Welsh regiment. He admitted that he did not find it
too difficult as he was born and brought up in the Forest of Dean, so close
to the border that it seemed a good choice for him to be stationed close to
his family home. He first got me sorted with a billet in a barrack block where
most of the MT drivers lived in two of the large communal rooms on the
first floor. The corporals had the luxury of a small private room each and I
had been allocated one at the end of the largest barrack room. He said I was
lucky because the last occupant was only posted last week so the room was
available. I was grateful and went to collect my kit from the guardroom, then
he left me for half an hour to settle in.

The officer in charge of the section was away on leave, so I was introduced
to the second-in-command, Sergeant Powell, who outlined my training
programme for the next three weeks at Chepstow. Corporal Staithe would
show me the workings of a typical motor transport section in support of an
active service unit during this week and Corporal Brown would teach me
how to drive each of the vehicles I was likely to come across with the siege
company, in preparation for taking the test for a driver's permit. I would have
the opportunity to experience working on all the vehicle engines, pumps' and
electric motors that you would have to be familiar with in the unit. There
will be a day of range practice to requalify for my marksman badge and an
opportunity to meet Major Rees-Evans to discuss joining the siege company.
He then threw in that I would be entitled to a weekend pass from 15:00 on
Friday until Monday 07:00 every week and when my embarkation date s

fixed, some embarkation leaves too. I was happy and that evening I wrote a letter to Ruby telling her the news that I would be home for the weekend, and also a short note to Mum to tell her the same, in the privacy of my own room. Corporals did not have their own mess but where possible had single rooms in the barrack blocks and were able to eat in a curtained-off section of the main cookhouse reserved for them. This established a little distance between the NCO and the ordinary soldier, which reflected a corporals' higher status and was good for discipline. This, of course, only happened in the barracks; when the regiment was on active service, they were expected to mess with the men.

I started learning to drive the range of vehicles likely to be used by the siege company in the line from motorcycles to cars, small vans, larger trucks, mechanical diggers, and bulldozers. I enjoyed driving them all. I especially liked trying to dig holes with the digger and fell in love with the motorcycle. Corporal Brown was an excellent instructor and had the knack of making everything seem so easy. He gave me the army driving manual to study for the driver's test and was certain that the best way to achieve a pass was practice and for a couple of hours each day, he let me take one of the vehicles and drive in the lanes around the camp to build my confidence. He thought I had made such good progress that he booked my test for Friday morning with the regiment driving examiner, who turned out to be none other than Charlie Staithe. At 08:00 on Friday morning, I was sat at the desk in the MT office with the question paper in front of me. I had one hour to answer all the questions and then would have the practical driving test. The examination paper was straightforward as all the questions had been culled from the driving manual and there were no trick questions. I was then directed to the general purpose three-ton lorry. Charlie climbed in the cab on the passenger side and said he wished me to drive from here to the Admiralty Stores Depot at Caerwent and back again and wished to see how I managed driving on the open road, related to other vehicles and navigated our journey by the best route.

Luckily, I had a fairly good idea of where Caerwent was, although I was not exactly sure where the depot was located. Charlie had a notebook open on his lap and as I was driving, he scribbled things down and made little sounds as if he were judging my ability as a driver. Some of the sounds were encouraging and sounded positive, whilst others seemed to be quite the opposite. I was confident I was driving well but these little sounds were making me feel less so. I made good progress on the journey through Caldicot and on to Caerwent but became confused when I got to the crossroads in the centre of the village to discover that there were four directions to choose from and no mention of the Admiralty Depot on any of them. I had no idea which way to go and knew that pass or failure hung on getting this right. I realised that I had made a basic error by assuming I knew the way when I did not and realised that if one of the drivers behaved like this he would be in trouble. I should have looked at the local map in the MT office to check the route before leaving the yard, which is what all drivers are trained to do. Getting lost in France and finding oneself in enemy territory could have disastrous consequences. I was about to stop and plead ignorance when I caught a glimpse of a small van with a naval number plate coming towards us and turning to the left. I thought this is fifty fifty, took the gamble and turned right to follow him. Charlie made another one of his strange noncommittal noises and then scribbled more notes in his notebook. I kept quite a way back from the naval vehicle, but I knew after about three-quarters of a mile that I had made the right choice because I could see a tall perimeter fence coming up through the trees. I heaved an internal sigh of relief and pulled into the side of the road for further instructions from Corporal Staithe, who looked at me knowingly and then told me to drive straight back to Chepstow. He didn't say a word on the return journey, nor did he write any more notes in his book, so I could not gauge whether I had made the grade or not. I pulled into the MT yard, backed the lorry into its parking place and switched off the engine. Charlie turned to look at me, smiled and then said that I was a lucky devil because if I were a driver, he would have failed me for not preparing the route properly with a route card etc.

"However, I think you realised your mistake," he added, "and were fortunate in Caerwent village when that naval van showed you the right way. Remember, you will be operating close to the German lines and taking a wrong turn could end you in all sorts of trouble. You must always prepare thoroughly before leaving the yard. However, as you are not a driver but a corporal, I will pass you." So, we went into the office, and he prepared my driving permit immediately. I realised that I was extremely lucky to have passed the test, thanks to the kindness of Corporal Staithe.

As I was a new arrival, I was not yet added to the duty corporal list for guard room duty over the weekends so I was able to return home from Friday afternoon to Monday morning, provided that the guard room had a record of my accommodation address should it become necessary to be called back to barracks. Sergeant Powell passed by my desk and congratulated me on passing the driver's test, asking me if I were intending to return home for the weekend because he lived in between Risca and Magor and would be happy to give me a lift on the back of his motorcycle, and drop me off at the nearest station to his home. I readily agreed and he said I could get a return lift on Monday morning from the same station. This day was turning out well, not only passing the test but now I was going to miss the crowded train to Newport and changing to the valley line, all of which were bound to be busy on a Friday afternoon. Riding a motorbike would make the journey much quicker using the country roads to bypass Newport and taking the valley road, which ran parallel to the railway line most of the way. Joe Powell was a regular soldier and his wife and young family lived in a cottage on the outskirts of the village of Risca, which was just under eight miles from my home. He was not a local boy, coming from somewhere on the coast close to Barry Island but since joining this regiment on its formation, he had set up a permanent home close by to provide some stability for his family growing up.

We met at 15:10 outside the MT yard, I hopped on the rear seat of the motorbike and we were off. As we passed through the main gate and turned right, I could see the crowd of soldiers thronging the entrance to the station booking hall and platform for the next Newport train. Joe had given me a pair of goggles to wear to protect my eyes from dust and insects and we set off at a lightning pace. Joe seemed to know the roads very well and made excellent progress as we skirted around Newport and began the climb up the valley road. I was amazed when we pulled into the frontage of Risca station in just twenty-five minutes, which was less than half the time it would take the train. I thanked him profusely and said I would be standing at this spot, Monday morning at 06:00 and, with a wave, he let out the clutch and roared away on the bike.

The next train on the up line was due in three minutes, so I had just enough time to buy a return ticket and get over the footbridge to the platform. I could not believe it when I walked out of our station at four pm that afternoon. I did not look for Ruby as I knew she would be still at the office until 5pm, so I took a leisurely stroll up High Street to Mog's café to enjoy a cup of tea and wait for her to finish work. At five minutes to five I was posted right outside the front door of the gas office and waited expectantly for her to emerge but, of course, my patience was stretched to its limits as she was one of the very last to come out and almost walked right past me, so deep was her conversation with

Freda. It was Freda who spotted me first and even when she went silent as if struck dumb by some catastrophe, Ruby did not stop her stream of chatter until Freda shook her arm and she looked up and saw me standing there. Ruby's face was a picture as she looked aghast in absolute surprise to see me standing there right in front of her, and she threw her arms around my neck and kissed me. She stammered that she was not expecting me until later this evening, and she hadn't had any time to do her hair or put on a clean dress, and she pushed me away and told me to go home so that she could get herself ready for me later that evening. I just stood rooted to the spot as Ruby and Freda in her wake rushed down the hill without even looking back.

After what seemed ages stood in the middle of the pavement, completely perplexed at Ruby's behaviour, I reconciled myself to being too young and inexperienced to be able to understand their feminine wiles. When I came in through the door to the back kitchen, there was one woman who was more than happy to see me as Mum hugged me and then put the kettle on for some tea. Dad and Gwyn had come off shift at five had already bathed and were upstairs changing their clothes. Within ten minutes we were sat round the table with our tea and Mum was putting the finishing touches to our meal. She had made a large shepherds' pie with lamb mince from the butcher and vegetables from Dad's allotment. It was plain but wholesome food, and we were grateful that we could afford to have full bellies and a warm comfortable house, for there were many in the valley who did not have these necessities. Dad and Gwyn wanted to know all about my first week at the regiment and I gave them an account of what I had been doing, especially learning to drive all the different vehicles, and passing the driver's test. They were glad I could come home at the weekend, but I warned them that it might not be every weekend as I could be called for duty sometimes. I was able to tell them that I would be home for Christmas and maybe the New Year too as I would complete my three weeks' training at Chepstow and be posted to the siege company in France in January. The length of my embarkation leave would depend on my joining date in France.

Gwyn's face looked a bit glum when he turned to me and said that Josh Andrews had collared him at work. He pressed me about when your leaves were and as we had had the note you sent, I told him that you were home each weekend, and he has put you on the team sheet for the away game tomorrow at Cross Keys. I will be playing too so it would be good to have us both in the same team.' My face said it all because the disappointment was written all over it; I had hoped to spend tomorrow with Ruby, I explained. I thought perhaps she could come with us because a supporters' bus usually went with the team to away games that are not too far. Cross Keys was further down the valley from our village, but only by about seven miles. I did not know what to do; I could let the rugby club down and spend the day with Ruby, but I knew she and her father both liked rugby and maybe she could come with us. I told Gwyn that I would ask Ruby's father and if he agreed that she could come to the game then I would play, but if not then I would stay behind and spend the day with her her. Gwyn hoped he would say yes as he had my freshly laundered kit here and had got out my old boots and dubbined them for me, ready for the game.

At seven-thirty that evening, I knocked on Ruby's front door and waited for it to open. Mr Thomas stood there smiling, shook my hand and welcomed me into the warmth of the sitting room. He offered me a seat and sat down himself by the side of the fireplace, where I could see the half-read edition of the *South Wales Gazette* on the arm of his chair. He said that Ruby sn't ready yet but s still doing something with her hair, making herself look more beautiful and heaven knows how long she will be and as Mrs Thomas is apparently assisting in this delicate operation, 'we best relax and wait at their pleasure. He said that Josh Andrews had told him the good news that I was playing at Cross Keys tomorrow and I said that I was not sure that I could play. Mr Thomas looked disappointed and asked what was stopping me playing. I admitted that I would rather spend the day with his daughter, and he laughed and said if that is all I was worried about then just ask her to go with me. He said he could not go himself because he was on duty and was thinking of asking me to take her to the game anyway.

I couldn't believe my ears; the barrier I had built up in my head over the last few hours had just melted away in an instant. Mr Thomas must have seen the relief pass across my face, he dropped his voice a little and said almost conspiratorially so that his wife could not hear, even though she was not in the room, "Derfal, you have shown me already, in the short time I have known you, that you are a respectful and decent young man who can be trusted to treat my daughter properly. The effect you have had on Ruby is almost miraculous, for you have reawakened the lively and sweet young woman she used to be before the tragedy struck her, and we are grateful to have that happy young girl back with us. Lastly," and he dropped his voice even further, "I get to go to the rugby club on the Saturdays when I am not working, without Mrs Thomas you understand.' I did not really understand but I guess it was why on the occasions he went to the Miners' Welfare Club he left Mum at home.

Finally, Mrs Thomas came into the room, greeted me warmly and said that Ruby was almost ready and would be out directly. I was not really prepared for the vision of loveliness that approached me a few moments later, with her hair done to perfection so that reddish tinge stood out more vividly and her make-up highlighting the natural beauty of her face. Her eyes were bright and glistening and she was the loveliest girl I had ever seen. I could feel myself going weak at the knees as I gazed at her and I knew I would be so proud to be seen walking out with her. We gave our farewells and putting on our coats, set off into the cold night. I promised to be back by ten at the latest, although I did not have any real clue about where we were going to go this evening. I certainly did not want to lurk behind the school wall or sit on the bench on the rugby club veranda this evening, I wanted to show off my girlfriend to the world. I decided we would take a short stroll down the hill to the main Newport Road where the Bedwas Hotel stood on the corner. We could sit in the plush surroundings of the saloon bar lounge. I had only been there once before to a family wedding about five years before, and I remembered it being quite splendid with potted palms and leather furniture. I knew that the people who frequented this hotel were among the most well-off and respectable in the village,and they would be dressed well for an evening out. I reckoned that Ruby was dressed perfectly, for she was wearing a new dress that her mother had made for her this week, copied from the latest fashions and I was wearing my best uniform with bright buttons and badges.

When we entered the main door to the reception, the young bell boy asked us if we had a reservation for dinner or had come in to have a drink. I replied that we had come in for a drink and he showed us into the lounge bar to the right of the reception hall. The lighting was quite dimly lit, and we could hear someone was playing softly on a grand piano in the corner of the room. He showed us to a table and pulled out the chair for Ruby to sit, and then for me when she was settled. He took our drinks order, a port for Ruby and a whisky and soda for me, and he said the waiter would bring our drinks directly. Nobody seemed to take much notice of us although I recognised one or two faces from the village; one of the colliery managers and the branch manager of the bank in High Street but most people were unknown to me. The waiter brought our drinks, I paid the bill and realised that the drinks were over twice the price that they were in the Railway Tavern and even more than twice those in the Miners' Club. Ruby seemed to settle well into the quiet atmosphere with the piano music playing softly in the background, which was intimate and cosy. We just talked silly stuff, stared into each other's eyes and as I held her hand under the table, I realised that I was falling ever more under the spell of her charms. Was this falling in love? It certainly felt special enough to me. We had a second drink and passed an hour and a half quietly sitting together in the lounge before it was time to think about walking back up the hill to the Station House.

As I stood up to get Ruby's coat, I noticed an officer in mess dress escorting some ladies from the dining room into the bar. I stood to attention as he approached me and as he turned to acknowledge me, I saw it was Captain Willoughby-Jones who mumbled, "Thank you, Corporal," and then exclaimed, "'My God, its Morgan!" His face was wreathed in smiles, he shook my hand and said how glad he was that I had gone to the Engineers and I had done well to be a corporal already. I introduced him to Ruby,he was charmed by her smiling eyes and said, "You have done well, my boy." He wished me good luck in France and then went to join his ladies, who I assumed were his wife and daughter. We left the hotel and walked back up the hill arm in arm. I explained how I came to know the captain and the significance of his excitement of seeing me tonight. We were so wrapped up in each other I almost forgot to ask her if she wished to come to the game tomorrow. She said she thought I would never ask and then got all coquettish with me, she had already booked a seat on the supporters' bus whether I was playing or not and did I think she only liked rugby when I was playing? My heart dropped, then she threw her head back, laughed and said that she would come straight from her half day at the office at 12:45 and would not miss it for the world. We just managed five minutes for a kiss and a cuddle before we got back to the station and Ruby had to go in.

I was exhilarated as I rushed up High Street and so excited that I did not want to go home yet but I could not decide where to go. There was the Railway Tavern, or I could see if my brother Gwyn was in the Miners' Welfare,which would be preferable because the drinks were the cheapest in town and after the hotel prices that would be good for the pocket. I looked through the front window of the Miners' Club and searched for Gwyn but at first, I couldn't see him and was about to change my mind and go on to the Railway when I saw him standing at the far end of the bar drinking with Dai Rees. I rushed into the front door and asked the doorman if he knew Gwyn Morgan and he said he did. I asked if he would go in and ask Gwyn to come out and sign his brother in; grumbling under his breath, he went through the door into the bar and was soon back with Gwyn behind him. We went in and joined a small group at the end of the bar including Dai who was in the team last week, and Gwyn got me a pint. There was some talk about the match tomorrow, then the talk turned to the war and they asked me which unit I was with. I told them I was at the regimental headquarters in Chepstow but was joining the Monmouthshire Siege Company in January in France. They all approved as the company was made up, almost exclusively, of coal miners from this locality and each seemed to know someone who had served with them. Dai said that I could become an honorary member of the club as a member of the siege company and then drink here anytime. I enjoyed a happy hour with these boys until closing time and Gwyn and I walked home together by 11:30.

The club at Cross Keys was larger than our small village club, but very friendly to the visiting team. I waited for the supporters' bus to pull in behind us and went to meet Ruby but could only spend a few minutes with her before I had to go to get changed for the match. Josh Andrews gave us a team talk before the game and warned us that their outside half had an awesome reputation as a sprinter and an excellent ball-carrier, so he was the one to mark closely. When we ran out onto the field, I was surprised to see Joe Powell lined up in the outside half position on the opposing side, when he smiled and gave me a nod. The game was different from the Maesteg game for it was much more open and free flowing. Both sides seemed happy to move the ball out and run the ball through the backs. I could see that the main value of Joe Powell was his ability to read his opponent's mind and mastermind the overall direction of their response. He was sharp and when he had the ball in hand, was the fastest runner on the pitch. Tries came easily for both sides as the game was played in a fast and furious manner and at half time the scores were level. The second half was just as thrilling but in the final minutes they managed to edge a try into the corner to win the game. We were exhausted as we came off the field but proud of our performance. The spectators had enjoyed an exciting match which ranged from end to end with lots of running tries scored.

After a bath and changing, I joined Ruby and the others in the club room to enjoy a few beers and good company for the rest of the evening. Joe Powell came over to me smiling and congratulated us on a well-fought match. I expressed my surprise when I saw him on the field but congratulated him on his prowess as an outside half. I introduced him to Ruby, Gwyn, Dai, and the rest of our crowd and then we sat together to eat. Joe was in deep conversation with Dai Rees about rugby tactics and swapping outside half stories between them. I noticed that Freda had sat on the other side of Dai and seemed a little put out that he was talking to Joe so avidly instead of her. After half an hour, Joe got up from the table, came across to me and said he would have to leave as his wife was at home with the children. After Joe left us, I noticed that Freda did start to chat to Dai, they seemed to be getting on well and I said a silent prayer that this would become a relationship that would keep Freda away from us in the future. When it was time to leave, I managed to sneak on to the supporters' bus so I could ride home with Ruby, we wedged ourselves into a double seat at the rear and held each other tightly in the dark as the bus rolled back home. As we walked back from the rugby club, Ruby said she had never been so happy and hoped I felt the same. I had never enjoyed such happiness before and already knew that I probably never would in the future, but I could not find the words to express this clearly to her at that moment. I was afraid she would think that I was silly and unmanly for exposing my emotions so openly, so I kept quiet.

The next few weeks, drawing up to Christmas, passed very quickly as I was made ready for embarkation and joining my new unit. The most informative time was the hour I spent with my new CO, Major Rees-Evans, a qualified mining engineer who had worked in coal mines in Wales and England before the war. He gave me some insight into the secret mission entrusted to the siege company to prepare subways for a new push in Passchendaele, near Ypres, in the spring of next year. The job of the company was to tunnel out the communication lines for material and supplies to be brought up safely and secretly to the start point for the attack. Much work needed to be done to prepare the communication lines so that the Germans were unaware of what was going on. Closer to the attack itself the company would tunnel, secretly, under the enemy positions and lay explosives and mines to be set off when the artillery barrage was under way on the morning the first wave was to begin. He stressed that it was vital work and the importance of maintaining our supply line with men and materials was the main job of the transport section, which would be under my direct supervision and part of the company headquarters platoon. Although the majority of the time the drivers would be operating behind the lines, loading and bringing forward the equipment that the sappers and miners needed underground, there would be times when they I would have to assist in carrying this equipment below ground and help to maintain it. The vehicle fleet was to be kept in good working order for day-to-day operations only requiring planned maintenance at the depot or emergency repairs. He was relying on me to ensure that the work of the transport section was carried out in a disciplined manner so that the work of the siege company would be successful.

After the major had left the barracks, I was given my orders and joining instructions. I was to complete my training in Chepstow and my posting to the siege company would become effective on the Friday before Christmas. I was to report to Crickhowell Barracks, near Abergavenny, on the 2nd of January, 1917 and take charge of the Monmouthshire Siege Company transport section which consisted of ten driver/mechanics, two specialist vehicle fitters and a clerk. I was to inventory all our vehicles and equipment and prepare them for shipping. Our equipment and stores were to be crated and loaded onto the vehicles for the journey and I was to prepare convoy orders for the journey by road to the port of embarkation in Kent. We were to be at the port of Ramsgate for loading onto SS *Maid of Kent*, cross channel steamer, by 06:00 on the 8th January for the crossing to Dunkerque in Northern France. I could see that this would be an extremely hectic week in Crickhowell, and that we would have to depart by early morning on the 6th of January to complete the journey on time. In addition, we all had to withdraw our battle kit, arms, and ammunition as we were going to the front. This was quite a lot to take in all at one time, but I was excited to see that I would get eleven days embarkation leave before I had to report to Crickhowell. I would be able to enjoy Christmas and New Year with Ruby and my family.

My embarkation leave was all mapped out for me between Ruby and my mum, who were constantly vying for my time, but they did not fall out over it. I did manage to spend lots of time with them both, but Ruby was my prime concern, and we became even closer than before. I was a frequent visitor to her house and her parents always welcomed me warmly into their home. I also took Ruby to meet my parents at our house and Mum enjoyed cooking a special dinner in her honour. Of course, I played for the rugby club several times over this period, and there were carols and extra Christmas services to attend too. As was usual over this family period, I did not get too much time to be alone with Ruby and to have her to myself, but I did feel that we were getting quite comfortable with each other and people were beginning to see us as a couple. As my departure day came closer, Ruby and I did talk more frankly about the risks of going to the front; she was obviously frightened for my safety and what she would do if she lost me too. We embraced and caressed and I kissed the tears running down her cheeks to console her. I told her that I was not going over the top like the infantry and would be relatively safe. I do not think she fully believed me, but I think it gave her an illusion of comfort for the time being. We promised to write as often as possible and exchanged love vows to each other before I left for Crickhowell the next morning.

FIVE

Transport Section

Crickhowell Barracks was a small transport depot at the foot of the Black Mountains between Abergavenny and Brecon. It would have been a relatively easy journey from home by road taking the Heads of the Valleys Road, but I had to go by train, which meant two changes at Newport and Abergavenny. The camp was situated in a beautiful location close to the river on the edge of Crickhowell village with wonderful views towards Pen Y Fan in the distance. I was anxious about meeting the men in my section for although it seemed ages since I became a corporal, this would be the first time that I would take responsibility for the supervision of men and for delivering the level of support to our comrades on the frontline. I wondered what kind of men they were, who they were, where were they from and would they take orders from me?

The barracks sergeant major had allocated a large hangar/workshop with bays for checking and servicing the vehicles, storage space and a small office for my use until our departure. I spent an hour with the duty corporal checking through the inventory before the buildings and all they contained were signed over to me on Monday morning. I moved into the office and went through the orders and signals for my attention and prepared what I would say to the men when they reported. The first parade of the transport section was to be at 10:00, so it was quiet and peaceful for a little while longer. Around nine there was a knock on the door and a short lance corporal with round glasses and a smile on his face poked his head into the office and introduced himself as Ivan Lewis. He explained that he had been a wages clerk at the colliery in Treorchy but had decided to join up in 1914 and had been with the South Monmouthshire RE ever since. I already knew from the papers I had received that he was an experienced clerk, he would soon have the administrative affairs of the section running smoothly and his fitness reports suggested he would be a good right-hand man. He carried an attaché case with him, which he said contained the personnel records of the section, inventories, and convoy orders for our journey to join the main company. He said he had already been working on them and would brief me on the orders in detail after the parade. Over the next thirty minutes or so the rest of the section reported in, so by ten I was ready to go on parade and formally take control of this new section.

We paraded in front of the hangar, where the concrete pan was large enough for parking several vehicles. The section was called to attention by Ivan Lewis, and he handed over to me, I stood them at ease and then called them back to attention and accompanied by L/Cpl Lewis I inspected my new command where I was able to greet each man face to face and learn his name and role in the section. They were arraigned in ranks of four with Ivan Lewis out front acting as parade adjutant. They seemed a mixed bunch; some were young and had come directly from the training camp, whilst others were experienced soldiers who, hopefully, had the skill and knowledge we would hope to rely on in action. I was extremely pleased to find that in the rear rank the lance corporal fitter was George Smithers, from my basic training entry at Lidsing. I had last seen George on our passing out day from basic training and knew that he had also gone to the school of military engineering in Chatham although had not been accelerated to a faster course like me. I remembered that he was a time-served apprentice and a fully qualified tradesman before he joined up. Before I dismissed the section, I told them to take a short tea break and report back to the hangar at 11:00 for a detailed briefing and allocation of duties. The fitters were easy to arrange, as L/Cpl Smithers was the senior fitter and Sapper John Davies was his junior. Four of the drivers had seen service at the front before and one of the drivers, Gareth Hughes, had just received his first stripe so he was an obvious choice to be lead driver. Sapper Welsey Owen seemed a reliable and steady soldier and was great friends with Billy Williams, who also had a good record of service. However, Bryn Edwards, the fourth experienced one, had served for two years in three different battalions and one specialist company and his charge sheet was full of many minor disciplinary charges, usually involving too much drink and lateness on parade as a result. I wondered if he was being dumped on us and would have to keep a watch on him closely. For the young drivers, this was to be their first posting to active service, but they seemed a decent enough bunch. They were Edwin Jones and Alan Jones, who were not related, Maurice Griffiths, Arnold David, Jonathan Bennett, and Wesley Chambers. I felt that we would soon get to know each other well as we would be working and living together in the field. Although they all seemed to be quiet and a little nervous as we were all new boys, I knew that in the days and weeks ahead characters would begin to emerge that we would love or hate. At the briefing I outlined our tasks for the next few days and allocated individual and collective responsibilities to ensure we were ready for departure from Crickhowell promptly on Saturday morning. I also issued us all with the Monmouthshire Siege Company patch to be sown on to the right shoulder of our tunic, which would distinguish us as members of this specialist company from now on. I expected that we would all be wearing them by morning parade on Tuesday and I could hear a buzz of excitement amongst the men as they took pride from the transition from the depot to becoming part of an active service unit at the front.

Progress went well during the week as we all seemed to be pulling our weight to complete our own tasks and to help others with theirs too, and I could see the beginnings of a team emerging and friendships beginning. I was still a little worried about Bryn Edwards who had not settled in as well as the others. He shied away from the other experienced soldiers, preferring to offer not very constructive criticism of the younger men and to set himself up to them as the expert in all things. However, I was confident that the other experienced men went out of their way to counteract his negative influence and L/Cpl Hughes was an effective buffer between Edwards and the others. As I had hoped, Ivan Lewis proved to be an excellent organiser, he took all the administrative tasks in hand competently and was able to use his own initiative to get work done ahead of schedule. Remembering the important lesson taught to me by Charlie Staithe, Ivan and I worked together to produce the detailed convoy orders and route cards, maps, stopping places and refuelling depots. George Smithers worked out mileage and fuel consumption for each vehicle and although we could carry some additional fuel in large cans, we knew we would have to fill up at army fuel depots several times on the way. George's calculations enabled us to plan where we could refuel on the way to Ramsgate to avoid too much refuelling by the roadside. I realised that apart from the experienced drivers, most of us were unfamiliar with convoy driving and we would need to practice avoiding mishaps on the way. George and his assistant were great workers and managed to check and prepare each vehicle for the road so that by mid Thursday, all our vehicles were roadworthy and ready to go. Gareth Hughes had a full schedule of practice for the drivers to experience driving all the different types of vehicle and for the whole section to have a convoy driving practice from Crickhowell to Sennybridge and back on Friday morning first thing.

Thursday afternoon was set aside for drawing our personal weapons, range practice and the delivery of a stock of ammunition for the section's immediate use. Ivan arranged for the supply of rations sufficient for our journey to joining the siege company and had identified a couple of lads, Bennett, and Owen, who fancied themselves as cooks. The vehicles were loaded and sheeted down securely, our personal kit packed by Friday afternoon, and I stood the section down at 14:00 so that they could get some rest and be ready for the early departure on Saturday morning. We were all in high spirits, but I knew that the long hours and hard work had tired everyone considerably. I still had to hand back the hangar and office to the barracks and this took most of the afternoon for Ivan and myself, after which we treated ourselves to a couple of beers in the Corporal's Club and were in bed by eight o'clock. We had planned an early start and were up at 05:00; the section paraded at 05:45 and we hoped to depart by 06:30. It was cold and pitch black with quite a heavy frost on the ground and we were anxious to be on the move; warm and cosy in the cabs of our vehicles as we drove along the deserted roads into England. As I came to take over the parade, I noticed a gap in the ranks and my heart sank as I realised Edwards was absent on parade. No one had seen him this morning, so I despatched L/Cpl Hughes to find him. Hughes was only gone a few minutes, he came back and reported that Sapper Edwards was still in his tent asleep and, when he had woken him, he appeared to smell strongly of alcohol. I was furious and sent two L/Cpls to get him up and dressed and bring him to me as soon as they could. Ten minutes later he appeared before me in a dishevelled state as if he had slept in his uniform, his eyes were bleary, and he stank of a mix of vomit and alcohol. I told him he was a disgrace to the Royal Engineers and to his comrades in this section and that if it were in my power, he would be facing a serious charge right now. I told him that he was on report and he would be referred to the company adjutant when we joined up with them. He had ten minutes to clean up and be ready to depart but I was not prepared for him to drive in the state he was in for the safety of the rest of us so I ordered that I would not have him ride in the comfort of the passenger seat in the warm cab but in the back of the stores truck at the rear of the convoy. Sapper Davies, who would be sharing driving the workshop truck with George Smithers, would take over driving Edward's truck until he had sobered up. I would have preferred to hand Edwards over to the guardroom at Crickhowell for punishment, but this would cause a real disruption and extra pressure on us in our forthcoming journey. I now knew, more than ever, that Edwards was a weak link and would report the matter to the adjutant when we arrived at the company headquarters.

We managed to set off just ten minutes behind schedule and drove out of the gates, through the silent village and turned right on the A40 London Road which would take us between the Black Mountains and Brecon Beacons to Abergavenny and into Gloucestershire, all the way to London. This was a main turnpike road so there were places we could stop for a brew and rest every couple of hours, and we intended to camp at Uxbridge on the outskirts of London for the first night where we could refuel ready for an early start again on Sunday. Our intention was to cross London on Sunday morning and take Watling Street, which would lead us southeast towards the channel ports to reach Ramsgate harbour by late afternoon. The journey was slow with only an average speed of around twenty miles per hour on the open road, so it took over seven hours' driving to reach our campsite for the night. All the vehicles were refuelled, checked and ready for the second stage of our journey in the morning. Bennett and Owen broke out the rations and soon got a good fire going and a hot meal on the go with plenty of tea. Edwards had sobered up and was rather sheepish but did not complain when I put him on the latrine digging duty. Our volunteer cooks served up an excellent chicken hot pot with carrots, peas, and potatoes, which made us all feel warm inside. Even though the evening temperature dropped to near freezing, the fire was kept stoked up with logs from the surrounding woods, the camp was sheltered and quite warm and by eight-thirty that evening we had all turned into our blankets and slept. When we woke in the morning Bennett and Owen had a great pan of porridge on the go, which served us all well for breakfast. We had to wait a few minutes for Edwards again this morning, but this time it was because he was filling in our overnight latrine hole. He was sober now so could be returned to his driving duty and Sapper Davies resumed his partnership with George Smithers.

Crossing through the centre of London, even on a Sunday morning, was busy and took all our concentration to keep the convoy together amongst the melee of motorised and horse-drawn traffic on the city streets. It was vital we stayed together, for getting separated could lead to a wrong turning and getting lost in this massive city. I was amazed to see some of the sights so familiar from books that I had never seen before; Marble Arch, Buckingham Palace and the Houses of Parliament where we crossed the Thames at Westminster and picked up the old Roman road, which led us out of the city and across Blackheath into Kent. Watling Street was a straight road and although busy with military traffic heading for the channel ports was still a much easier drive. When we descended Strood Hill and saw Rochester Cathedral and castle standing over the other side of the River Medway, I remembered joining up and reporting for basic training at Rochester nearly a year ago. We crossed the bridge and passed through the busy military town of Chatham where access was controlled by the military police who checked our convoy papers and said they were searching for absentees and deserters.

We rested in a field next to apple orchards just before we reached Sittingbourne for some bread and cheese and strong tea and then pushed on towards the coast in the afternoon. Watling Street ran through Canterbury to Dover, but we were routed to join a ship in Ramsgate Harbour so several miles past Faversham we switched left onto the Ramsgate Road, which took us out on to the Isle of Thanet, the most south-easterly tip of Kent. On arrival at the harbour entrance, I reported with my orders to the port marshal's office. The port marshal greeted us warmly and showed us where SS *Maid of Kent* was berthed and where we could park up overnight. The ship would begin loading at midnight but as our vehicles were to be deck cargo, they would be last to be loaded before sailing in the morning. He gave us a leaflet that showed how to secure our loads and tether our vehicles to stop them moving at sea. The crossing to Dunkerque would take approximately three hours, and he reminded me to report to the port marshal before leaving the Dunkerque docks to ensure that we had the latest intelligence on enemy movements and access to our destination, as the situation in Northern France and the Belgian border was quite fluid.

It was rather strange to the first timers in the section, including myself, to hear the guns firing and see the flashes reflected in the evening sky across the channel that we were about to cross within twelve hours. We parked the vehicles close together and created a sheltered area for us to sit and relax, although we were going to sleep in the cabs for warmth on this cold night. There was no need to cookas there was a large transit canteen near to the dock gates where an evening meal was served, hot drinks and breakfast in the morning. I gave strict instructions that no one was allowed to leave the dock area and to ensure that Edwards was not tempted I placed him on guard detail until 22:00, giving him no chance to slip away to taste the brews in the dockside pubs. I emphasised that the whole dock area was under surveillance of the military police; offenders would be arrested and thrown in the cells to be brought before the provost marshal. Anyone who missed the ship would be posted absent without leave but because we were due to sail to join the war, this would be construed as desertion. Sappers Davies and Bennett took first stag so that the rest of us could go together to be fed, and they would be relieved by Edwards and Jones A. by 19:00, so that they could eat as well. There was a good choice of food for departing troops, but we all chose vegetable soup, minced beef and onion pie with vegetables, mashed potato and thick gravy followed by plum duff and custard. This went down well, we all felt satisfyingly full after it and were pleasantly surprised to receive from some Salvation Army volunteers a Bible, two bars of milk chocolate and some fruit.

After our meal we sauntered back to our camp, we did not stand around talking too much but climbed into the cabs of our vehicles and wrapped our blankets around ourselves to try to sleep. My mind was in a whirl as I tried to make sense of all the things I had to remember to do in the morning and what awaited us when on the other side of the channel. At best my sleep was fitful and by four am I was wide awake again and my feet were like ice blocks. I decided to get up, opened the door and jumped down to the ground only to see others with the same idea. Ivan Lewis was on last guard duty and was glad to see the section coming round slowly. Even though it was cold, and my breath was streaming in clouds in the cold air, I stripped off my shirt and shaved as best I could in cold water. The chalky water in Kent was hard so it was difficult to get a reasonable lather in the shaving bowl, but I worked my brush hard and finally managed a reasonably clean shave without getting a knick on my chin. I felt invigorated after a wash and although I did not put on a clean shirt, felt presentable for the day. As soon as we were ready, we made our way over to the canteen where there were mountains of bacon and fried eggs and you could help yourself. We ate our fill, drank a couple of mugs of tea and I hurried back to relieve Ivan and his companion on guard to go for their breakfast.

By five-thirty we were mounted and ready to move the convoy forward to the berth alongside the *Maid of Kent* for loading by crane at 06:00. The stevedores were skilled in attaching the strops under each vehicle to ensure an even distribution of weight for the crane driver. We stood on the dockside as each of our vehicles were loaded onto the foredeck of this steamer and tethered down securely by the deckhands on board. When all was completed, we marched up the gangway and were directed towards the passengers' saloon, already crammed with soldiers from many different regiments and from all parts of the Empire. Within minutes this little ship cast off its mooring ropes and began slowly to edge away from the dockyard wall with blasts of its hooter, and slowly turn its bow to face the open sea. This was the first time I had been on a ship and I was excited to enjoy the experience. The weather was fine, and visibility was good even though it was not yet daylight. The sea was gently rolling with the kind of swell that you couldn't feel whilst sitting down but seemed to make your knees feel wobbly as soon as you tried to stand up. The master was on the bridge and directed the ship slowly through the exit from the harbour and once into open water, turned to port on a heading for the French coast just as the morning artillery barrage opened up. We could not tell whether it was the Germans or our guns, but it was just like rolling thunder and sheet lightning. One of the able seamen told us that it happened every day at this time in the morning and again at dusk, but usually only lasted a couple of minutes unless it was before a big push when it could go on for half an hour or more to soften up the enemy before a big attack. It was obviously not going to be a big push by the infantry today because after three minutes, the guns fell silent, and dawn began to inch up from darkness to twilight and then into a bright anti-cyclonic January day. Many soldiers were seasick and the atmosphere in the saloon became quite fetid and unpleasant, so to stop myself feeling bilious too I went out on to the upper deck where the air was fresh and bracing. I found a spot on the rail and found I was soon joined by most of the section, who also wanted to escape the foul air in the saloon.

Although *Maid of Kent* seemed to be the only ship leaving Ramsgate harbour that morning, I was surprised to see that once we were out in mid-channel there were dozens of ships making the passage to and from the French coast; some in the grey livery of the Royal Navy, many merchant vessels carrying stores, troopships and we saw two former passenger liners converted to hospital ships. I was fascinated to see aircraft dotted high up in the sky, skittering about like insects with little plan except for chasing each other about. I guessed this was the Royal Flying Corps engaging with the Germans over the front lines but could not be sure. I did know however that I was envious of the freedom of the skies to engage the enemy in chivalrous combat like the knights of old in their jousting competitions. Suddenly, it dawned on me that we could no longer see the English coastline but that grey smudge appearing increasingly on the horizon was France. I was excited but also anxious, and a churning in my stomach was proof of the lack of confidence I felt about my ability to perform my duty well when I got there. I felt some fear but knew I was not a coward; I would not run away or be unable to fight, but I did have some doubts that I would be able to lead my men and get them all home safely.

I knew that I had something to get home for now my family and, of course, my beloved Ruby. The thought of her in my arms, cheered me and I resolved to write a long letter to her tonight to tell her about the journey and that we had arrived safely. We could see the entrance to the Dunkerque port from a couple of miles out at sea but there was a traffic jam of ships coming and going so we had to wait our turn before we could dock alongside. It was just after midday when we were finally alongside and we were amongst the first to disembark as our vehicles were to be lifted off the deck on to the wharf where the drivers were waiting, ready to drive away from the unloading area for about 200 yards to wait for the whole section to be unloaded. When all were present and correct, we went back into convoy formation and drove to the port marshal's office to receive the latest routing information.

I was welcomed into the port marshal's office by a short, middle-aged lieutenant who introduced himself as the deputy port marshal. He read through my orders and then took me through into a closed room where large maps of the front line were maintained with the latest positions of all Allied and German units marked. The door was locked and guarded twenty-four hours a day, but the guard let us in and the I was shown where to find the Monmouthshire Siege Company location on the big map. He pointed out the route I should take and what to avoid, and he advised me that as there was only a few hours of daylight left this afternoon, we should find a place to camp tonight and set off in the morning. It is not a particularly long journey, being less than forty miles, but with the amount of motor and horse traffic and marching columns we would be lucky to make ten miles an hour. We were heading for a hilly area in Flanders, Belgium and needed to approach from the French side of the border into the area controlled by the British Second Army to the southwest of Ypres. The siege company were billeted in woods near to the village of Dranouter in the entrance to the Ypres Salient. He wished me and my men the absolute best of luck and I saluted and returned to the convoy to tell them that we would camp near Dunkerque tonight and join the company in the morning.

I studied my maps and discovered that there was a suitable village to stop for the night about five kilometres inland at a hamlet called Berques, where there was a bakery to get fresh bread and milk and replenish our water supplies. We headed for this village and the old lieutenant was proved right, for it took us nearly an hour and a half to get there because of the volume of military traffic. We found a meadow by the river where we could camp for the night and I delegated Edwards and three others to replenish all our water containers with fresh water. He protested and said he spoke the French lingo well, and he should be the one to go into the village to buy the milk and bread. I knew he could not be trusted and could see through him straight away, for if there was a café in the village, he would feel that he should make a call there as well and who knows what state he would be in when he returned. I delegated our two volunteer cooks to go for supplies knowing I could trust them to buy what was necessary to feed the section properly, and I was proved right when they returned with adozen fresh loaves, five litres of milk, some butter and cheese, fresh vegetables and three bottles of red wine. George and Davies checked all the fluid levels on the vehicles so that they were ready to go in the morning.

Our cooks still had plenty of rations left because we had eaten in the dock canteen last night and for breakfast this morning, so were able to rustle up an excellent Welsh lamb stew with plenty of French onions, parsnips, carrots, and local cabbage. The smell of the stew cooking was delightful, and we hoped it would taste as delicious as it smelt. We all had plenty of fresh bread to wipe up the gravy from our mess tins, hot mugs of tea and washed it down with some cheap red wine and as it was another cold night, I found the half bottle of brandy that I had in my pack and put a little nip into every mug to ward of the cold. Nobody said anything but the silence showed their appreciation, nevertheless. After breakfast we broke camp, reformed the convoy and I placed Ivan Lewis at the rear on the motorcycle to ensure that we lost no one on the way. We threaded our way along small country roads from village to village in the general direction of a small town called Bailleul, where we needed to turn towards the larger town of Ypres. At no time were we able to get up any speed but crawled along slowly, avoiding the shell holes and wreckage of damaged vehicles and buildings that littered the roads everywhere. Some villages had been completely flattened, whereas others had seemed to escape without too much of a mauling.

We were often stopped at checkpoints and our orders checked by regimental and military police, but mostly we passed soldiers from many regiments who waved cheerily as if they were on a school outing. There were Scots in kilts, Indian Army troops in khaki turbans, Africans, Canadians, and Australians from all parts of the Empire. We saw hardly any French or Flemings because the landscape appeared completely devastated by the fierce artillery barrages of both sides. The bigger town of Bailleul, although showing signs of damage, still managed to give the appearance of a thriving community despite the war and although thronged with Allied soldiers on every street, some of the local businesses were open and doing a brisk trade. It had taken us six hours to reach here already but I knew that company headquarters was only three kilometres further, so after a quick brew-up and eating the remains of the bread and cheese we drove on. In about forty minutes I caught a glimpse of our shoulder-flash colours painted on a piece of wood with an arrow pointing down a narrow lane, suspended from the branch of a tree. I turned into the lane and we drove down a track for about half a mile towards a half-demolished farmhouse, which was our company headquarters with a tented camp all around. We halted in the farmyard and I went inside to report.

The remains of the old farmhouse were reasonably warm and dry and provided a base for the company commander, adjutant, and company sergeant major. The administrative personnel who made up the headquarters platoon also worked in and around the farmhouse too. The other three platoons were dispersed in the field behind the headquarters. This was only a temporary home, as the company was expected to move forward into the Ypres Salient within a few days. The Transport section was part of the HQ platoon under the command of 2nd Lieutenant Craddock-Williams, who in turn reported directly to the adjutant, Captain Herbert Vaughan, and on entering the HQ I saw a sign pointing out the way to the adjutant's office. The door was open so I knocked and entered a small parlour which seemed to serve as an office and inside I could see a large desk in the middle of the room occupied by the captain and too smaller ones either side occupied by the CSM and 2nd Lt. I came to attention, saluted, and presented my orders to the captain, who looked me up and down in a rather circumspect manner and caustically remarked that we were late and were expected to arrive yesterday. I pointed out the orders of the deputy port marshal at Dunkerque who had advised us not to travel after dark and to camp for the night before darkness fell. He had annotated our orders accordingly. The adjutant did not seem interested in my reply and dismissed me, pointing at the young subaltern on his right, who appeared young, like a schoolboy in uniform, but he smiled sheepishly at me. I saluted the captain again and suggested to the lieutenant that he might like to meet the men in his section who were parked outside in the vehicles. He jumped up, saluted the adjutant, and rushed out of the door in a great hurry with me trailing behind him.

When I caught up with my officer in the cottage garden in front of HQ, I managed to step between him and garden gate to slow him down and brief him on the section before he burst upon them unannounced. He seemed overexcited and stressed and plainly had little or no idea about what he was doing. I calmed him down and explained that I was Cpl. Derfal Morgan and I came from Bedwas, he said he knew it and had stayed at the Bedwas Hotel once with his parents. He said he was from Treorchy originally but now lived in Penarth where his father was a solicitor in a local practice. He had only left Penarth Grammar School last summer and had hoped to go to university to study Civil Engineering, but he was called up and sent to OCTU instead. He had been commissioned in December and posted to join the siege company until there was a vacancy for him to study at the School of Military Engineering. I told him that I had graduated from there with a diploma in Engineering, Engines in November last and had been appointed corporal on graduation. He said he envied me having taken the army diploma because at least I knew what I was talking about and I had successfully brought the section here in one piece and all the vehicles in good order, which showed that I was competent at my job. I felt sorry for him but felt that he would soon shape up working alongside myself and Ivan Lewis. He said the adjutant did not like him much and he gave him all the rotten jobs to do because he said that he was not a proper officer and call him a sissy because his Christian name s Vivian. If it were not illegal, he said he would challenge the bully to a duel with pistols and force him to take that insult back. I told him the only way to get back at the adjutant was to make the transport section the best it could be and prove to him what a good soldier he was. I promised him that he could rely on the men in the section to support him in this. In these few minutes he calmed down and I sensed he thought that he could trust me, and he smiled, put out his hand, we shook, and he said he was pleased to be working with me.

Our conversation had not been overheard and took place in private, and 2nd Lt Craddock-Williams had perfectly composed himself to meet the men. L/Cpl Lewis called them to attention as we approached, he handed the parade over to me, marched away and took his place at the rear of the section. I stood the parade at ease and then called them to attention, about turned, saluted, and handed command over to 2nd Lt Craddock-Williams. I then invited him to inspect and meet the men. For the next half an hour, he spoke to each man individually and was friendly to each so that he made quite a good first impression for such a young officer. After he had withdrawn the CSM came and introduced himself and gave us directions to the large barn where we could set up the transport yard stores and showed us space behind the barn where we could pitch our tents. Just before he was due to leave us, he drew me to one side, dropped his voice and warned me that the adjutant was quite an unpleasant man and a bully, and that I should be on my mettle to protect my men and the young officer from the captain's attentions. I asked about the other officers and he said they are fine and quite decent, but because they are mining specialists, they spend nearly all their time underground with the miners and sappers. They were more than happy to leave most of the running of the company to Captain Vaughan. The CO s a decent man and an excellent officer but would not take kindly to complaints about his officers unless there was strong evidence to back it up. He intimated that Mr Craddock-Williams, although inexperienced, seemed to have potential to be a good young officer and he reminded me that it would be my duty to train him as best I could. I was grateful to have been taken into the CSM's confidence but also concerned that I did not want to direct the adjutant's attention at me or my men unnecessarily.

For the next couple of hours, the whole section worked hard, unloading the lorries, breaking out our stores and stacking them away in the barn. L/Cpl Smithers and Sapper Davies cleared away an open area large enough to work on two vehicles at once, and where they could work undercover in all weathers. The drivers erected the accommodation tents under the direction of L/Cpl Hughes whilst Ivan Lewis and I, with the assistance of Sapper Edwards, erected the half marquee that would serve as the section office and a sleeping space for me. Our volunteer cooks were stood down as the company had established a field kitchen, which drew rations and cooked for us all. We all hoped that they were as skilled as Bennett and Owen who had done a first-class job of cooking whilst we were in convoy. The evening meal was served at six and two sappers acting as orderlies went to the kitchen to collect meals for the section. Ivan Lewis had set up a table under an awning at the rear of the barn where we could sit and eat together. We were all grateful for the hot food and extremely tired after a very full day, so that most of us turned in by eight o'clock to catch up on some sleep. There was no settling in period as transport requests started landing in Ivan Lewis's intray by 06:00 in the morning and drivers and vehicles were despatched almost immediately, even before the duty driver roster was published.

Every request was considered urgent by the requesting section but with a limited number of vehicles and drivers they had to be prioritised and scheduled according to availability. Two lorries had to make a return journey to the docks at Dunkerque, where a consignment of mining supplies had been unloaded from a ship early that morning and needed to be cleared from the dockside as soon as possible. Ivan allocated a senior driver to each lorry and a junior driver as a driver's mate, as this was going to be a two-man job. They were despatched from the yard at 06:45 but we knew that they would not be able to reach dockside until midday at the earliest, so were not expecting them back until the morning. The adjutant requested a driver to take him to Second Army headquarters at 08:00 and the CO wished to undertake some reconnaissance towards Passchendaele in a light vehicle with a driver at 09:30. The two light vans that we possessed were not suitable for rough terrain driving but if we attached a light sidecar to the motorcycle, we would be able to get almost anywhere close to the enemy lines. Ivan sent a runner to the major to seek his approval for our plan and then George Smithers set about attaching the sidecar immediately and getting the bike ready for use. The runner returned within ten minutes and told us that the CO would be happy to use the motorcycle and sidecar which should prove ideal for the purpose he had in mind. He requested that I should be the driver and report to company headquarters at 09:15 for briefing. Edwards was the relief driver which meant that he had to stay close to L/Cpl Lewis and busy himself with clearing away stores unloaded the previous evening: again, he was surly because he had not been sent back to the docks but I explained to him that he had not yet earned our trust and until he proved he could be trusted, this was how it would be. Other drivers were in and out of the office to pick up job cards and disappeared to carry out their requested journey, and I could already see that the transport section was going to be a busy place to work.

I duly reported to company headquarters on time and leaving the motorbike and sidecar in the farmyard, I went inside. The duty corporal called me over to his desk and asked if I was Cpl. Morgan and then showed me to a closed door at the end of the hallway. I knocked and waited. Major Rees-Evans shouted to come in and I marched in and saluted him. He was poring over a large military map of the Ypres Salient: he called me over and showed me where we were situated now and where he wanted to go.

"I told you when we met in Chepstow that we have been tasked with a special secret mission in preparation for the next big push out of Ypres in the early summer this year," he said. "We are to map out and then construct the subways for men and materials to be moved up closer to the front line without the Germans being aware that we are massing our forces for a new attack. I also wish to survey the best points for tunnelling under the enemy positions and laying explosives to be set off to coincide with the opening attack.' He said he had quite a clear idea of the terrain from the map, but as this piece of land had already been fought over twice already in the past year or so he wanted to see close-up and first-hand what damage ha been done to the landscape and our ability to tunnel safely there. He said that I was sworn to secrecy and must not discuss anything about this reconnaissance to anyone in the company.

We went to the motorbike, and I gave the major a leather overcoat and helmet, goggles and gauntlets to wear in the sidecar to guard against the cold. I explained that I wished to disguise the fact that he was an officer, who might attract attention from enemy snipers or sympathisers amongst the local population. I put on my coat, helmet etc. and it was now impossible to tell who was the major and who was the corporal. We slid my rifle on the floor of the sidecar in case we had need to defend ourselves and set off in the direction of Ypres. The bike was an excellent choice because the major wanted to leave the roads and ride across open country, getting as good a look at the terrain as he could. He would often stop and make sketches or more detailed drawings of features that caught his attention, to append to the bigger map later. Although it was extremely cold, we were fully engaged in our work and did not really notice it too much. I was surprised how freely the major talked to me about the task in hand and tried to involve me as much as possible. We stopped for a short break in a small dell just below the ridge, about 600 yards from the German redoubt where we thought we were sheltered from view. I had collected a flask of tea from the kitchen before we left camp and we sat on the grass enjoying the brew and chatting about home. It was quiet, and all we could hear were birds twittering in the leafless trees around.

I thought I heard a metallic click, which sounded somehow out of place in this peaceful pastoral scene and jumped up to take a quick look. At first all seemed clear, but I was suddenly aware of movement in the trees to the left of us and realised that there was a patrol of German soldiers about 150 yards away, moving fast to our right to cut off our escape. Another thirty seconds and we would have been caught unawares but I had just enough time to jump on the bike quickly and kick-start the engine, which roared into life immediately and shouted at the major to climb on board, let out the clutch and opened the throttle wide, praying that I would not flood the engine and stall. A couple of shots rang out but as the patrol was running through woods, they were not taking settled aim and their shots went wild. Our adrenalin was running high, and we were shouting at the top of our voices as I sped the bike and sidecar away from the approaching patrol as fast as it could go until we had covered at least half a mile from the site where we were so nearly captured. I could feel my heart pounding in my chest as I realised that I had just experienced my first taste of enemy action and although I did not think I felt afraid, I didn't like the experience very much. The major was excited too, it was more like game to him but after we had calmed down, he thanked me for my vigilance and prompt action which undoubtedly saved us from certain capture. He declared that he was satisfied with his reconnaissance today and we should return to camp. When he climbed out of the sidecar Major Rees-Evans thanked me again for my bravery and quick action. He then reminded me about the need for secrecy, not a word to anyone about today's events, and walked away to his quarters.

I did not say a word to anyone about the mission, although Ivan was keen to know. I just said that the CO wished to see the terrain for himself, and we were able to go off-road on the bike and get a closer look at the enemy positions, but I didn't mention the reason behind the mission or the incident with the German patrol. I was now beginning to see that life in the siege company had the potential to be exciting and more than a little dangerous; because of operating in such proximity to the enemy positions, anything could happen to put us in danger. I completed my tasks for the day and after supper I wrote a long and loving letter to Ruby and a shorter one to Mum and Dad before turning in. I felt tired and my head was in a whirl, thinking of our little brush with the enemy this afternoon, and realised that the war was serious and right on our doorstep. I imagined what it would be like to be taken as a prisoner of war, how we would have been treated by the German soldiers and I hoped that I would never have to find out for myself.

SIX

Sapper Edwards

The problem of Sapper Edwards needed to be dealt with promptly and I vowed that today I could not put this unpleasant duty off any longer. The offence for which he was charged, being late on parade and drunkenness, was committed on Friday night/Saturday morning last and it was now Thursday. I felt that the longer it went on without resolution by military sanction the more that Bryn Edwards thought he had got away with it. His surly attitudes when given orders by the NCOs was beginning to undermine their authority through his bragging to the junior soldiers that he could do as he liked because I was too weak to do anything to him. At this moment, he was a minor irritation but if not dealt with effectively, he could seriously undermine the discipline of the section. I spent the first hour of the morning writing up the charge sheet and report of the offence to be presented to the adjutant's office later in the day. When I was done it felt as if a considerable weight was lifted from my shoulders and I sent a runner to company headquarters to deliver the report to the adjutant.

I went about my duties in the section where we were as busy as ever with transport requests and under pressure because we were still three vehicles and six drivers down, as they had not yet returned from the docks at Dunkerque. We were to find out soon enough that this run to port and back was to become our most regular journey as tunnel work used a great deal of equipment and resources in construction and operation. There always seemed to be at least one vehicle every day tasked with a journey to Dunkerque or other channel ports to collect vital stores. I knew that this was part of the build-up for the new mission for the siege company that was coming up fast. Ivan Lewis and I sat together at the desk and thought about how we could accommodate this and maintain the high level of local journeys that would be required, especially when we moved forward. We reconciled ourselves to insisting that as the drivers became more familiar with the conditions in the area, they could make the journey in darkness as well as daytime, to reduce the need for staying overnight. The days were getting longer as January went on and within four weeks or so the days would be significantly lighter.

I was surprised when a runner appeared with message that I was to report to the adjutant at 13:00 today. I reported at the appointed time, but he kept me waiting outside for twenty minutes before I was called in to his office. He was alone, for the two smaller desks were empty. I came to attention, saluted and would have expected to be stood at ease before we conducted our business but I could see that the adjutant was red in the face and flushed with anger when he raised his voice and demanded what was the meaning of this report on his desk. Why had I not followed the chain of command and presented it directly to him? I attempted to explain the circumstances and why it had landed on his desk, and that at the time of the offence I was not aware that we were to have a junior officer in command. In addition, Edwards' past record was littered with many similar charges, which coupled with his frequent postings between battalions and specialist companies of the regiment were evidence of his frequent infringements of military discipline, which all added up to something that was more serious. The adjutant roared back at me that all it showed was that I was not able to discipline my men properly and this should be dealt with in the section. He told me to bring Sapper Edwards before Mr Craddock-Williams so he could deal with this. I tried again to persuade him of the potential seriousness of Edwards' behaviour and the threat he posed on good order and discipline, but he would not listen. He said that if the army court-martialled every soldier who got drunk and disorderly, we would have great difficulty in putting an army in the field on any day. He finished his tirade by saying that if I weren't up to the job, he would have me replaced with someone who was. I then saluted, about turned, and marched out of the office.

I was fuming inside from the injustice of the accusation made by the adjutant about my competence but as I crossed the yard back to the section, it dawned on me that this was probably a deliberate strategy by him to divert any tasks that he considered not worthy of his attention or beneath himto somewhere else. He did not want to be bothered with the business of Edwards' charge, which undoubtedly would have gone further up the line to the company commander or above and would have involved him in a fair amount of work in drawing together all the evidence for presentation at a court martial hearing sometime in the future.

I felt sorry for Mr Craddock-Williams who I believed had neither the experience nor the authority to impose an appropriate sanction on Edwards that would serve as a deterrent to preventing the repetition of this kind of behaviour. Luckily, I caught up with the lieutenant in the section marquee where he was waiting to see me. Ivan Lewis made himself scarce so that I could talk freely. I told him about the charge and showed him the report that I had sent to the adjutant. I described how the adjutant had refused to deal with it, as he said it was not serious enough to be escalated to him and that he should deal with it. I explained to him why I did not bring it to him in the first place, because the offence took place in Crickhowell, where Edwards got drunk, then missed the morning parade and was unable to perform his convoy driving duty. I suggested that as a subaltern, he had little more authority than me to impose a sanction on Edwards which would bring about any change in his behaviour. We discussed this for an hour but then agreed that we had no choice but to bring Edwards before the section commander immediately after morning parade on Friday, and the charge would be heard. The discussion of the severity of the punishment was not supposed to take place until after guilt or innocence had been established, when the officer opens the sealed antecedents of the charged soldier and considers the appropriate penalty in the light of his previous record. We had both read Edwards' record and we knew that it was packed with many previous appearances before section commanders, adjutants, and company commanders in every unit he had served with. I believed that to teach Edwards an appropriate lesson, he should be committed to twenty-eight days' detention but neither I nor Mr Craddock-Williams had the authority to give him that sentence. The most severe sentence penalty we could impose on him was fourteen days' extra duties, plus fourteen days' deduction of pay and fourteen days confined to barracks. I was sure that Edwards would see this as water off a duck's back and walk away smiling.

When I was alone with Ivan later in the day, I confided in him what had transpired over Edwards with the adjutant earlier in the day and what Mr Craddock-Williams and I had decided we could do, given the constraints imposed on us. He understood and advised me to bide my time because he was sure that Edwards would, almost certainly, see himself emboldened to offend again, especially if he thought he could get off lightly. We were now in the theatre of war and men unable to carry out their duties because of incapacity through drink were dealt with much more harshly than at home. As always, I could rely on sound advice from Ivan; I decided that I would keep a close watch on Edwards and bide my time.

At 08:00 the next morning, I marched Sapper Edwards escorted by two L/Cpls into the marquee in front of the section commander. I read out the charge and the corroborating evidence from L/Cpls Hughes and Lewis, 2nd Lieutenant Craddock-Williams listened attentively and then asked Edwards if he had anything to say. Edwards replied that he had only slipped out for a couple of drinks and was not drunk, but just overslept in the morning and was only a few minutes late on parade. Mr Craddock-Williams sat silent for a few minutes and then spoke quietly and with an authority that belied his youth, cleared his throat and addressed him formally, "Sapper Edwards 892, I find that the evidence is conclusive. You were the only member of the section to absent yourself from the barracks that evening to drink in the public houses in Crickhowell village. This in itself was not an offence as you were not confined to barracks as such, but you knew that the section was leaving in convoy early the following morning and blatantly drank so much alcohol that you overslept, and the convoy was unable to leave on schedule. You had a responsibility to restrict your alcohol intake so that you would be able to perform your duties in the morning. You are guilty of being absent on parade. The second charge of drunkenness is also proved because of the testimony of members of your section, who had to drag you out of your bed and who have sworn that you were dishevelled and smelt strongly of alcohol and vomit. I take note that you slept in the back of one of the trucks for most of the day and Sapper Davies had to take over your driving duties."

He then told Edwards that he was going to look at his antecedents, opened the sealed envelope and read through the contents in some detail. He looked up and continued in the same authoritative manner, "Edwards, you are an experienced soldier who has served at the front before and as such have a responsibility to serve as a model of behaviour for junior soldiers to learn from and emulate, but I notice from your records that you have frequently been charged with similar offences stretching back over two years. I count eight charges of drunkenness, six of being late on parade and can see that you are a habitual offender with little regard for discipline and the safety of your comrades when you have been drinking. I am going to put you on report for the next three months to monitor your progress in this section and you will be fined fourteen days' pay, given fourteen days extra duties under the supervision of L/Cpl Hughes and stoppage of all leave until your report is satisfactory."

He concluded his remarks by saying that this was an extremely serious matter, and this kind of behaviour would not be tolerated in this section. Any further occurrence of this offence would lead to serious repercussions and far more serious consequences as we were now about to go to the frontline and every man in the section must be able to rely one hundred percent on his comrades. Edwards saluted and was marched out of the tent, and I turned to congratulate Mr Craddock-Williams on his performance to see the resolve in his face capitulate with relief that this unpleasant duty was over with. I realised that a performance was what he had steeled himself to give and he had delivered it excellently. I told him I was really impressed with the way he had heard the charge and delivered the sentence in an exemplary fashion. He smiled and then admitted that he was so scared that his voice would crack and that there were shivers down his back.

Edwards was very subdued that night and I do not think that he expected to be so closely supervised and punished to the maximum by the young subaltern. He kept himself to himself and did not join in the conversation around the makeshift dining table that evening. I think that he realised that his card had been marked and we would be watching him for further infringements. Edwards kept his head down over the next few days, and perhaps this led to a false hope that he had mended his ways. Although we still did not know what date we would be moving forward to begin the tunnelling work, there was a great sense of anticipation and all sections were busy in the next few weeks with the necessary planning and preparatory work for the secret mission. Mr Craddock-Williams and I were kept extremely busy in planning the schedules for moving all the equipment and stores to our forward base in the most efficient manner, given the limited number of drivers and vehicles in our possession. The sapper companies would have to march to our new positions with their kit on their backs, but a small advance party would have to go forward and prepare the ground to receive them without drawing too much attention from the German lines. Every one of us was fully engaged in the tasks at hand and the boys of the transport section were increasingly becoming known and accepted by the sappers in the other companies.

About four days or so after my heated interview with the adjutant, he summoned me again but this time he was less choleric and reasonably civil in manner. He asked me how we were settling in and how was I coping with the second lieutenant who he realised must be a burden to me. I did not rise to this and commented neutrally that things were shaping up well and we were already well prepared for the move forward when it came. I would not be drawn on commenting on the performance of my officer in this informal manner, as I did not think it was my place to comment unofficially on his performance behind his back. The adjutant did not press me further but made a request for a driver to be allocated to him in the run-up period to the start of our new mission. He needed to visit Second Army HQ regularly, at different times of the day and short notice. I said that could be arranged and I would get L/Cpl Lewis to study the driver schedules and allocate a driver accordingly. He immediately replied that there was no need to disrupt the schedules as we had a driver who was on report and restricted to work around the camp only. I realised he meant Sapper Edwards and was about to protest that he was under punishment and could not be trusted fully. The adjutant smiled and replied that he would ensure that Edwards performed his duties to the letter whilst he was under his supervision. I had no choice but to agree to his request, although I felt that Edwards was going to feel some satisfaction that he was escaping some of his punishment by being the adjutant's driver instead of being confined to camp.

When I broke the news to Mr Craddock-Williams and Ivan Lewis back in the section, they were incensed and disappointed but realised that we could not disobey a direct request from the adjutant. The first request for Edwards to drive the adjutant came that afternoon. He was to drive the adjutant to Armentièeres for a meeting at the adjutant general's office at 19:00 that evening. Ivan Lewis detailed Edwards to undertake this task and gave him stern warnings about the need for his behaviour to be exemplary, because he was driving the company adjutant who was a stickler for correctness. Ivan could see that Edwards was elated that he would be getting out of the camp and to Armentièeres, which was a large and lively town by all accounts. Edwards took one of the light vans and set off to pick up the adjutant at a few minutes before seven. The duty watch of drivers were still working during the evening, whilst those on the schedule for tomorrow morning were relaxing, writing letters, or lying in their beds.

By midnight, the duty watch was stood down, but Edwards had not yet returned with the adjutant and L/Cpl Hughes volunteered to stay up to see the vehicle checked back in. I thanked him but sent him to bed as I slept at one end of the marquee only separated from the main working area by a curtain, so I would certainly hear them return and do the necessary. I lay on my bed lightly dozing but keeping an ear out for the return of our vehicle and as the time passed, I found myself falling more heavily asleep. At 02:45, I got up and made a brew and was just thinking of going back to bed when I heard the engine of a light vehicle approaching and I took a peep out of the tent flap to see the light van pull up outside of the farmhouse and the adjutant get out. A couple of minutes later, the tent flap was pushed open, and Edwards came in to drop off the vehicle movement order and keys and sign the book with the mileage and time. I stood in the shadows by my curtain,watched him do this, then spoke and Edwards nearly jumped through the marquee wall with surprise. I asked if he had a good trip, were there any problems, and he said all was well. As I moved closer to him, I thought I could detect a whiff of alcohol on his breath but then thought that not even Edwards would risk drinking when he was driving the company adjutant, and I dismissed the thought from my mind. He left saying he was anxious to get to bed and I turned in too, but as I was putting my clothes away, I looked at my pocket watch on the bedside cabinet and it was 03:10. I thought that there must have been a lot to discuss with the adjutant general's staff for a meeting deep into the night. Armentieeres was only a twenty-minute drive each way and staff officers don't usually work beyond dinner time. Anyway, it was late, so I dismissed this from my mind, climbed back into bed and was soon sound asleep.

In the morning, I couldn't get these thoughts out of my head, checked the log and signing sheet and could see that the mileage was consistent with a return trip to Armentières but that Edwards had signed the vehicle back in at 01:15, nearly two hours before the actual time of his return. I asked L/Cpl Hughes to ask Edwards to drop by the marquee to speak to me some time during this morning, deliberately suggesting that it was not urgent. About an hour later, Edwards appeared at the entrance of the marquee, I called him into the tent and asked him, as casually as possible, what his trip was like the previous evening. He said it was alright, he had dropped the captain at the adjutant general's house in Armentières and waited in the back kitchen whilst the meeting was on and then brought the adjutant back here when it was finished. He said it was very boring, just waiting around but one of the kitchen maids had given him tea and a cake to eat while he waited. I said I just wanted to check what time he returned because the log says 01:15 but as he knew he woke me up and I was sure it was later. He brushed this off and said that he was sure it was at a quarter-past one and he was very glad to get to bed as it was so late. I smiled and said to him not to worry as it was only a feeling I had, and I must have been half asleep and read the time wrong in the dark. When he left, I knew that he was trying to conceal something by putting the incorrect return time in the log. There was two hours unaccounted for when, according to the log, the adjutant and Edwards were in camp when they quite clearly were somewhere else. I did not doubt that the adjutant had attended an official meeting in Armentières but I would like to know where they went for the late evening and early hours of the morning, and then I remembered the hint of alcohol I thought I smelt on Edwards' breath last night and my suspicions grew.

I decided to share my suspicions with Ivan Lewis and Gareth Hughes and after they had listened to my story, they quizzed me closely about whether I was sure about the time and that I was not just befuddled by sleep. I was certain because I had deliberately looked at my pocket watch and saw that it was ten-past three in the morning, which I thought far too late to be returning from a meeting in Armentières. I admitted that I was not sure about the alcohol but was certain about the time. Eventually, they believed that I was probably correct about the time but without corroborative evidence of the actual time of the return, it would be my word against Edwards'. If the adjutant had decided to go on somewhere to eat and drink before returning to camp, Edwards would have no choice but to obey.

I agreed with their cautious words, and we decided to watch for any further log discrepancies that might occur when Edwards was driving the adjutant. We did not have to wait too long although the next two trips took place during the day, they were quite short and there were no log discrepancies. However, the next one in the evening came up early in the following week and was another meeting at Second Army HQ. Edwards collected his passenger at a few minutes before 19:00 and when they returned, signed back in at 00:45 and went to bed. Unbeknown to him, Ivan and Gareth were waiting for his return and checked the actual time of return as 02:15 and again the log had been filled in incorrectly. Both L/Cpls made a note in the log affirming the inaccuracy and signed it. We now had some proof that the log was being falsified by Edwards, but we did not have a clue why he would be doing this. If he was simply having to wait for the officer whilst he was carousing in town, why was it necessary to conceal the time of their return? It appeared as if he was trying to establish an alibi for himself and the adjutant, but why would he feel that he had to falsify the vehicle log to protect the reputation of this officer that he hardly knew?

On three further occasions in the next two weeks, Edwards drove the adjutant to Armentières and on each of the occasions, he returned late and entered a false return time in the log. We were confused and perplexed about what we could do about this and decided that the next time, one of us should follow them on the motorcycle and see where they went and why they were so long. We drew straws and Ivan Lewis drew the short one and we planned how he would follow them from a discreet distance and make notes of where they went and times etc. Three days later, a request came for an evening trip to Armentières and Edwards was assigned as usual as the driver. Ivan was ready on the bike hidden from view and was totally unrecognisable under goggles, leather helmet and greatcoat. As soon as Edwards turned left out of the farm track towards Bailleul, Ivan set off slowly behind them because he knew they were heading for Armentières, he could keep well back so as not arouse their suspicions of being followed. He pulled up much closer when they reached the town, but always kept another vehicle between them where possible and when the van pulled into the driveway leading to the adjutant general's offices he followed but pulled off the road and into the trees so as not to be seen.

He put the bike on its stand and silently made his way to a position where he could see the van stopped at the back entrance of the house that he presumed were the servant's quarters. There was no sign of the adjutant, but the van's rear doors were wide open, and Edwards was coming out of the house carrying boxes and stacking them behind the van. Ivan could see through his binoculars that there were four crates of good quality champagne and two boxes of brandy. The adjutant appeared and shook hands with another man who Ivan did not recognise and ordered Edwards to load the van. As there was only one entrance to this property, Ivan sprinted back to the bike to be ready to follow the van when it left in a few minutes. Following the van would be more difficult this time because the traffic was less than there had been earlier, and he would have to keep close as he did not know their destination, but he still managed to follow them undetected. They were making their way to the centre of town and the streets were busier with off-duty soldiers thronging the cafes and bars that populated this area. The crowds were so thick that progress was almost at walking pace and he almost missed the van turn up a side street. He waited at the corner and could see that it was a dead end, so reckoned that they must have reached their destination. The van had backed up to a door, which had opened at the rear throwing a shaft of bright light into the darkened street. The building itself would have its frontage onto the next street, and he decided that he would have to go around to the front to identify specifically what kind of establishment it was.

He parked the bike against the wall and keeping his motorcycling gear on, sauntered up the darkened street keeping in the shadows as much as he could, and could see Edwards unloading the boxes into the back door of this premises but no sign of the adjutant. When Edwards completed unloading the six boxes of alcohol, he shut up the van and disappeared inside the door, which was slammed with a loud bang. Ivan crossed the road, took a closer look and in the dim light he almost missed a small sign to the right of the door which said, "Club Casbah, kitchen entrance only". Ivan discovered nothing more here and decided to wander around to the front but removed the motorcycling gear so as he would blend in with the crowds who were mostly in uniform. It took him nearly ten minutes to make his way to the corner and then turn into the street where he was sure the nightclub would be. About a hundred yards ahead there was a substantial frontage lit up with a large sign,"Club Casbah";it looked a rather smart establishment and judging by the clientele who seemed to be exclusively Allied officers, it would be expensive too. There were a couple of liveried doormen in French Algerian costumes to control entry at the door, and he could hear dance music and glimpse couples dancing on a crowded dance floor. It seemed obvious to Ivan that this was a high-class brothel set up to make fat profits from the officer class. Ivan, as a life-long chapel man, did not really approve of this kind of immoral behaviour. He returned to the bike and redressed in the motorcycling gear for warmth and to be ready for a quick getaway when they decided to leave Club Casbah and return to camp. Ivan moved the bike to the end of the dead-end street so he would be hidden in the darkness and waited. It was now nearly midnight and he guessed he would have a couple of hours to wait before they would leave.

It was 01:45 when they finally emerged from the back entrance and climbed into the van and neither of them gave even a glance towards the end of the street, so he was reassured that his cover was still intact. Edwards drove off and turned right but by now the crowds had thinned considerably and he made faster progress. Ivan kept well back until he was sure that they were not making any more illicit calls tonight so when they were about halfway to Bailleul, he overtook the van and sped away so that they would not see him turn for camp and suspect they had been followed. He was back in camp ten minutes before Edwards and sure enough he again entered a false return time like the previous occasions.

The following morning Ivan Lewis told us the full story and said that he would submit a full report of all that he had observed. We knew that we did not have enough evidence to bring an accusation forward against Edwards and certainly not against an officer. The evidence that we had now collected told us that Captain Vaughan was using meetings at the adjutant general's office as a cover for some illicit black-market trading in high-quality wines and spirits, possibly in partnership with an unknown member of the staff there and then selling the alcohol on to a nightclub establishment in the town. We reckoned that this would probably be quite a lucrative trade because deliveries seem to be made every four days or so, and we estimated that 120 bottles a week would probably bring in the equivalent of at least £200 a week in profit which, even shared between two, would supplement an officer's income nicely. The captain seemed to spend three or four hours enjoying the entertainments of the nightclub after each delivery. Edwards was also observed to be inside the nightclub but given the high status of the clientele, we surmised that he waited in the kitchens until Captain Vaughan had completed his business to his satisfaction. We guessed that Captain Vaughan had an arrangement with Edwards, which probably involved additional payments or privileges to buy his cooperation.

We wondered why the adjutant had selected Edwards as collaborator in this venture so quickly after our arrival, but we guessed again that his attention was drawn to Edwards by the report of his conduct and the charge sheet I sent to him a few weeks earlier. He had noted that Edwards had been involved in many breaches of discipline during his service career and could probably be persuaded to be a willing participant in his criminal venture. The evidence was very flimsy and would be unlikely to attract much attention from the provost marshals in any case. We were frustrated that there was so little we could do to put a stop to their escapade.

It was nearly a week before another evening trip was booked by Captain Vaughan and this time, I drew the short straw and would follow them. As we knew that the destination was the same as on all previous occasions, I rode on the motorbike to the wooded area with a good view of the servants' entrance and waited for the van to arrive. Within fifteen minutes the van arrived, parked close to the door and the captain went in. Edwards opened the rear doors ready to receive the load, which this time seemed to be a larger consignment as I counted nine crates of champagne and four cases of brandy. Captain Vaughan came out, when the loading was complete, accompanied by a man in the uniform of the army commissariat, they shook hands, the captain got into the van and they drove off. I ran back to the bike, kick-started the engine and followed them discreetly in the direction of the centre of town. I knew from the details given by Ivan Lewis in his report the approximate location of Club Casbah so did not have to keep too close behind them. Just as before, they turned into the back street behind the club, unloaded at the back door and after a further thirty minutes, as they had not come out, I decided to go back to camp and await their return. I heard Edwards parking the van at 03:25 and noted the time and then checked the log the next morning to find that he had signed the log with a return time of 01:05. We were now sure that Captain Vaughan and the commissariat lieutenant had a regular racket supplying army stores illegally to civilian businesses. The Commissariat were responsible for the supply of all stores and equipment, including food, wines and spirits for officers' messing and it was not too difficult to see how, with the large quantities being supplied, that a few crates and cases went astray. What we were not able to understand was what was the connection between Vaughan and the commissariat officer and how and why they were involved together. We were at a loss as to what more we could do to put a stop to this sordid illegal trade.

Orders had now been received for the siege company to move forward to new positions much closer to the front line,,to begin work on the subways leading towards the German fortifications in the Passchendaele Valley and our attention became more focused on the preparations for the move in three days. Ivan and I were busy with the route cards and convoy orders, liaising with the section NCOs to ensure that nothing was left behind. The CO asked for me to take him right forward to the front line on the motorcycle and sidecar again for a second look at a couple of places where he needed more information. He wanted to see the areas that afforded the best view over the valley towards the village of Passchendaele. This time, I kept the bike engine running when we stopped close to the enemy lines to avoid another close shave with a German patrol. General Haig and the high command wished to make greater use of the tunnellers, not only to lay explosives underneath the enemy fortifications but also to construct subways underground that would enable our troops to attack the enemy without crossing the open ground of no-man's-land and to save the large number of casualties caused by withering machine-gun fire in every such attack in the war so far. There was much confidence that if we could break through around Arras and break out from the Ypres Salient, the Germans would be dealt a massive blow and be pushed back many miles. At the same time, there were rumours circulating that the Americans would be entering the war sometime soon and this would certainly lead to a German capitulation by the end of the year. These frenetic preparations took precedence over our detective work to uncover Captain Vaughan's illegal trade and it was decided to put it on hold for the time being as we felt that our move into action would probably curtail their activities immediately. However, we could be proved wrong because when the company moved up much closer to the German lines, the HQ support was to be located three kilometres to the rear in the village of Westhoek, which gave good access to the main road to Armentières and allowed for transport to reach the channel ports easily. Ironically, it turned out that the journey to Armentières from here would be less difficult than in our present location.

The transport section set up its base in some sheds that were still standing on the eastern side of Westhoek, about half a mile distant from the main company HQ who were housed in a deserted village house. We needed sufficient room to accommodate our vehicles, especially as we had taken delivery of three larger lorries and a light car with three more drivers to swell our numbers. The larger vehicles could carry much heavier loads, meaning we could keep the tunnellers supplied with sufficient lumber and equipment to keep pace with their construction work underground. The movement day was set for the 2nd of March and the officers decided to hold a St David's Day dinner in their mess the night before. They pulled out all the stops to have an excellent affair, inviting guests from Second Army HQ and other surrounding units. Our officers dressed for dinner and the CSM had managed to find a quartet of musicians from the regimental band of a light infantry battalion billeted close to us to provide music for dinner. Sergeant Evans, the senior cook, had procured some Welsh lamb to be served as the main course of the traditional Welsh dinner. Corporal Haley from one of the tunnelling sections had assembled a small choir of about ten voices who would sing some traditional Welsh songs and lead the singing of, "Land of My Fathers" and, "'God Save the King'" Mr Craddock-Williams, as the most junior officer in the mess, had been detailed off to assemble half a dozen young and presentable sappers to volunteer to act as stewards for the evening and three of our young drivers had agreed to do so. He also wanted to ask Ivan Lewis if he would write the name cards for the table settings in his lovely copperplate handwriting. Ivan agreed and the lieutenant left the table plan with a list of officers plus guests with their ranks, decorations and medals and units on his desk.

Later when Ivan sat down to write the name cards, he called me over and showed me a name on the list, Lieutenant C. J. Vaughan, Army Commissariat Corp. We were both struck with the coincidence that he had the same name as the adjutant and whether he was the mysterious commissariat officer that Ivan and I had both seen at the adjutant general's offices in Armentières. This seemed to be a major coincidence; we both agreed to find out who he was and who had invited him to the dinner. After Ivan had completed the name cards, he wandered over to company HQ to deliver them to Mr Craddock-Williams. He entered the office, saluted the adjutant, gave the 2nd lieutenant the completed cards and then in casual conversation he dropped in that one of the guests was called Vaughan and he asked the adjutant directly whether he knew him. Captain Vaughan bristled but then replied that it was his younger brother who was serving in Armentières and is coming to the dinner as his guest but what it had got to do with us? Ivan removed himself from the office and hurried back to the section to impart what he had discovered.

We had now found the connection between them and how they came to be in this together. The little pieces of the jigsaw were beginning to come together and perhaps we would be able to find the proof to bring them all to justice. I did not think that Edwards was a partner in this venture but just the hired hand who drove the delivery van when required. I was sure that Edwards was dispensable and would be ditched when he no longer suited their purpose. Ivan and I decided to position ourselves so that we could see the guests arriving for the dinner, to see if we could positively identify the mysterious commissariat officer when he arrived. We were in luck because his small car stopped close to us, the driver got out to open the door on our side and we got a good close view of Lieutenant Vaughan, who did appear to have some family resemblance to his elder brother. He looked straight towards us, and we were certain that he was the officer we had both seen in Armentières on our surveillance trips. We now knew this was a family affair and that we would have to prove the guilt of both of them to stop their criminal activity for good.

The mess dinner seemed to go very well, and our officers and their guests dined on an excellent meal and enjoyed the music and choral singing afterwards. The evening ended around ten-thirty as we were to be on the move by 06:00 in the morning, so the guests began departing just after ten o'clock. The young sappers, who served as stewards, had enjoyed it too and had been fed with some of the leftover lamb and a glass of wine for their trouble. The CO had decreed that there would not be any excessive drinking given the operational circumstances and the camp was quiet by eleven o'clock, as we all needed to be on our mettle for the move forward in the morning. I was soon asleep but after what seemed ages of deep sleep, I was roused by sounds of drunken singing close by and so I dragged myself out of my bed, pulled on my boots and went to investigate the cause of the commotion outside my tent. I did not have to venture far to see Sapper Edwards rolling around and shouting at the top of his voice in a drunken state. He was holding a magnum of champagne and swigging from it as he lurched about the yard. Ivan Lewis, Gareth Hughes, and George Smithers appeared, and I knew that we could handle this together. Gareth removed the bottle from his right hand and laid it on the ground and the three lance corporals carried Edwards, who had now lapsed into a kind of stupor to his tent. We put him to bed, covered him over with a blanket and hoped he would sleep it off by the morning.

I was sure that this time he had gone too far and was certain that a custodial sentence awaited him when he came before the CO. Ivan looked around the tent and found a second bottle of champagne empty. It looked as if Edwards had consumed nearly three litres of the stuff and it was not surprising, he could hardly stand up. Ivan carried the evidence back to the marquee and we began to wonder where he had got two magnum bottles of expensive champagne. Gareth surmised that Edwards had probably pilfered from the cases delivered to the farmhouse before the mess dinner and we decided to check in the morning. As it happened, I did not need to check as one of the new sappers, Billy Williams, who had been a hotel wine waiter before the war saw the bottles on the table and remarked that someone had expensive tastes. I asked him what he meant, and he explained that the labels showed that these bottles had contained Dom Perignon 1914 vintage and were expensive to buy. I asked him whether this was the champagne served at the table last night, for I knew that he had been one of the volunteers the night before. He said that the mess had served a Bollinger non-vintage, which was good but not so expensive as the Dom Perignon. We were now quite mystified as to how Edwards had acquired these expensive bottles of champagne and I summoned Mr Craddock-Williams so that we could charge Edwards and prepare a report to go this time to the adjutant for punishment.

In the meantime, I tasked Ivan Lewis to pull Edwards from his bed and give him a cold bath to wake him up and present him in front of the section commander at 05:30. Edwards looked pale and ill when he marched in front of Mr Craddock-Williams, who formally told him he was to be charged with drunken and disorderly behaviour with further charges probable if he did not answer our questions honestly. He was asked where he got the champagne from because its value was many times more than a sapper's pay could afford. He said that he had not stolen it; the bottles of champagne were given to him as a gift. We found it hard to believe him because who would he know who could afford to give away such expensive presents, or be inclined to do so? He said that it was his business but when it was impressed on him that he would be charged with stealing them he relented and admitted that Captain Vaughan had given them to him to thank him for all the times he had driven him, "He told me not to drink them as that might cause unnecessary questions regarding where he got them from. The captain told me that I could sell them for a good price to any of the café owners in Armentières. He told me to hide them carefully until such time as I got some leave when I could sell them for some extra spending money."

The fact that he had implicated Captain Vaughan made things much more complicated because he could now no longer hear the charge against Edwards. I advised Mr Craddock-Williams that we must take this to the CO, who would know how to deal with it. We presented ourselves at Major Rees-Evans' door, knocked and waited for an answer. After a couple of minutes, the major opened the door, and it was clear that he had been shaving when we knocked. He listened carefully to the full story, fell silent while he thought for a few minutes, then he said to us both that we must keep silent and keep the lid on this for twenty-four hours. We needed to make our move to our forward operating area that day and could not be diverted from this but would deal with this in the following morning. He said he would call the provost marshals and ask for an investigator to join us at our new headquarters, who would interview Edwards and Captain Vaughan separately and get to the bottom of this business.

"I don't want rotten apples in our company whether they are drunkards or thieves," and with that statement he dismissed us to carry on.

SEVEN

Captain Herbert Vaughan

Major Rees-Evans kept to his word and even though the move was hectic we all worked throughout the day and well into the night to move our positions closer to the enemy, he had signalled the provost marshal who designated Major Rydall as the chief investigator. Major Rydall was at company headquarters the following morning, accompanied by a provost sergeant, and began the day by interviewing Sapper Edwards for over four hours in one of the rooms upstairs in the requisitioned house. We were all still preoccupied with completing the move successfully and moving the tunnelling supplies up the line to each of the mining sections so that they could start work. This was much more dangerous than working a few miles back from the front line and the drivers were now fully armed with a pistol and their service rifle in case of attack. Driving vehicles close to the front lines could be hazardous as they often attracted enemy attention from snipers or aircraft, so all drivers had to be always on alert for possible attacks. After lunch, Major Rydall indicated that he wished to interview L/Cpls Lewis and Hughes, myself and then Mr. Craddock-Williams to take our statements before speaking with Captain Vaughan. Edwards was held in detention in one of the upstairs bedrooms where a guard was placed on the door. There had been no opportunity for Edwards to communicate with the adjutant since the events of last night, so it was hoped that Captain Vaughan was ignorant of the specifics of what was going on today. We did recognise, however, that he would know that Edwards was drunk and disorderly because it was common knowledge amongst the men, but we hoped that he did not know that he had been implicated by Edwards' profession of innocence of stealing the two magnums of champagne.

Rydall and his sergeant were thorough in their questioning and re-covered our involvement in the events several times before we were asked to commit them to paper in the form of sworn statements. I was close questioned, more than once, about why I did not proceed against Edwards as soon as I was certain that he was falsifying the vehicle logs which should have been my first duty. They were right and I admitted that I did not charge Edwards because I believed we could find out the reason behind the false return times and possibly discover something more criminal. The major reminded me that in military law the end does not necessarily justify the means and my failing to prosecute one offence to catch the perpetrator in a bigger, more serious offence was a breach of my responsibility as the section corporal. He went on to state that our amateur detective work enabled us to discover a great deal of circumstantial evidence over a long period of time whereas if the provost marshals had been informed at the earliest opportunity of our suspicions, an escalation of the crimes could have been avoided. Suitably chastised I left the room and realised that I had just been taught a useful lesson in how army discipline worked by the major. If I had put a stop to Edwards falsifying the logs at an earlier juncture and investigated the reasons why he did this on every occasion he drove Captain Vaughan, the provost investigators could have stopped the theft and sale of contraband to civilian businesses much sooner. Later in the day, Mr Craddock-Williams came to the section after his interview and told us that he had been chastised much in the same way as I had. However, he had just seen the provost major and his sergeant go into the adjutant's office and close the door.

We heard no more that night but the next morning there was a request for a driver and the light car to take Major Rydall to Armentières. Sapper Davies was despatched at 08:00 to collect the major and his sergeant and they did not return until well after eleven. We were anxious to know where they had been, and Davies told us about the trip to the adjutant general's offices in Armentièees and that they had picked up a commissariat lieutenant who had accompanied them back here. He said that he thought he was one of the guests at the St David's dinner the other night, but he was not certain. Lieutenant Vaughan was interviewed most of the afternoon in the same upstairs room and then held in detention in the bedroom next door whilst Edwards was interviewed again at length. At eight thirty that evening, Mr Craddock-Williams, and I were summoned to the CO who met us in his room with Major Rydall. Major Rees-Evans told us that Major Rydall had made excellent progress with the investigation and wished to thank us both for our cooperation.

"Although he has made some remarks about your initial handling of the situation, he feels that you have both conducted yourselves well and learned valuable lessons from this incident. Edwards and Lieutenant Vaughan have made full confessions of their part in this criminal venture and an arrest warrant has been sworn out for Captain Vaughan, who seems to have disappeared from company headquarters sometime this afternoon." Major Rydall continued that it was now imperative to arrest the civilian business owners who were receiving the stolen military supplies and he was pleased to say that Sapper Edwards had volunteered to be part of the subterfuge and drive the van for the next delivery to the Club Casbah scheduled for tomorrow night. We would be on hand to arrest them receiving the stolen goods in person. They had hoped that Captain Vaughan would be persuaded to confess and take part, in exchange for a more lenient sentence, but his disappearance had made that impossible. However, Sapper Edwards, he reassured us, would be dealt with severely for the further offence of drunkenness and for falsifying army records, and would receive twenty-eight days in the military prison near Arras, but on the charge of handling stolen goods they were satisfied that he was coerced by Captain Vaughan into keeping quiet on the threat of being punished by the adjutant more severely, the next time he was in trouble. Captain and Lieutenant Vaughan would be tried by court martial after the full extent of the thefts has been established by a thorough audit of the wine and spirit stores in Armentieres and the captain apprehended.

I was then dismissed and left the room, but Mr Craddock-Williams was asked to remain. I waited outside for him to come out and about five minutes later he appeared with a grin on his face. I could not guess what the reason was for his happiness and pressed him to spill the beans and not keep me in suspense. He said that he was to be promoted to acting lieutenant with effect from today and to take over as adjutant on a temporary basis until a replacement could be appointed.

The CO said he was reluctant to take a more experienced officer from one of the tunnelling sections now that we are about to start underground operations in earnest. He said I had improved greatly in my performance over the past couple of months since taking over the transport section. He said that working with you and the others in the section had boosted my confidence and made me tackle military life as an officer more seriously. I shook his hand, congratulated him, then saluted him, called him Mr. Adjutant and we went across to the section sheds to impart the news to the others. We were delighted and a bottle of red wine was found to toast our new adjutant.

We were pleasantly surprised by the way in which Mr Craddock-Williams settled into the responsibilities of his new job, almost from day one he seemed to master what needed to be done and forged a good working relationship with the CSM and the section heads to meet their administrative needs as effectively as he could. The one blow to me though, although I could see why he had done so, was to arrange to transfer Ivan Lewis from the transport section to be office manager in the headquarters section. This would be a loss to the efficiency of the transport section because we all relied on Ivan for such a lot, but the transfer was a good step up for Ivan and was accompanied by the addition of a second tape, which was good news too. I sent an urgent signal to Regimental HQ in Chepstow requesting a replacement section clerk but in the interim, I acted up Sapper Bennett into Ivan's role. This meant that I was now short of an experienced driver just at a time when the demands on our services were increasing dramatically so I was spending more time driving than I should, but it also gave me the opportunity to become proficient driving the mechanical earthmover currently in high demand to initiate the earthworks at the commencement of each new tunnel.

The subways were larger than the underground tunnels, for they were large enough for fully equipped soldiers to move up closer to the enemy line and launch an attack without being seen. They were dug about fifteen feet below the surface and were wide enough for a column of marching men to move freely in either direction. They were relatively easy to keep aerated so that soldiers could breathe normally in them. Some deeper tunnels needed pumping systems to circulate the air to enable the miners to work safely underground, but the subways did not as they were closer to the surface. The subways were dug out from our trenches under no-man's land as far as we could safely go without discovery, and the intention was to allow our troops to launch surprise attacks from right underneath the enemy trenches. In theory, this seemed to be a great idea and would hopefully save the lives of many infantrymen, but in practice the terrain of the land under which they were to be dug had often been badly ravaged by continual artillery fire from both sides so did not present a level surface for the sappers to work on; the preceding winter weather had waterlogged many areas around Ypres which meant extensive drainage work had to be undertaken in some places, before tunnelling could begin. Work had to be conducted in as near to absolute silence as possible so as not to alert the enemy of our intentions too early before the attack. The other unknown was the location of the German tunnels for we were aware, that the enemy were using tunnellers as well as us. Each of the sapper sections had an expert listener and surveyor, who would spend hours underground, listening for the sounds of enemy digging and mapping it on our underground charts. These charts were vital for the avoidance of a collision with a German tunnel somewhere in the middle.

There were several unfortunate incidents in the next few days when I was called on to use the earthmover to dig an entrance for a subway for the miners to start digging out the larger tunnel when the roof had collapsed on top of the men, one was killed and three wounded. This was an early setback, but the sappers were keen and eager and were soon back at work. I returned to the transport section to find Major Rydall's sergeant waiting to speak with me. The major had asked for support from the transport section for the raid on Club Casbah since we were providing Edwards and the van. He wanted L/Cpl Hughes, Smithers, and me to hide in the rear of the van armed with revolvers and for a driver and the light car for the major, Mr Craddock-Williams and himself. The plan was to arrive at the club at the usual time and for Edwards to open the rear doors of the van as usual. He would knock on the door and when it was opened, we would rush the door with our revolvers in our hands and secure the rear entrance whilst at the same time the major, lieutenant and the sergeant, supported by four military policemen, would arrest the doormen and secure the front entrance of the premises so that a proper search of the premises could begin.

We synchronised our watches so that we would be able to undertake action in coordination. That evening we assembled at company headquarters and set off in the two vehicles at eight o'clock; we drove straight to the street behind the Club Casbah and were in position in the dark street by nine. Major Rydall left us to go to the front of the building and rendezvous with the military policemen and we waited for zero hour, which was set for nine forty-five, about the normal time that Vaughan and Edwards usually arrived. Dead on time, Edwards banged on the door, and it opened as expected. The man inside recognised Edwards but was expecting to see Captain Vaughan, so was a little apprehensive as things were not quite right but before he could close the door, the three of us tumbled through it, knocking him over and brandishing our pistols in front of us. I could hear a similar commotion out front and then a single shot and some screaming from inside. I was later to find out that one of the doormen had attempted to stab Major Rydall with his ornamental dagger, but Lt Craddock-Williams had shot him dead in the entrance to the club. The military policemen soon secured the ground floor and sealed the doors so none of the guests could leave until their identification had been checked and noted. George, Gareth, and I followed the major, ran upstairs behind him and began checking each of the rooms on the first floor, many of which were occupied by officers of varying ranks entertaining ladies of varying ages in different stages of undress. The major shouted to us to forget about these officers caught with their trousers down because we were only interested in capturing Captain Vaughan and discovering the ownership of the Club Casbah on this occasion. We ploughed on room by room until the first floor was clear and then mounted the stairs to the second floor, when several shots rang out just as we reached the top of the stairs. We all ducked back behind the balustrade into cover, waited a few seconds and the major ventured up again. I moved quickly behind him and threw myself across the landing into the relative cover of the door frame of the room opposite. I had a good view along the hall and caught a glimpse of Vaughan as he snatched two shots back down the hallway ducking through a door into the room at the end. We rushed down the hall together and crashed through the door to discover Vaughan and an attractive French woman in fine clothes attempting to exit via the sash window, which led to the fire escape. Unfortunately for them, we were so quick in our headlong rush through the door that they had not managed to make good their escape, but it was obvious that they had planned to get away, as there were two packed suitcases in the room. Vaughan had taken off his uniform and was wearing civilian clothes, which meant that he intended to be a deserter as well as a thief. The major opened the first case and found over £50,000 in used notes and the deeds of the Club Casbah, held jointly in the names of Herbert Vaughan and Madame Cecile Beauchamp.

Vaughan was put in handcuffs and the lady, who we presumed to be Madame Beauchamp, was placed on the chair next to him. The room was searched thoroughly, and more incriminating evidence was soon found which pointed to the extent of the theft of expensive wine and spirits from the military stores. The officers' mess was able to procure expensive food, wine, and spirits for entertaining at wholesale prices through the military stores. The Vaughan brothers had been systematically stealing small amounts from many consignments and covering them by falsifying records or by writing them off as breakages in transit. It started as a small enterprise just to liberate a few bottles of good champagne for their own consumption but rapidly developed into a very lucrative business. Major Rydall removed Vaughan and the lady to military custody at the provost marshal HQ for further questioning. He thanked Lieutenant Craddock-Williams for saving his life at the front door by his prompt and accurate shooting and for the support of the rest of us, and said we were free to return to our unit. He reminded the lieutenant that he would need to give a statement of the circumstances of the shooting of the doorman for the report but that this was only a formality. Edwards was also taken into custody again and removed to the provost holding cells for transport to Arras military prison to begin his twenty-eight-day sentence. Gareth Hughes drove the van back and we all chatted excitedly about the successful conclusion of events of the night so far but by the time we reached base, we were coming down from the high and tiredness was setting in. I managed to write a short letter to Ruby describing the events leading up to tonight and expressing my love for her before turning in.

Subsequently, we heard greater details that filtered from the provost marshal investigations, and it was announced that both brothers were to be tried by court martial at Second Army headquarters in seven days. Madame Beauchamp was handed over to the Belgian civil authorities for action and the Club Casbah closed permanently. Court martial procedures differ from civilian courts as the accused are not required to plead, guilty or not guilty, for it is the purpose of the members of the court martial to establish guilt or innocence of the charges brought before them by examining the evidence. The court usually consists of five officers appointed by the presiding military authority. In this case, the General Commanding the Second Army, General Haig, who had selected as members of the court Lt. Col. Jordan, Royal Engineers who was to be chairman of the court and Lt.Col. Colston, Royal Artillery; Major Alston, Army Commissariat Corp; Major Llewellyn, South Wales Borderers and Captain Millington, Adjutant General Corp. The judge advocate's representative was Col. Hannan whose role was to ensure that the court proceedings were conducted properly within the constraints of military law and to advise the court members in his summing up of the evidence of points of law before they retired to consider their verdict. The case was prosecuted by Major Weston, who had been a noted barrister in civilian life, and the Vaughan's represented by Captain Thomas who had been nominated by both of Vaughans, as prisoner's friend. The events of the court martial did not concern us much, except that I was called to give evidence on day one mostly concerning the vehicle logs, the recording of frequent journeys made by Captain Vaughan to Armentieres and the false entry of the return times. This evidence was not disputed by Captain Thomas and I was dismissed very quickly, but as the week went on the story began to unfold.

Lieutenant Vaughan admitted that it had started when he pilfered one or two bottles of good champagne or brandy to share with his friends or his brother from time to time and soon found that his false entries in the paperwork were never questioned, that it was easy to take bottles on a more regular basis, to sell them to friends and acquaintances. Captain Vaughan, however, seemed to be the driving force behind turning this into a more profitable business venture. Herbert Vaughan had been stationed near Arras and became a regular visitor to the cafes and nightclubs in Armentieres when he could. He became enamoured with a pretty courtesan and hostess in the Café Pigalle, Cecile Beauchamp, and visited her whenever he could. Herbert was totally besotted with her and would do anything to be with her. On some occasions, he would take one of the bottles of fine quality champagne he got from his brother to share with her. She recognised the business opportunity that lay here and persuaded him to work with his brother to secure a more regular supply of wines and spirits so she could use her contacts to gather a circle of discreet customers amongst the café and nightclub owners. She was a good saleswoman; their business grew extremely fast, and it became more difficult for the younger Vaughan to keep up with the demand.

Herbert and Cecile made so much profit that they became equal partners in the purchase of the freehold of a large building in the centre of Armentieres and converted it into the exclusive Club Casbah. The nightclub was a roaring success serving high quality wines and spirits in an excellent dining room and bar, live music and dancing on the ground floor and twenty-four private rooms on the floors above where her guests could indulge their personal tastes with the array of beautiful hostesses who worked for her. Cecile adopted the title "Madame"and retained a commission of fifty percent of the fee the girls charged each client. She had stopped entertaining clients herself and reserved herself solely for Herbert. The Club Casbah soon became the popular venue for senior officers from the Allied forces, but its prices were such that only field and staff officers above the rank of major could afford membership. Some local civilian dignitaries were also regulars, and it was rumoured that even enemy agents and German sympathisers frequented the club to pick up loose-tongued gossip from drunken staff officers about the progress of the war. Cecile and Herbert had little concern about that as the profits were vast and they were becoming seriously rich from the proceeds of their joint venture. They had reckoned that when the British broke through the Ypres Salient and at Arras, their trade would decline as the Allied war machine moved, further forward, into Belgium. Herbert and Cecile were already planning to liquidate their assets and to disappear under false identities to America before that happened.

The presentation of evidence lasted for four days, and the judge advocate summed up the evidence and directed the court to consider some points of law before returning a verdict. He warned them to be careful not to be persuaded that the guilt of the brothers was unequal. They may understand from the evidence that one brother was far more deeply involved than the other in this criminal venture, but did this mean that the other brother was less guilty? He counselled that guilt and innocence were finite and that it was not their job to allocate shades or degrees of guilt for each defendant, but to decide simply whether they were guilty or innocent of each of the charges they faced. If the accused were found guilty then the court may hear mitigation arguments, which may determine that a sliding scale of sentence imposed on each defendant is appropriate. He directed that the first charge of theft and the second charge of handling stolen goods were straightforward enough but indicated that on the third charge of deserting his post that there was little evidence to the guilt of one of the accused to this charge. He finally instructed them not to think about sentences at this stage but only consider guilt or innocence. The court retired to consider the verdict and the court martial was adjourned. The five officers did not take long to consider the evidence against the accused and returned a verdict after five hours.

On charge one, they were both found guilty and the same for charge two but on the charge of deserting their post in time of war, Lt. Vaughan was found not guilty whilst his elder brother was found guilty. The court was adjourned and would pass sentence on the following morning after hearing any mitigation arguments from the defence and recommendations for sentence from the prosecutor. There were three days of arguments over the sentence but finally the court sentenced Lieutenant Vaughan to be stripped of his commission, reduced to the rank of private and sentenced to five years in prison. If the war were still on when he was due for release, he would continue to serve as a private soldier until the war was over. If the war had ended before his sentence, then he would be dishonourably discharged. After his sentence he was immediately led away in custody and the court moved to sentencing Captain Vaughan who was also stripped to the rank of private, and sentenced to ten years in military prison for the thefts and handling of stolen goods, but on the charge of desertion he was sentenced to death by firing squad or twenty years in prison if commuted by the General Officer Commanding Second Army. The execution was scheduled to be carried out at the military prison in Arras within five days. We felt no pleasure in hearing this sentence and although we had no kind thoughts about our former adjutant, nobody in the section wanted him to pay for his crimes with his life. As a postscript to this unfortunate episode Lieutenant Craddock-Williams was mentioned in despatches and I received a commendation from the General Officer Commanding for our part in the raid on the Club Casbah.

The court martial was soon forgotten as we became immersed in the main business of the siege company as the subways proceeded at pace under the stretch of land between the frontline trenches. We were spending most of our time right up at the frontline and we became friends with the mix of Australian and New Zealand troops who occupied the frontage under which the sappers were tunnelling. Sometimes we too had to go underground to help transport bulky and heavy items down the tunnel to those working at the face. This was slow work as noise had to be kept to a minimum and sometimes it took several hours to move a pump or motor just one hundred yards. Seeing the drivers underground helped build a bond between the sappers and us; good friendships and banter were enjoyed on both sides. The forward trenches often came under sporadic fire from enemy snipers and spotters directed artillery fire of aerial attacks on vehicles that could be observed bringing supplies to the front line. We lost Sapper Jones W. and one of our largest lorries loaded with lumber for roof supports in one such incident when two German aircraft swooped out of the clouds, machine gunned Jones and dropped two bombs which set the lorry on fire. Despite some heroic efforts by some of the sappers to get Jones out of the burning cab, he was found to have been shot through the heart and was dead already. This was our first casualty of the war, and we were severely affected by it. Sapper Jones was a quiet young man who worked hard and was loyal to his mates, we his loss greatly. We did not have much time to mourn his passing because the pace of the work had to continue, and we were not able to send anyone to his burial. I promised myself that I would visit his grave the first spare moment that I got.

A couple of weeks after this, Ivan Lewis sent me a note asking me to drop in to see the adjutant at some time during the day. Later that afternoon I found time to present myself at company headquarters and was received warmly by my old boss. He asked Ivan to get us a brew asking how things were going with the section and how the boys were coping with the loss of Walter Jones. I answered all his enquiries but knew that this was not the real reason he had summoned me. I felt that there was something else more serious that he wanted to talk about. Finally, he got to the point; he had received a signal from the provost marshal that Sapper Edwards was to be released from the Arras prison next Monday after completion of his sentence and would return to duty with the section. I was taken aback, mainly because I had given no thought to the fact that an offender would be returned to his old unit after his release from custody, but the adjutant confirmed that, apparently in cases with only short sentences, this always happened. I was not sure whether I wanted him back or not because of the effect he might have on discipline within the section, but also was well aware that my shortage of drivers meant that there was plenty of work for him and he would be kept busy. Mr Craddock-Williams could see I was concerned and said that I could request to transfer him to another company, but in the short term I would have to have him whilst the transfer went through. I thought for a few seconds and then made up my mind. I had always thought that transferring Edwards between units was passing the buck and had been done too many times already in his career, in part contributing to his poor record. I decided that we would try to make something of Sapper Edwards as best we could by making him an essential part of our small section rather than shutting him out.

That evening I took all my NCOs into my confidence about this and although there was some dissent amongst them, we agreed eventually to work together on this. After the others had drifted off, I spent twenty minutes or so talking this through with Gareth Hughes in greater detail. Gareth, as the lead driver, would have direct supervision of Edwards within his team. I was certain that the fact that Edwards had been on report and restricted duties had built a wedge between him and the rest of us. We both agreed that Edwards needed a chance to show he could work as part of the team rather than skulking around the transport section looking for mischief. Gareth suggested that he would immediately take over Walter Jones' tasks in shipping the lumber for the tunnellers mining underneath the German command and control post in the centre of their front line. This was a difficult task because it was operating closest to the enemy line by some hundreds of yards and considerable stealth was required to bring in the loads and unload without stirring up the curiosity of the watchers from the enemy lines. The tunnellers were working mostly at night and consumed the wood for the roof supports daily. Edwards' task would be to ensure that he resupplied the mining team during the day ready for their night shift.

News had filtered through the camp, and it was later posted in daily orders that Herbert Vaughan's sentence had been commuted to life imprisonment with hard labour by General Haig; he was to be returned to Britain to serve his sentence in Colchester Military Prison. Most of us were glad that he had escaped death by firing squad, even though nobody had a kind word to say about him within the siege company. Sapper Edwards reported for duty the following Monday after his release from the Arras detention centre; he had managed to hitch a couple of lifts from Arras to Armentieres and on to our forward positions. My first thought when I saw him was that he seemed smarter and less surly than before, which I thought was a welcome change. I wondered whether this would be only a temporary phase and he would revert to his usual behaviour once he had settled back in but through our conversations that morning and observing his behaviour, I realised that he was somewhat embarrassed to have to come back to the transport section. He had nowhere to hide; every one of us knew his background and record. The opportunity for him to brag about his past exploits had all but disappeared as all the young sappers had now got frontline experiences under their belts too. I think he would have preferred to have been given a new start by the army, but this easier option was not open to him, so he had decided to be cooperative and keep his mouth shut. I found this a bit disconcerting as, at any minute, I was expecting his old surly manners and his true self to resurface. However, as the days went on there was no sign of this happening and his comrades were remarking what a difference there was in his character. I also noted that he had thrown himself into working with the ridge tunnelling boys with more enthusiasm than I had observed in anything he had done before. He seemed to relish being part of something productive and the loads he brought up each day were enabling the miners to extend the tunnel further out and closer to the enemy lines. He seemed to take pride in this task and that when the explosives were finally laid and set off, he had played a part in it. I had asked Gareth to keep a watch for any signs of his past behaviour with alcohol but again he seemed to have this under control too. He would drink some wine with the boys in camp and once went to the village with some of the tunnellers and although he had consumed a fair amount, he was not drunk or disorderly on his return.

Our confidence in Edwards was increasing and I was certainly encouraged to see he was trying hard to show that he was a valued member of the transport section. The routine continued almost twenty-four hours a day and was largely determined by the schedule set for the mining operations and the availability of the resources the sappers needed to complete their job on time before the planned attack. Sapper Bennett had struggled in the first few days to get a grip of the administrative side of the work of the section, but he proved to be a quick learner, and as he did when he was one of our volunteer cooks, he was proving to be more than capable. He lacked the years of experience of Ivan Lewis but was not afraid to ask him if there were things he did not understand. Bennett showed that he had a good head for organisation and soon had the work rota running smoothly.

The pressure was building on the siege company and the other "mole" units operating along the front line to complete all their tunnelling work before the date of the big push to break out of the salient towards Passchendaele and further south from the Arras area. General Haig believed that the tunnelling was vital to our success in this attack, as this would be the first time that the infantry first wave would not have to run across the divide between the trenches exposed to the enemy machine guns. The highest toll of casualties was always in the first wave of the attack when large numbers of men were killed or wounded as they went over the top. The sappers had constructed subways that approached right under the enemy positions and would enable the first wave of infantry to attack the enemy trench free from the machine-gun fire. This element of surprise was to be reinforced by the setting off a large explosive device under the areas where the German command posts were situated immediately after the artillery stopped firing to prevent the enemy from regrouping and organising themselves to receive the attack by infantry which inevitably followed the artillery barrage. This was to be the first time that this tactic had been tried and there were high hopes that if I was coordinated accurately, it could prove decisive, break the German line and allow a significant advance across a wide front. There was massive frustration amongst the British and French forces because of the stalemate that existed along the French and Belgian border, where both armies had been at a standstill since the last autumn. The main attack was planned for the early summer; it was hoped that this would break the back of the German resistance and victory for the Allies in Belgium would be achieved by the onset of another wet Flanders winter.

In early May, the main tunnel works hit a setback as Staff Sergeant Roberts who was the main surveyor and listener for the company had detected an enemy tunnel within twenty feet of ours. He could hear German voices clearly through the headphones attached to the various microphones he had placed in the tunnel and by triangulating the sounds, he could work out the direction of the German tunnel. The proximity to the enemy tunnel, was highly dangerous and could lead to the discovery of our tunnel or the risk of a surprise attack by the Germans, before we were ready to attack them. Major Rees-Evans and several other sapper officers went below ground to inspect his findings and to plan what needed to be done. Staff Roberts was well-respected and knowledgeable, having worked nearly eighteen years underground in the Welsh coalfield; he was certain that the enemy tunnel was on the same trajectory as ours but about six feet above our level which posed a high risk of discovery and of a collapse of our roof as they tunnelled above us. His solution was to withdraw forty feet from the current end of the tunnel, backfill, then continue by diverting the direction of our tunnel by twenty degrees for a hundred yards and to go deeper. He suggested we needed to be thirty feet below the German tunnel to ensure there was no chance of roof collapse caused by enemy activity. After the hundred yards of new tunnel was completed, he recommended returning to the original heading and level and continuing to the target as planned.

The CO accepted this solution, but everyone knew that this would cost another three or four days of delay until the backfill was completed and the new direction and depth started. It was agreed to use the earthmover to bring additional ballast and topsoil to fill in the existing tunnel and make it safe. The CO also decided that whilst this remedial work was underway, the HQ section would provide an armed detail of four men, to guard against any surprise attack by enemy soldiers, under the command of Cpl Lewis. The transport section was required to suspend all non-essential journeys and to locate suitable ballast and earth to dig out and transport by lorry to the opening of the damaged tunnel. Staff Sergeant Roberts had estimated that there was a requirement of between eighty and hundred tons of ballast required for the backfill job and that he would revise the requests for lumber and equipment to cope with the additional length of the diversion, which would also require transporting to the entrance to the tunnel. Transporting the extra ballast through the tunnel had to be completed by the sappers and there was a call for volunteers from other sections to help with this task. It was back-breaking work as each man had to fill a canvas bag with earth and rock and drag it to the work site in a constant rota. Very soon the men working underground really did begin to look like moles, and I was astonished to see that even Major Rees-Evans and his officers had stripped to the waist and were working alongside their men to get the job done.

I knew that I could not operate the digger all day and all night, so I needed to train a couple of others to support me in this work; I was surprised that Sapper Edwards was the first to put his name forward so I took him into the digger cab and showed him how the controls worked to manoeuvre the digger on its tracks and to manipulate the digger arm and claw to lift earth and rock on to the back of the lorries. He caught on quickly and when I gave him control of the vehicle, he showed no fear in moving it freely and digging out the ballast as required. I decided that he was to be in charge at the digging site whilst I went to help the drivers, and he smiled and mouthed some words that I could not hear clearly over the noise of the digger's engine but judging by his face, he was happy to be left to get on with the job. I left him for most of the day whilst I attended to a lot of loose ends and arranged for lorries to collect additional lumber and equipment from neighbouring tunnellers and from the docks. When I returned to the digging site, I realised that I had left Edwards for over seven hours on his own and hoped that he had coped. I need not have worried for he was working as speedily now as he had been when I left, and I could see that he had moved a fair amount of material judging by the size of the hole in front of the machine. I said I would relieve him and when he stepped down from the cab, he thanked me for the trust I had placed in him and said he would be back after getting something to eat, to finish the task. He was only gone for about forty-five minutes and he was ready to resume his job again.

Three hours later, word was passed that the men underground would be taking a break to sleep and recuperate and would resume at 06:00. They had blocked the original tunnel and backfilled fifteen feet which meant that the initial danger had passed for the time being and they hoped by an early start tomorrow they could backfill to almost the required distance enough to start on the new tunnel the following day. I drove up to the dig site in the small van to collect Edwards and drive him back to the section for the night. He looked whacked out, having spent ten hours behind the digger controls, but there was not one word of complaint from him. He said he was starving and then slumped into the passenger seat and was asleep within a couple of minutes as we made our way back to Westhoek. Sapper Bennett had drawn our rations;a hot meal was ready for us when we arrived back, the whole section tucked in together with gusto and then drifted off to their beds to sleep away their tiredness. The next day was equally busy as we were all engaged in the effort to bring the tunnelling back up to speed, even George Smithers and Sapper Davies left their workshop to help with the driving duties and I sent them to Dunkerque docks to collect a large load of machine tools that had arrived the previous day.

I arranged to spell Edwards on the digger at four-hour intervals, which would give him some breaks and enable me to coordinate the work of the section in liaison with the sappers underground. It was even harder work today, as the CO was determined to complete the backfill by the end of day two, so we worked on until nearly midnight before the forty-foot backfill was completed. Staff Roberts declared that he was satisfied that we now had a safe buffer between us and the German tunnellers, who seemed have turned away from us judging by the latest sounds he was picking up. Major Rees-Evans thanked us all for a supreme effort and called the CSM to issue a rum ration to every man for their efforts. The volunteers underground stood down and the section tunnellers would resume digging the new tunnel the following day at 10:00. The transport section had now to catch up on some of the routine journeys that had been postponed but I told them that we would not begin operations until 10:00 also to allow them all to get some rest.

EIGHT

Transport Section in Action

It had been decided and a suitable site mapped out for a more secure location for the company headquarters closer to the operational digging sites. The sergeant major had drawn up a team of transport section personnel and additional sappers to clear and mark out the site for the construction of some hangar-type buildings and huts for the company administration and cookhouse to be located. As this was much closer to the German lines, the additional sappers were tasked with patrolling the area to ensure that the construction work was not disturbed by enemy action. Bryn Edwards and I took alternate shifts driving the mechanical digger to clear and level the required pitches for the various buildings. The work was moving on at quite a fast pace and we reckoned to have the site ready for the building work to begin within three days or so when the work on erecting the huts and the hangar workshop could begin in earnest.

I was impressed how Sapper Edwards was applying himself to the task in hand and when he was not actually driving the digger, he would lend his weight to the teams clearing and levelling on the ground. I would not have thought that such a turn round was possible for someone with a poor record of drunkenness and indiscipline, but I could see the evidence before my eyes. I was still a little sceptical, but perhaps he had changed for the better and his time in the military detention centre had been the catalyst for the change in his behaviour. I had been reducing the amount of direct supervision that I put on him and had noticed that he was beginning to take on the experienced soldier role, using his greater skill and experience at the front to build the confidence and ability of the younger soldiers in the section. It must have been hard for him because most of the members of the section knew of him before or were aware of his reputation, and yet he was winning their respect. This was good for the section, good for Edwards and of course, good for me as I was able to devote more of my time to running the section more effectively. We worked from dawn to dusk without any complaints, for we all knew that the faster we completed the work the quicker we would be relocated in better accommodation. In the evening we gathered around the campfire with a hot meal brought up from the cookhouse and it was not long after that we turned in with full bellies for much-needed sleep.

On the morning of the third day, we were nearing the completion of the clearing of the site and trucks started to arrive with the steel frames for the hangars and the huts and almost all of us were involved in unloading and stacking the equipment ready for assembly in the next couple of days. I was driving the digger, completing the levelling for the accommodation huts when our attention was caught by a spectacle in the sky above us where we could hear aircraft engines and machine-gun fire. Two German and one of our aircraft streaked across the sky whirling and turning in a desperate dogfight. The first German aircraft was being chased by a British SE5 who was firing successive bursts of prolonged fire into his adversary whilst he himself was under fire from the second German fighter. We cheered as we saw that the SE5 pilot was scoring hits on his target as we could see bits of wreckage breaking off his fuselage and smoke billowing out from under his engine cowling. The SE5 immediately pulled up and broke to starboard, which took the second German by surprise and managed to fire passing shots at the second adversary as he overshot. The chaser had now become the chased and the SE5 pilot pressed home his advantage with a cool and professional detachment whilst the German pilot dodged and weaved seeking to escape before he too was shot down. I remember wondering who this pilot was and thinking how I would like to meet him.

The SE5 kept on his tail, scoring hits all the time but was forced to break off when he too started to show some smoke trailing from his engine. The SE5 now began to circle the field, getting lower each time he came round as he appeared to be looking for a place to land safely. My wish to meet him was going to come true quicker than I expected as I saw him settle into an approach towards the ground from over the German lines to drop into no-man's-land. He was obviously a good pilot as I could see how gently he put the aircraft wheels down on to the ground in the middle of the field, some 400 yards from our positions. Almost at the same time I was aware of German soldiers running from their lines with the intention of capturing the British pilot and as I saw him climb from the cockpit, he was hit by a bullet and fell to the ground beside his stricken plane. I did not think that he was dead as he seemed to be still moving, but it looked almost certain that he was going to become a prisoner of war unless we did something about it.

I called out to my men to grab their rifles and climb on the back of the digger. I opened the throttles and headed across the field towards the aircraft and wounded pilot. In the absence of a lance corporal, I saw Bryn Edwards rounding the boys up and mustering them at the rear of the earthmover as I moved forward, and I lifted the digger blade up in front to provide some protection from the German rifle bullets coming our way. We made faster progress towards the aircraft than the German patrol because we did not stop to return fire, and they were still 150 yards short when we reached the wounded pilot. I placed the mechanical digger in a position to provide protection from the enemy fire. Without orders from me, Bryn Edwards placed a defensive screen around our position and laid down fast and furious fire on the advancing Germans, which halted them in their tracks and bought me enough time to examine the pilot and ascertain the extent of his injuries.

A quick examination showed that although there was quite a lot of blood over his flying coat, the bullet wound was only to his shoulder and was not too serious. With a little help, I was able to lift him, and he was able to climb up to the cab of the digger unaided. I then ran the tow cable out and fixed it to the front axle of the undercarriage of the aircraft and dragged it back to the safety of our positions. I helped the pilot down into the hands of the medical orderly, unhitched the tow rope and then turned the digger back towards the fire fight to provide cover for the withdrawal of the boys maintaining the defensive screen. I swung the bulk of the mechanical digger between my men and the advancing Germans to enable them to detach from their individual positions and climb up on the superstructure at the rear of the vehicle, whilst still laying down covering fire at the enemy. This was going well, and we had not sustained any casualties until the last man to break off was hit twice as he stood up to run for safety behind the digger.

I could see that it was Bryn Edwards, and I could tell from the way he had collapsed and the awkward position he was lying in that his wounds were serious. I shouted to Sapper Davies to keep up the covering fire at the Germans, sprinted out of the seat of the digger and zig-zagged across the ten yards towards the slumped figure of Sapper Edwards. I could hear the bullets whizzing around me, but I was not hit. I had no time to be gentle with the wounded man but just grabbed him as quickly as I could, threw him over my shoulder in a fireman's lift, ran as fast as I could towards the safety of the digger and was glad that Davies had used his initiative, jumped into the driver's seat and swung the digger round to enable me to place the wounded Edwards on the rear of the vehicle then run behind it back to safety. By this time, the sergeant major had set up a strong defensive line and immediately we had passed through it, began targeting the German patrol with intensive and accurate fire.

I could see that Bryn Edwards had multiple wounds and was in a serious way, but by now the medical orderly was able to devote his attention to the wounded sapper when the lieutenant doctor arrived on the back of the motorcycle and they both began to work to save Bryn's life. The ambulance was on its way and the doctor said there was a good chance that he would survive if he could reach the base hospital for a major operation to repair the damage to his lungs and kidneys in a reasonable time. They had managed to stop the bleeding and although Bryn's breathing was laboured, he opened his eyes and asked to speak to me. A half smile came on to his face when he saw me, and he said in a very low voice. " We make a good team Corporal Morgan… keep my place open in the section for when I am fit again," and then he closed his eyes and was unconscious. A minute or so later the ambulance arrived, Bryn Edwards was lifted on to a stretcher into the back of the ambulance and the doctor accompanied him to the base hospital in St Omer.

I then turned my attention to the rescued pilot, who had been bandaged up and given sedatives. It appeared that his wound, although it would be painful for a couple of weeks, was not serious because the bullet had passed straight through missing the vital parts which make the shoulder work, and it was estimated that he would be fit to fly again in two to three weeks. When I approached him, he was sitting on a chair holding a mug of tea and I could see that he was a lieutenant. I saluted and introduced myself, he told me he was Jamie Dalrymple of 354 Squadron RFC and he thanked me for my bravery and quick thinking that saved his life and could I telephone the squadron and arrange for a driver to pick him up and a lorry to collect the aircraft. The sergeant major took charge of the young pilot and very soon he was driven away to company headquarters to be entertained in the officers' dugout until his transport arrived.

When he was gone, I went over to the aircraft and walked all around it, lovingly touching its fabric all over and then climbed up and sat in the cockpit, just dreaming about what it was like to fly. I was aware that the smoke we had seen as he landed on the field had gone and there was no sign of any fire or heat damage anywhere around the engine compartment. I sent a message to George to bring his toolbox and we would see if we could get this beast in flying condition again. Twenty minutes later George arrived with a big toolbox, and the pair of us opened the engine compartments and began to diagnose what might have been the problem to cause some smoke and a loss of power but no apparent serious damage. A careful engineer's diagnostic testing narrowed down what it could possibly be when I spotted that there was a split in one of the hoses which carried coolant from the radiator to the engine and it looked as if the coolant were dripping down on to hot engine exhausts producing the smoke and overheating the engine, causing the loss of power. We did not have any kind of hosing like the piece that was broken but George said that this wasn't a problem; he would fabricate a temporary hose from thin plate steel that would do the trick to get the aircraft back to base in one piece.

By the end of the afternoon, we had fixed the temporary hose in place and refilled the engine coolant to the right level. It was now time for the acid test, but we were not sure how to start the aircraft safely. I decided to send a message to Lt Dalrymple at the officers' dugout that we had repaired his aircraft and would he like to inspect it. Within ten minutes he appeared in a car accompanied by the CO and Vivian Craddock-Williams. Lt Dalrymple looked at the repair we had affected to his engine and we wondered whether he would like to test whether it would work or not. He was game to try and climbed into the cockpit and started flicking switches and moving lever; shouted to me to swing the propeller. This was much harder than I thought it would be because of the compression within the cylinders of the engine but after half a dozen attempts, I managed to get a splutter or two and then two swings later the engine fired and sprung into life. The lieutenant shouted that he would take off and circuit the field and if all remained well would return to base, but I was worried because of the wound to his left shoulder. He laughed it off and with a hearty wave swung the nose around, opened the throttles and set off across the field. At the furthest point he turned about, giving him the longest runway to take off and then hurtled down the field and into the air just short of trees closest to the German lines. He pulled up sharply to gain altitude and circled back towards us, waving, and waggling his wings, then disappeared to the south-west back to his base.

The SE5 was soon out of my mind as I wanted to go to St Omer to check up on Bryn Edwards and to see how he was doing. I borrowed the motorcycle and set off for the ride to the base hospital. After some waiting and enquiries, I was able to track down the surgeon major who had operated on Bryn, who told me that he had performed an operation to repair a hole in his left lung but the damage to his right kidney was too great for him to repair at the same time. However, Sapper Edwards was stable, out of immediate danger, able to breathe more freely and no longer bleeding internally, so he had been evacuated to a hospital ship in Dunkerque port where a specialised team of surgeons would repair the damage to his kidneys immediately. He said, "The prognosis is good that your friend will recover but the seriousness of his injuries will probably mean that he will not return to full fitness again. If the operation is a success, Sapper Edwards will spend about four weeks in recovery at the Naval Hospital Dover and then three months convalescence near to his family in Wales." I knew that this was the best I could hope to hear and that the boys in the section would be pleased that Bryn was not going to die.

With the excitement over for the day I knew we had to work faster tomorrow to keep up the pace of the construction of the buildings if we were to finish on schedule. I called all my team together to give them the news about Bryn Edwards, the emergency operations he had undergone and that by now he would be in the Naval Hospital in Dover to start his long recovery. This cheered us all up and I was glad that Bryn had managed to become such a popular member of the section since his return from detention. It was a credit to him but also to the men in the section who had been willing to accept him back with a clean slate. As soon as it was light, we set about erecting the steel frames for the shells of the hangars and larger buildings. This work proved remarkably quick and easy to accomplish but I knew that the harder work would be in attaching the roofing sheets and the wooden cladding for the walls, which was far more intricate and time-consuming to complete. The sappers laid down a concrete base for the large petrol generator that had been delivered several days ago. George and I set about locating it securely on the base and laying the cables to supply the workspaces and accommodation with electricity before the buildings were occupied. It felt good to be busy and to see my team working alongside the sappers to create the new company headquarters.

The sergeant major had a second team of men from the nearby Pioneer's company building sandbagged emplacements and parapets that would protect this facility in the event of further enemy action. In the mid-afternoon, we were interrupted by visitors when a convoy of staff cars were observed approaching the site from the direction of the Ypres road and there were four or five cars which seemed to be filled with officers. As the convoy grew nearer, we could see that in the first car was Major Rees-Evans and the adjutant, but we could not recognise who was in the other cars. As the cars drew up and the officers began to alight, we could see that the second car contained several RFC officers including the wounded pilot from yesterday, Lieutenant Dalrymple, who now looked smart in his uniform and was easy to recognise because he sported a white sling bandage to stop him using his damaged shoulder too much. The other officers I did not know, except I saw that most of them wore the red tabs of staff officers and were probably from Second Army headquarters. I wondered why they were interested in us.

The sergeant major called a stop to the work going on, calling the men to gather round in front of the cars and their distinguished passengers. When everyone was assembled Major Rees-Evans addressed us all in a clear voice that he was proud to bring distinguished guests to the site of our new company headquarters and to honour the action of the men of the Monmouthshire Siege Company Royal Engineers in successfully rescuing a Royal Flying Corps pilot brought down through enemy action and salvaging his aircraft.

"The men of the Monmouthshire Siege Company have a proud record of valiant service under the ground, but I am pleased that we have demonstrated that we are equally valiant above ground too."

There was some applause and then one of the RFC officers stepped forward and said that he was Major John Harcourt, commander of No. 354 Squadron RFC and had brought with him Captain Moss and Lieutenant, the Honourable Jamie Dalrymple, who he was sure we would all recognise from the events yesterday. He went on to say that he was speaking on behalf of all the personnel of No. 354 Squadron and wished to convey their profound thanks to the men of the Monmouthshire Siege Company for their prompt and brave action yesterday in fighting off the strong challenge from the German patrol who would have almost certainly captured Lt Dalrymple and destroyed a valuable aircraft.

"You will be pleased to know that Lt Dalrymple was wounded, but not too seriously, and will be able to resume flying duties within fourteen days.

You will also be pleased to know that both, of the enemy aircraft involved in the dogfight with Lt Dalrymple were destroyed by his action, and finally that your prompt action has saved one of our finest young pilots who will be able to take the fight to the enemy again in a few short weeks. The RFC are working hard to establish complete air superiority over the battlefield so that future offensives will have the benefit of air cover as you go into action. We have come here today to say thank you, but also to honour the bravery of two Royal Engineers and I can inform you that I have written citations for the award of the Military Medal for Corporal D. I. Morgan for his swift thinking and leadership in using the mechanical digger to affect the rescue of Lt Dalrymple and his aircraft but also for going out unarmed and under fire to rescue his wounded comrade Sapper B. Edwards and bring him back to safety. The second citation is for Sapper Bryn Edwards for his single-minded support of his corporal in organising and deploying the defensive screen to enable the rescue to happen and then remaining in position providing covering fire so that his comrades could withdraw safely. Sapper Edwards was seriously wounded when he came to withdraw himself and would have been left for dead had it not been for the actions of Corporal Morgan."

He addressed Major Rees-Evans directly and said that these two men showed the highest standards of gallantry expected in the British Army and bring real honour to the reputation of the Royal Engineers. There was some cheering all round and then Jamie Dalrymple stood up to say that he was glad that all the talking was over, that the boys of 354 have donated some cases of wine and beer so we can all share a drink to show our appreciation and he called for some assistance to unload the alcohol from the rear of their staff car.

Work was stood down for the afternoon and there was enough beer and wine for everyone to have a celebratory drink or two. I was quite taken aback by the whole proceedings as I had only thought that we had done what any soldier would do, and I did not think that I was particularly brave as I had just done my job. The credit should go to the whole section who took part and acted without question and to Bryn Edwards who assumed command of the defensive screen although it was not his responsibility to do so. He showed incredible bravery to lead from the front without fear for his own safety and to stay under fire until all his men had retired to cover. He was the brave one but when I tried to say this, everyone told me to stop being modest and enjoy the accolade. During the afternoon, I had an opportunity to converse with Jamie Dalrymple who was an engaging character and was profoundly grateful for what we had done for him and then to talk more seriously with Captain Moss and Major Harcourt. They were interested in the repair that George and I had affected on the SE5, which had apparently impressed the engineer officer on the squadron and had returned the aircraft to full serviceability almost immediately. They believed that someone had some knowledge of aero engines by the skilful diagnosis and repair, and I admitted that both George and I had both passed out as engines technicians from the Royal School of Military Engineering. I told them that I specialised in aero engines but on promotion to corporal had taken charge of a transport section and did not work on them anymore. Major Harcourt told me that the RFC was desperate to recruit more fully trained technicians, especially those who could supervise and direct a team and perhaps, I might consider applying for a transfer to the RFC. I indicated that although I loved playing with engines, I would much prefer to be able to fly an aircraft. Captain Moss asked if I had ever been up in a plane and when I said that I had not, he said he would arrange with my CO for me to spend a day with 354 Squadron at their base at La Couple to see the engineering operations and to fly a familiarisation sortie with him in the two-seater Bristol.

After a pleasant hour or so our guests began to drift away, and things began to return to normal. My head was in a turmoil with my unexpected citation, which was not yet confirmed, but I was glad that Bryn Edwards was being recognised although I thought that the medal would be a small consolation for the loss of his fitness and good health. I was not sure whether the invitation to spend a day with the RFC would materialise, but I hoped that it would. I knew that I had plenty to write in my letters to Ruby and to Mum and Dad when I got a quiet moment.

There were few interruptions to our work on the construction site and within a few more days the structures were up, the cladding and roof sheeting were all in place, the fittings were being installed and I was sure that the company would be moving in within a few more days. I thought the underground tunnellers would be glad of the huts that would become their homes instead of the tents they were in now, and the availability of running water for bathing after many hours digging would be a godsend. We all knew that the big offensive was coming soon; the preparation of the subways was well advanced and some of the tunnellers were diverted to tunnelling to lay explosives under the enemy lines in strategic places before the start date for the attack. I had almost given up any thoughts of being able to visit the RFC in La Coupole when I received a message from Ivan Lewis that it had been arranged for the following Wednesday,and that I was to report to Major Harcourt by 08:00 that morning.

I arranged to borrow the motorcycle again, left by 06:00 as it was at least a journey of twenty-five miles and although I had a rough idea where the airfield was in relation to St Omer, I was not certain of its exact location, so I had left adequate time to make the journey and find the airfield before my reporting time. As I rode through the slowly waking up countryside, I was excited but also full of some forebodings of how I would behave once I was in the seat of the aircraft. I had heard stories of people suffering terrible bouts of air sickness and vomiting uncontrollably or passing out in tight turns when doing aerobatic manoeuvres across the sky. Would I have a strong stomach for flying? I did not know but I reasoned that I have never suffered from seasickness on a boat or ship at sea so maybe I would be OK. There was little military traffic moving this morning and I was able to make good progress without being entangled with convoys or too many checkpoints, and the further I got away from the battle zone the quieter it became. I took the road through Cassel to Arques where I knew that I needed to make a left turn after I had passed through the small town in the opposite direction from St Omer. Many of the road signs were missing so I had to keep my wits about me and rely on my sense of direction at some road junctions.

At the end of the Arques I came to the junction I wanted and confidently took the second left turning having rejected the first left as it was little more than a farm track. I was now on a bigger road; I opened the throttle a bit and was able to move faster for a couple of miles until I had to slow down and stop at a checkpoint where military police were checking movement orders. The corporal approached me politely, asked for my papers, read them through before returning them to me, then informed me that I was on the wrong road for La Coupole airfield and said that I should have taken the first turning. I argued that it was only a farm track, he laughed and said that I was approaching the back entrance to the airfield and the main entrance was on the road between St Omer and Montreuil. I thanked him, turned the bike round, headed back to the junction and this time took the farm track which did widen out a little after several hundred yards. I could see beyond the hedges a vast open space which I assumed must be the airfield. After about a mile and a half I came to a gateway in the high fence which was guarded by two soldiers in a small hut. They looked at my ID and papers, then opened the gate and directed me to go left around the perimeter track until I came to the main gate on the other side of the airfield. 'There are no airfield operations yet this morning, so you will have a clear run. If, however, you sight an aircraft you must give way as they have precedence over ground traffic.'

I set off and I found it was another two miles around the perimeter track to find the guardroom by the main gate where I found Lt. Dalrymple waiting for me. He jumped on the back of the motorbike and directed me across to the squadron command hut to meet Major Harcourt. When we pulled up and got off, I could see that Jamie was not wearing the sling anymore, seeming to be able to move his arm freely without too much discomfort and he told me that the doctor was going to pass him fit to fly again for next week. As we walked across to the command hut there were half a dozen young pilots sitting on deckchairs or lounging on the grass who started shouting ribald comments at us as we approached. "Hey, corporal, why did you save him? He is no use to us!" and other similar catcalls. Inside the hut I met Major Harcourt and Captain Moss again. They were glad to see me and after a few minutes the major handed me over to Captain Moss who was going to take me flying. First, he took me into the briefing room where we got some coffee and sat at the map table to study the air charts for the part of France we were going to fly over. He pointed out that although we were in a relatively safe area some thirty or so miles away from the front line that did not mean we could be complacent because we still needed to be alert and keep a close watch for possible enemy aircraft that might prove a threat to us. He emphasised how important this was as we would have no weapons to fight back with and our only defence was to outfly any potential attacker. A combat pilot's number one rule is to keep a close lookout for potential threats. He then showed me the flight plan he had drawn up for today's sortie which would take us north-west towards the coast avoiding the exclusion area over Dunkerque port, crossing the coast at LoonPlage and turning west to follow the coastline towards Calais and Boulogne sur Mer, where we will head inland again and fly south towards Montreuil, then proceed north-east into an area of farmland where there should be no other aircraft where we can try out some aerobatic moves as far as the two-seater is capable. Then we would return to base. The whole sortie should be about one hour.

"My objective is to give you a taste of what military flying is all about but also let you have some hands on of the controls so that you can see what you have to do to control an aircraft. The aircraft is a two-seater trainer where the instructor sits in the rear cockpit and the student is in the front. It is equipped with a Gosport system which is a speaking tube linking the two cockpits so that we can speak to each other during the flight. He explained further that he would taxi out and take off and when they reached their operational altitude, he would demonstrate the use of the hand controls, the throttle, and the rudder bars. He then explained what would happen when he handed control of the aircraft to the trainee, I will say, you have control and you will reply, I have control. This procedure will be followed in reverse when you hand back control to me."

We went out and inspected the aircraft for any faults or fuel leaks, broken linkages, or tears in the fabric of the fuselage and then climbed aboard and were strapped in tight by the ground crew. I heard Captain Moss going through certain procedures and flicking switches then shouting "Contact" and the ground crewman swung the propeller. It took about three swings for the engine to cough into life but soon all I could feel were the vibrations reverberating through the airframe and my body and I could not hear anything other than the sound of the engine clattering in front of me. I felt the brakes come off as the aircraft surged forward, and I was thrown back into the seat as we taxied across the grass to line up for take-off. I had the map with the course we had agreed drawn on it. Captain Moss had stressed how important it was for a pilot to be able to relate what he sees on the ground to what is on the map and to keep his eye on the compass to orientate his position at any one time.

We took off towards the east and gently adjusted our course more northerly towards the English Channel and as the minutes went by, I was able to see the Straits of Dover laid out before me, the fortified ports on the French side clearly visible and the major ports of Ramsgate, Dover, and Folkestone on the other side. I could not help thinking of Bryn Edwards recovering in the hospital at Dover, then marvelling at how close we were from the English coast even though the Western Front seemed so completely detached from the people back at home. I learnt how to bank, turn, climb, and descend and adjust the throttle setting to increase and decrease power. When I was confident using these controls, he gave control to me, and I flew the aircraft on the leg parallel to the coastline until we were off Boulogne and made our turn inland towards Samer and Montreuil. I continued in control until we were several miles beyond Montreuil and all we could see below us was open farmland with small farms and hamlets beneath us. Captain Moss took back control, saying he was going to show me a barrel roll and when I was ready. He performed a slow barrel roll which I thought was rather fun. He then went into a series of rolls but this time much faster which was exhilarating but quite confusing to know whether you were right way up or not when he was finished. I remembered that a pilot had to remain alert constantly and be able to orientate his position, so I looked out of the cockpit and then at the map and thought I knew where we were.

He then said we would loop the loop and pulled the stick back hard into our stomachs, opened the throttles for more power and we began to climb hard up to the top of the loop. As we went over the top upside down, I watched the earth rotate before my eyes as we raced back down to our starting position. This was fantastically exhilarating and immediately it was over I wanted to do it again, but Captain Moss said through the speaking tube for me to take us home. I knew this was a test to see if I had been paying attention and whether I had any potential to be a pilot at all. After a few seconds of blind panic, I looked out of the cockpit all around and then compared what I had seen on the ground to the salient features on the map. Being in a predominantly agricultural area there were not too many man-made landmarks to help me, so I looked carefully at the physical features of the landscape, and I could see the outline of the coast over my left shoulder which meant I was pointing roughly easterly. I was able to confirm this with a quick glance at the compass and then I picked up the line of the small river that flowed west of the airfield and toward the sea via St Omer and Dunkerque. So, using the course of the river to guide my heading, I proceeded towards La Coupole, which I was able to see clearly four or five minutes later. Captain Moss took back control, landed and taxied back to the hangar and then took me back inside the briefing room for a debriefing session.

He expressed his satisfaction at my flying which he said was exemplary for someone on their first ever flight. "I am certain that you have the potential to become a good pilot because you have an almost innate sense of airmanship and are able to keep a good fix of where you are in the sky at any one time. None of the aerobatic moves fazed you in any way and when asked to navigate your way back to base you made good use of the map and your powers of observation to bring us directly home. Corporal Morgan, you have a natural ability as an aviator, and I would recommend that you put in for a transfer to the RFC immediately."

I was greatly encouraged to hear this from such an accomplished pilot, but I was not sure yet whether this would be right for me or not. With the briefing over we went to join the other pilots for lunch on a trestle table set up in the open air and they all wanted to hear the report from Captain Moss when we sat down. Although they were loud and had a rebellious air, I could tell they were all dedicated pilots and respected Moss for his great skills as an instructor and as a combat pilot. He told them that if he could find three or four more soldiers like Corporal Morgan here to train as pilots, he would be able to rid the squadron of this whole gang of indolent, upper-class playboy pilots that we have now and then we would show the German air force what for. There was pandemonium and uproar which only subsided when Major Harcourt joined us for lunch. I enjoyed my day very much and spent quite a time talking with Jamie Dalrymple who was the first person from an aristocratic background I had ever had cause to talk to at any length, but I was surprised to find that we had so much in common and I imagined that we would become firm friends in the future. So many thoughts were going through my mind as I rode back to the siege company headquarters contemplating whether I had the courage to apply for the transfer to the RFC.

NINE

Passchendaele Day 1

Section heads were briefed by Major Rees-Evans the evening before the attack was scheduled and all of us in the siege company knew that the attack was imminent because of the build-up of infantry soldiers in the communication trenches, ready to advance through the subways on the morning of the attack. With the explosives laid, and all the charges set and primed the main role of the sappers and miners was over for the time being. The task of setting off the charges was coordinated by Major Rees-Evans and the section commanders synchronised to go off twenty-five seconds before the artillery barrage was due to end so that the enemy's ability to reorganise and be ready to receive the first wave of British infantry was seriously disrupted. Small detachments of men were placed at the end of the subway to break through the final barrier into the open, so that the infantry could pile out as quickly as possible into the enemy trenches. The secondary task of the company was to stand to in our trenches and in the entrances of the subways to repel any counterattacks should the first wave be unsuccessful.

At 06:00 the artillery barrage was set to begin, and the enemy positions were to be pounded by our heavy artillery for fourteen minutes. The noise of the shells passing over us and landing on top of the enemy positions was overpowering, the smell of the cordite and burning stuck in our nostrils and it was impossible not to think of the enemy soldiers on the receiving end of such a tumultuous torrent of destruction. We could not hear each other speak but just kept our heads down and counted off the seconds on our watches until it ended. Our explosives were set to go off under the enemy command posts just twenty-five seconds before the end of the barrage. The sounds created by the underground explosions were distinctly, different from those of the shells raining down from above as they produced a deep, rolling rumble of noise and vibrations radiating out through the ground beneath our feet. I hoped that the quantities of explosives had been judged right by our sappers and that the whole battlefield was not going to collapse underneath us. I was tempted to lift my head up and look over the parapet at what was happening; I could not see much because of the smoke swirling around over the German lines but could make out that a gap appeared to have opened where the main command post had been situated. I then heard the whistles blowing and saw our infantry pouring out of the ground like hordes of ants leaving an ant hill and charging for the gap. Luckily, the enemy machine gunners were completely outflanked as they were positioned to face an attack from the front when now their enemy was at their rear. Some of the gunners were rapidly trying to dismantle and reassemble their guns to bring them to bear before they were overrun but this proved a fruitless task as the numbers pouring out of the subways were overwhelming them too quickly.

The lead companies were from the Gloucester's supported by militia battalions from South Wales, Merseyside and Scotland who followed quickly behind them. The lead units headed straight for the gap and were quickly established behind the German front lines, but it was clear that even though the command centre had been eradicated the discipline of the German troops was not broken nor their willingness to fight diminished. The resistance they put up was fierce and casualties were high on both sides as they fought for every inch of the disputed territory. Reports were coming in that the three command posts in our sector had been destroyed and the South Wales Volunteers to the east of our position had captured 500 yards of German trenches, taken nearly 800 prisoners, and were now established in position with an unrestricted view towards the village of Passchendaele. The defenders immediately in front of our position seemed to be made of sterner stuff and held on for five and a half hours before when running low on ammunition they were forced to surrender. We were amazed to find out that most of their officers had been killed in the initial explosion at the command centre except for one junior lieutenant who supported by four sergeants, led his men brilliantly in defending their positions. To the west of us the King's Own Buffs and Royal West Kent's had punched a big hole in the German lines and moved forward nearly a mile into enemy territory. Similar success was being reported along most of the line and the first action was declared a big success.

The second wave of troops was moving up fast to overtake the first wave and continue the momentum against the Germans before they could establish a new defensive position. The advance of a few hundred yards did not secure a major victory but only reflected a slight change in the stalemate that had existed for so long already. We had not yet managed to break out of the Ypres Salient but rather just pushed the flexible edges of the balloon out a little further, The Germans had not broken and run away in terror at our advance but had simply fallen back and re-established the defensive line a little further behind their previous positions. The General Staff were celebrating the victory whilst the Germans were consolidating their new positions, but our line officers were warning the generals that the enemy would be preparing for a counterattack that they would mount within a couple of days. Some of the veterans of the previous winter in Flanders complained that if we did not get a move on during the summer and early autumn there was a strong likelihood of becoming bogged down in sopping wet wintry weather where all the roads and fields were waterlogged and muddy just like the previous year. It was popular belief among the soldiers that if the Germans were allowed to establish their positions again the subway surprise attack tactic would not work successfully a second time. We were surprised when the second attack wave was ordered to halt and consolidate a new defensive position in the German trenches, we had just captured rather than push forward as previously planned. No one on the ground could understand why this change of plan had occurred but our attack ground to a halt after the early gains.

The earthmover was brought into use again to break open the roof of the subways and clear away the earth to make use of them as supply routes to reach our new front line. The siege company moved into the former front-line trenches and set about surveying the new German lines for mining potential again. We were expecting that orders would come for a further attack on the new German positions to build on our initial success, but they did not come from Second Army HQ. General Haig had been proved right and his subway tactic had delivered surprise and reduced the number of casualties in the first wave of infantry drastically. There was a strong feeling amongst the front-line troops that we had dealt a blow to the enemy that could be capitalised on if we were to attack again swiftly. The large number of German prisoners taken that first morning suggested that their defence would be weakened unless they were given time to bring up reinforcements. However, the generals decided that caution was the best policy and whilst there were continued skirmishes and forays using tanks there was no concerted attack. To say that the ordinary soldiers were frustrated would be an understatement as this stalemate dragged on all summer and we were restless for some more decisive action.

I felt as frustrated too as we settled into a daily routine, but the siege company had no proper job in sight so spent its time rebuilding the captured trenches and strengthening the parapets. We had heard that Bryn Edwards was making good progress with his convalescence in the hospital in Monmouth which was good news. I received notification that the award of the Military Medal to Bryn and I had been approved and I was to be presented with the medal in a ceremony in Armentieres the next week. I immediately wrote to Ruby and Mum and Dad to tell them the good news and I was sure that they would be proud. I also decided that I would apply for a transfer to the Royal Flying Corp, filled the application for transfer and submitted it through the adjutant's office. I sent a request to Major Harcourt at 354 Squadron to ask whether he would be prepared to support my application and he wrote back that he and Captain Moss had done so.

The award ceremony was held in the ballroom of the grand chateau where Second Army HQ was situated, about two miles outside of the town itself. I travelled to Armentieres together with the CO and the adjutant in the light car driven by Ivan Lewis. The major was delighted that two of his men were to be awarded gallantry medals and although I was sad that Bryn Edwards would not be with us today, I was glad to have Ivan and Vivian with me instead. I later heard that Bryn received his medal in hospital from the colonel of the regiment a few days later. I was surprised by the grandeur of the chateau; the ballroom was a massive, magnificently decorated room, which was packed with those who were to receive awards and spectators. I was surprised to learn that there were nearly 200 recipients of awards and decorations, and we were marshalled by an imposing-looking sergeant major resplendent in his red tunic who arranged us in order in the front rows of the seats laid out across the dance floor. I noticed that the recipients were from all different ranks and that some of the lower awards were dealt with in batches. However, the higher awards for gallantry were dealt with individually and the citations for each were read out before the medal was presented. I counted sixteen of us in my row ranging from private soldiers to a major at the other end of the row. I knew that there were twenty-three awards in this category so surmised that some would be posthumous or that the recipients were wounded like Bryn Edwards.

General Haig was presenting the medals himself and sat on the dais surrounded by other officers from the general staff who were also resplendent in red and blue ceremonial uniforms with medals and swords. In contrast the majority receiving awards looked rather dowdy in our best khaki, direct from the trenches. The ceremony started off with the awards of commendations and certificates of good service that were presented in batches and then on to honours for meritorious service that were awarded by the King. Most of these were given to rear echelon senior NCOs or junior officers for performing their duties well in support of the front-line troops. Finally, it came to the awards for gallantry in the field and the medals of Military Medal and Military Cross were the first to be presented. The ribbon for each was identical but non-commissioned ranks received the medal whilst officers received the cross. Each citation was read out by a lieutenant colonel who stood at a podium to the side of the dais in a loud and clear voice. When he came to my name he read out:

> *Morgan, Derfal, Ieun 0209616, Corporal*
> *Monmouthshire Siege Company the South Monmouthshire Regiment, Royal Engineers*
> *For outstanding bravery and leadership in engaging an enemy patrol and preventing the imminent capture of Lieutenant, the Honourable James Arthur Dalrymple, 354 Squadron, Royal Flying Corps.*
> *Corporal Morgan without fear of the danger to himself used a mechanical earthmover to approach Lt Dalrymple's aircraft and provide cover for his men to engage the German patrol whilst the rescue of the wounded lieutenant was affected, and his aircraft recovered safely. Corporal Morgan then returned to the battlefield, and under fierce fire from the enemy ran forward to recover a wounded comrade, Sapper Bryn Edwards 0739392, from the same regiment and carry him over his shoulder to safety. This brave action enabled Sapper Edwards to receive urgent medical attention and survive his wounds and he is currently in convalescence.*

When he finished reading the citation, I marched forward to a point roughly four feet in front of the general where the orderly was waiting with the Military Medal on a blue cushion for the general to pin on my left breast above the pocket. He then shook my hand and quietly spoke a few words of congratulation to me. I took a short pace backwards, gave a little bow and about turned and marched back to my seat. As soon as I sat down the Lt. Col. started to read the next citation.

I was proud to receive the medal and the praise that went with it but deep down I could not see what the fuss was about. I felt I had just done my duty as any soldier would have in the same circumstances and particularly when I listened to the two citations being read for the award of the Victoria Cross at the end of the ceremony, I thought my actions paled into insignificance compared to theirs. However, Major Rees-Evans and Vivian Craddock-Williams were determined to celebrate my success and we dined together at the Café Pigalle in Armentieres on the way back. The dining room had an excellent reputation and a well-stocked cellar; we ate and drank well but ironically, I remembered that this was the establishment where Herbert Vaughan had met Cecile Beauchamp who was a hostess in the rooms upstairs but decided to keep that recollection to myself. I wrapped the medal in tissue paper and put it away safely in its leather case when I got back to my billet and got out the needle and thread from my ditty box to sew the medal ribbon on to my tunic. I felt more than a little humbled by the bravery and courage that I had heard of at the medal ceremony and was unsure whether I was worthy to be included in their illustrious company.

The next few weeks proved frustrating as there was no word about a new task needing the siege company's special talents lthough every attempt was made to keep the men busy by finding them things to do they were getting listless, and incidents of indiscipline were on the rise. The CO tried to give some leave if possible, prioritising married men with children to go first and for the rest he gave weekend leave passes to enjoy the delights of some of the small towns and villages in the rear area behind the front lines. The majority opted for the larger town of Armentieres, rather than the local villages, because they were attracted by the many bars and brothels that proliferated there. As a result, after every weekend there were long lists of sappers arrested for drunkenness or affray when they got into fights with soldiers from other units, and then were referred to their units for punishment by the military police who did not have the time or resources to deal with the sheer numbers of offenders. Worse still was that the medical officers were complaining of the increasing numbers of soldiers reporting sick with sexually transmitted infections every week and that this was using up their valuable time and stock of medicines to treat these avoidable conditions. Every section in the siege company was affected and the adjutant was run ragged holding punishment parades to deal with the offenders. We were hearing from other units nearby that it was the same for them but without a plan for moving forward against the enemy coming from Second Army there was little to break the malaise.

George Smithers and Ivan Lewis had both been given fourteen-day leave passes to return home and had left together to see their wives and families for the first time since arriving in Belgium. I was hoping that I might get home leave too; although I had been receiving lovely letters from Ruby every week, which had sustained me through the past six months, I was yearning to be with her again. No leave pass came my way and when I broached the subject with the adjutant he told me that the CO could no longer approve home leave for me because I had applied for a transfer and would have to wait until that was decided before applying for leave again. He said that this did not apply to local leave which would continue as normal whilst we were in this lull from the fighting. I was disappointed and just hoped for a resolution of my transfer application sometime soon. I did not have to wait long for just over a week later, I received a signal from Second Army declining my request for transfer from the RE to the RFC but approving my secondment to 354 Squadron RFC as Sergeant Technician acting, so I was to remain a Royal Engineer but be attached to Jamie Dalrymple's squadron on secondment for one year. I found that I had mixed emotions of happiness and sadness, happy to be closer to aircraft but sad to be leaving behind all my friends in the siege company who I had lived and worked with for the past six months. I was due to report to Major Harcourt at La Coupole airfield on the 1st of July 1917 so had just under two weeks to hand over the transport section to my successor and say goodbye to all my sapper friends. My successor was appointed and on his way from the regimental depot at Chepstow. I was pleased to see that it was Corporal Charlie Staithe who had given me a break during my driver training. I knew that he would run the section well and his infectious personality would enamour him to the siege company.

I wrote to Ruby and my parents immediately to tell them of my promotion to sergeant and secondment to the RFC explaining that I would now be working from an airfield over ten miles behind the frontline where I would be servicing the aircraft engines and that this was much less dangerous than my work with the siege company had been. I was hoping to be able to persuade my new CO that a couple of weeks' home leave might be appropriate for me, but I was by no means certain. On my last day with the siege company, I sought to have a few quiet minutes with the CO to thank him and pay my respects, so went across to his quarters and knocked on his door. He opened the door and invited me into his sitting room and offered me a seat. He told me to relax and produced a bottle of fine malt whisky from the cupboard and two glasses. He poured two fingers into each glass and passed one to me then raised his glass and we drank in silence for a minute. Then Major Rees-Evans said he was sorry to be losing me as I had been a valuable member of his company; "Right from that first day when we were nearly captured by the Germans, I knew that you had more to offer than many in this regiment. You have managed the transport needs of the company well and been an excellent support to the main work of the sappers and miners and have shown that your commitment to duty and personal courage are your greatest assets."

He offered me congratulations on my third stripe which he said was a parting gift from the siege company and not connected to the transfer request. He wished me good luck in my secondment to the RFC. "And I hope it turns out as they were desperate to have you as Command received several recommendations from them requesting your transfer." When I had finished my whisky, I stood shook hands with the major and left the room.

TEN

The Royal Flying Corps

Gareth Hughes had volunteered to drive me over to La Coupole airfield the following morning. I could hardly contain my excitement when we turned in at the main gate and I saw the squadron aircraft spread out in the field in front of the squadron command hut. This was achieving some of my dream to be working with aircraft and I knew that this was what I had always wanted to do except for becoming a pilot myself. I was happy to accept the role of keeping the aircraft in good flying condition even if I was not able to fly them. Gareth did not stay long and was soon heading back to the siege company. I knocked on the door to the command hut to report into the squadron commander and was greeted by Major Harcourt, Captain Moss and a sergeant major I had not met before who was introduced as the squadron warrant officer. Sergeant Major Perks would be my boss as he oversaw all technical support for the aircraft on the ground. I was to supervise the engine bays that would service, repair, and replace the aircraft engines as required. He said I should report to him in the hangar after the CO had finished with me and he would show me round and get me settled in.

Major Harcourt was glad to see me and then apologised for the little subterfuge they had to undertake to get me here. I was confused because I was not aware of what he was talking about but sensing my confusion he went on to explain what he meant. The reason I could not be transferred directly to the RFC was because I was in a territorial regiment and was unable to transfer to the RFC, which did not have any territorial units for me to be transferred to. "We then hit on the idea of seconding you to this squadron as an engines technician because you hold the Army Level 3 Diploma in Engines and this has worked, and we have got you here." Captain Moss then took over the story and explained further that after I had taken my first flight with him, he was so impressed with my flying potential that I should be sent on a flying training course and trained to be a pilot.

He said, "We have applied for a place for you on the next RFC initial flying course at South Cerney airfield, just north of Salisbury in Wiltshire. The course is six weeks long and allows for forty hours of flying training before the award of pilot's wings, when you could join a squadron as a fully-fledged pilot. Once you are a qualified pilot, we can apply to transfer you to the Royal Flying Corps as aircrew as most squadrons would give their back teeth to have a pilot who understood engineering in their ranks. In the meantime, we have great use for your engineering knowledge in the hangar on 354 because we are faced with a major problem. "We have become so overwhelmed by the number of aircraft unserviceable or in need of major repairs that the engines section has been unable to keep up. We imagined that seconding you into the section to reorganise and focus on clearing the backlog will get the squadron one hundred percent operational again." I was amazed to hear this news and excited to think I was going to get my hands on the aircraft engines and to learn to fly into the bargain.

The next four weeks proved extremely busy for Captain Moss had been right when he said there was considerable remedial work to be undertaken on over half of the squadron inventory of aircraft. The lull in the battle to the east of Ypres had given enough break from operations to work on these stricken aircraft and get them airworthy by the beginning of August ready for the next big push. The squadron pilots were able to maintain daily patrols along the German lines but would have been unable to maintain effective support had a major battle been in progress. The team in the engine bays was basically sound but it was apparent to me that they lacked the leadership and basic administration that was needed to prioritise and expedite the flow of work to keep up to pace with operational requirements. I knew that the basis of my success with the transport section at the siege company lay in my good fortune in having a first-class administrator in the mould of Ivan Lewis to underpin the work of the whole section and by allowing the lance corporals who led each sub-section to work without too much direct oversight from me but within the framework for the management of our work we had all agreed to. I knew I could trust these men to act independently to achieve the overall tasks set for the whole section and support each other to get the task done. In the six months or so that I led them they had become moulded into an efficient team.

Sergeant Major Perks showed me around the engine bays and introduced me to the corporal who was the engines lead, Anthony Smith. Anthony was young and keen but had made the basic error of not stepping back from his previous role as an engine fitter to concentrate his time on supervising the engines section effectively. It was obvious he was a good tradesman, but he was spending too much time working on aircraft and not enough time prioritising, coordinating, and ensuring that completion dates were met. The engines office was a mess and no admin clerk had been attached to the section to provide the foundation for managing the work on the aircraft. Anthony knew what needed to be done but did not know how to organise his time between the office and the engine bays to make it happen. The pace of work by the fitters was frenetic but disorganised so that priorities were often missed, and less important jobs completed ahead of time whilst vital tasks were delayed. There was poor coordination between the pilots and the fitters who often got little chance to talk face to face about how the engines were performing in flight to aid in the diagnosis and fault-finding. Job cards were not raised in the office with an initial inspection report and diagnosis of work needed plus requests to the stores for tools and spare parts. I found unused spare parts discarded along with specialist tools that should have been returned to the stores after each job was completed. There was also a backlog of incomplete service documents waiting to be written up and filed in the aircraft service log for future reference.

I shared my initial thoughts with the sergeant major; he agreed with my assessment and asked what was needed to improve the situation. The number one priority was to detach an experienced admin clerk to the engines section to bring some order into the office and get the record-keeping back in order. Secondly, I would train Corporal Smith, as best I could, how to run the section efficiently and to use the resources at his disposal to keep the squadron aircraft serviceable and fit for operations. I recommended that an additional skilled engine fitter be posted in to replace Corporal Smith in the bays so that, when I left for flying training, he was competent to run the engines section alone. We put these suggestions to the CO in the morning and after some discussion he agreed to our plan and the squadron adjutant would make the requests immediately.

Within a week, Second Army HQ had sourced an admin clerk for us and would transfer him within forty-eight hours and a request had been sent to the RFC HQ in England for a replacement engine fitter. A couple of days later the new clerk arrived and reported to the engines bay asking for Sergeant Morgan. He was directed to me, and I was surprised to see that he was middle-aged, probably over fifty, with thick spectacles that made him look rather like an owl and was a private soldier from the infantry. He introduced himself as Private Albert Gresham, King's Own Yorkshire Light Infantry on secondment to 354 Squadron as an admin clerk. I thought he looked an unlikely choice to be soldier at all but questioned him on his experience before the army. He was a Londoner and told me that he had worked as a stores clerk at the Woolwich Arsenal for over twenty years and had been prompted to join up in 1914 to work in the ordnance corps or artillery but usual military confusion placed him in the light infantry at the age of forty-nine. He told me that he had never been able to keep up in the light infantry but had been a clerk in battalion headquarters for the past two years. He said, "This request came across my desk from Second Army I didn't pass it on but volunteered myself because although I am not cut out to be an infantryman, I am a good clerk." As he was speaking, I found that there was something about him that I liked; he certainly had some spirit and when I described what I expected him to do he needed little prompting and understood exactly what I was looking for in the new clerk. It felt strange giving orders to a man more than two and a half times my age, but he showed no sign that this was a problem for him, working for a young sergeant barely twenty years of age.

Albert Gresham was almost instantly popular with the fitters because he sorted the muddle in the office quickly and efficiently; job requests were made and written up, entered into the aircraft record book and a job card issued to a named fitter with requests for tooling and spare parts to the stores. He drew up a job progress chart on the wall of the office so that we could follow the progress of each job, ensuring that all the records were kept up-to date and that I was kept informed. I spent thirty minutes with Albert every afternoon for him to report on progress of the work in hand and for me to discuss new priorities in the pipeline; I discovered that he was not bragging about his ability for he was a particularly good clerk. The fitters nicknamed him,"Pop" because of his age and the name seemed to stick because soon the whole squadron, including the CO, was calling him Pop Gresham. I included Corporal Smith in the afternoon sessions when I could but also got Pop to spend time explaining how the progress charts worked and gave us useful snapshots of the priorities in short, medium, and longer term. He showed him how good record keeping was essential in ensuring that the section met the operational targets for serviceability and how vital it was for the fitter to be able to read the service history of a particular aircraft before attempting to fix the problem. Pop's patient manner helped Smith understand how the system worked in our favour and made him feel confident that he would be able to manage this after I had gone to South Cerney.

Towards the end of August, the signal ordering me to report to South Cerney airfield to begin flying training on the 12th of September arrived from RFC headquarters. I was elated because I was taking the next step towards becoming a pilot but also equally exciting, I would almost certainly get an opportunity to get home and see my family and more particularly spend some time with Ruby. A further signal was received later that day informing us of the posting of Lance Corporal Martin Terry as an engine fitter to replace Tony Smith in the engine bays. I was satisfied that, although there were still more improvements to be made in the efficiency of the section, under the leadership of Tony Smith supported by Pop in the office the engine section would thrive and grow in effectiveness. Just ten weeks after joining 354 Squadron I was on the move again to a brand-new adventure.

Nine months after crossing the channel, I returned as a passenger on HMS *Dunoon*, a small frigate that carried the mail from Dover across the channel for the soldiers at the front and vice versa. She made the trip every day and as well as the tons of mail, she always had room for passengers travelling on official business. I joined the ship in the port of Calais, and she made a fast dash across the Straits of Dover in under two hours, giving me time to catch an afternoon train to Charing Cross from Dover Marine station. I had left La Coupole at 07:00 and would be arriving in the centre of London by 16:30 that afternoon. The trains for the south-west departed from Waterloo or Paddington depending on your destination, and I had discovered that the fastest trains to Salisbury were from Waterloo. I also discovered that adjacent to Waterloo Station was a club for SNCOs in transit who could get free accommodation and food provided they were travelling on a rail warrant. I had decided to put off my journey to Salisbury until Sunday morning, when I would be able to arrive at South Cerney in plenty of time to get settled before the course started on Monday morning. Waterloo was just across the river from Charing Cross and only a short trip on the Underground to the mainline station. The station was crowded with soldiers and sailors waiting for trains or just arrived, but I was able to ask directions to the Jackstay Club from a military policeman on duty at the top of the stairs from the

Underground station and after checking my transit papers he directed me to a station exit on my left and said I would find the club about 400 yards down Waterloo Road on the right. I thanked him, set off walking and within a few minutes I could see the entrance marked with the union flag and regimental flags above the door.

The club had a grand portico with a dozen steps leading up to the door which gave way to a large, open reception hall manned by a uniformed commissionaire who pointed me to a young lady sat at the desk. She was young and pretty, smiled a welcome and asked to see my ID and transit papers, then returned them to me and said she would see what rooms were available. After a few minutes she gave me a key to a nice room with a view across London on the fourth floor reminding me that dinner was served at 18:00–19:00 in the main dining room and breakfast at 06:30 in the morning. The rules of the club were that uniform was to be worn in the public rooms and no guests were allowed in the private rooms. The bar was open until midnight and drinks were to be paid for in cash. There was no lift so the climb up four floors with my kitbag was quite taxing but worth it for my bedroom was spacious with a large double bed, clean white sheets, and a bathroom with plenty of hot water just across the corridor. These were luxuries that I had not enjoyed very much in the trenches, and I intended to make full use of them. I dived into the bathroom opposite and ran a hot bath before dinner. I felt refreshed and renewed as if I had washed off the grime and dirt of nine months at the front when I dressed in my uniform with a clean shirt to go down to the dining room about half-past six. There was a good selection on the set menu so there was enough choice for everyone. I was happy to choose brown Windsor soup followed by Dover sole and finished with apple tart and custard for dessert which I really enjoyed. Feeling quite full and satisfied I went into the bar and joined a crowd of sergeants drinking and chatting at the bar. I ordered a pint of India Pale Ale, stood at one end of the polished bar top and was soon drawn into the chatter as the drinks loosened tongues. Most of us were returning from the front for courses of training like me or were transiting back to their units in France or Belgium. A staff sergeant stood next to me noted the ribbon of the Military Medal and asked in which battle I had earned the medal. I was reluctant to talk about it much and passed over the subject quickly by saying I was with a siege company in Belgium. After a couple of pints, I said my farewells slipped up the four flights of stairs to luxuriate in that lovely clean bed and slept soundly until about five-thirty.

Breakfast was hearty with eggs, bacon, and toast and plenty of tea and I had a leisurely time before wandering back to the station to catch the 09:15 to Salisbury.

Salisbury Cathedral spire dominated the skyline as the train approached the station and I stepped down onto another platform crowded with soldiers but this time I think it was mostly soldiers returning to their units from leave because I knew that Salisbury Plain to the north of the city was home to dozens of regiments. As I pushed my way through the barrier and joined the crowds, I caught sight of an RFC forage cap and decided to follow it and see where it went. As I got closer, I could see that the forage cap was on the head of an RFC corporal, so I lengthened my stride and caught up with him. I asked him if he were from South Cerney airfield and was disappointed when he said he was from Middle Wallop but then he said he could drop me at the main gate at South Cerney which was not too far from his route back to camp. He was very chatty and said I was lucky because he had just dropped off a group of officers at the station on their way to London so I could ride back in the staff car in comfort. After hearing his life story, I was glad when he pulled up by the main gate of South Cerney airfield, I lifted my kitbag out and he drove off. Approaching the guard on the gate he directed me into the guard room where I showed my ID and joining papers and they directed me to the sergeants' mess and the location of the flying school.

I had never been into a sergeants' mess before and was impressed by the size of this new building alongside the edge of the peri-track around the edge of the airfield. The mess was built to accommodate up to eighty SNCOs in single rooms and provided a comfortable home for those based there and those on courses too. I signed the warning-in book in the reception as a steward gave me a key to my room and helped carry my kit to my room. It was only a medium-sized room with a bed, side table and wardrobe but was big enough to have a desk and chair for studying and an armchair for relaxing. I thought it was grand and would serve me well during my time at South Cerney. I spent the afternoon walking around, exploring the camp, made sure I knew where the flying school was situated and then wrote another long letter to Ruby hoping that I would get an opportunity to get home to spend whatever short time I could get with her. I was hoping that the training schedule would allow for a forty-eight hour pass some time in its duration and I knew that it was possible to get a direct train to Bristol from Salisbury and on into Wales from there. I knew everyone at home would be excited to see me although I was most interested in spending as much time as possible with Ruby.

The first day at the basic flying school was long and packed full of so many new faces, many hours of listening and note-taking that it was hard to take it all in. I was surprised to see that most of my fellow students wore khaki breeches and putees to the knee and a white smock. They were addressed as cadets, displayed no badges of rank and were either direct entry or transferees from the infantry destined to be commissioned at the end of training if successful. There were, however, three of us who were SNCOs on secondment from our regiments; we were allowed to wear our uniforms and rank badges but were expected to put a white band around our hats to show that we were under training. The chief flying instructor, Major Low-Holmes, addressed us first thing in the morning and explained the course of training we were to undertake for the next six weeks was to consist of seventy percent classroom theory and thirty percent flying training. The object was to enable us to study the Principles of Flight, Engines and Airframes, Meteorology and Navigation and to pass the Pilots' Basic Proficiency Theory examination whilst at the same time learning to fly the Aero bi-plane trainer until we had gone solo for at least fifteen hours. He made it clear to us that this was only a beginning and at the end of the course we would be pilots but with only a basic proficiency in flying and nowhere near ready to face an enemy in combat. The RFC had in the first two years of the war sent pilots straight to operational squadrons after graduation from this course, but the losses had proved too heavy, with nearly 14,000 young pilots killed within weeks of joining their squadrons. This loss rate was disastrous for the air corps and had created a massive shortage of pilots in the front-line squadrons forcing a major change in training strategy to be adopted from the start of this year to address the shortage. On graduation from this course, you will be presented with Army Preliminary Flying Wings which you can wear on your uniforms and then posted to the advanced flying schools at either, Gosport or Croydon, where you will spend a further six weeks training turning you into a competent combat pilot.

There was much talk amongst the cadets about this new method of training which was called the Gosport Method devised by the chief instructor at Gosport, Lieutenant Colonel Robert Smith-Barry and quite a revolutionary method designed to give new pilots as much time at the controls of the aircraft they were going to fly in combat as possible. Most of us could expect to gather forty to fifty hours flying time on type in our pilots' logbooks. This meant that we would get experience of the SE5, Sopwith Camel and Bristol Scout and would also be taught to fly in hazardous situations and learn techniques that would enable us to recover from a spin, cope with engine failures, stalls, and other hazards. We would become proficient at aerobatics, combat formation flying and air to air gunnery before the award of our RFC wings and posting to a front-line squadron. The CFI went on to make us understand that command in the air is dependent on experience and ability, not rank, which is why most of us who were joining the RFC were simply cadets. "You may find that your flying instructor has a lower rank than the one you held before transferring to the RFC but that is of no consequence because he will hold his QFI qualification on his merit and ability as a pilot." He warned us about maintaining our discipline and that whilst we would be exempt from standing duties at South Cerney, we were expected to use that time for studying. The drinking of alcohol was allowed but not within twelve hours of flying and then only in modest amounts. He concluded his remarks by reminding us that there was to be no second chances and that failure on any part of the course would mean a return to unit and the end of our opportunity to become a pilot. Finally, he finished with some good news that the training continued Monday to Saturday 08:00–16:30, and that Sunday was a rest day. All trainees who were in good standing with their instructors may apply for a weekend leave pass at the end of week four if desired. We now knew what we were facing but I was greatly encouraged to think that I could get a whole weekend to be with Ruby in one month's time.

A great deal of the classroom work I found to be relatively straightforward and again I had cause to thank Yanto Richards for the great foundation he had given me in the village school. I was always a keen reader and spent hours reading and rereading *How to Fly a Plane"* the pilots' manual and had managed to acquire a copy of Lt. Col. Smith-Barry's book, *General Methods of Teaching Scout Pilots*, to immerse myself in the subject. I have always enjoyed studying and was anxious every time I climbed into the Aero trainer to try out something new that I had learned from the books. My flying instructor was Sergeant Major Parry, who had lost an eye in aerial combat and now looked like a pirate on the Spanish Main with a patch over his empty eye socket, who was very patient with me and managed to control my exuberance enough so that we did not come a cropper in the air. He did, however, recognise that I had a good sense of airmanship and with discipline would make a better than average pilot. His objective was to get me to fly solo by the end of the third week of training, allowing plenty of time to gain as many hours of solo flying as possible. At first, I could not understand how hard it would be to accumulate fifteen hours of solo flying until I tried to do it. The biggest priority was the practice of take-off and landings, and a great deal of time was allocated to these monotonous but essential "circuits and bumps" which, in themselves, only amass short bouts of flying time each. The airfield and surrounding sky were crowded with sometimes twenty or so aircraft operating at once which meant a lot of time was spent sitting on the ground waiting for your turn or stooging about the sky waiting for a slot to be available for the final approach. Despite these frustrations, I was loving every minute I was in control of the aircraft, and I could feel that I was growing into a pilot every time I went up.

I had completed sixteen hours of instruction with Sgt. Maj. Parry when he suggested that we should prepare for my first solo flight on Thursday of that week. I was exhilarated because I knew that no other trainee from my course had yet gone solo although I was aware that a couple were as close as me to achieving that rite of passage. This was a major milestone for us all but also required a change of mindset from flying with the safety net of an instructor sat behind you to shout down the Gosport tube when you had made a blunder or take control to avoid imminent disaster. When I went solo, I was aware that the instructor would climb out of the aircraft and we would have no contact until I taxied back in after the flight, and this was a daunting feeling. The idea of being the first to go solo also brought some pressure of its own with a feeling that everyone would be watching me for signs of failure, but I need not have worried because when I walked into the trainees' crew room I heard Cadet Hubert Moreton telling a group of his friends that he was about to go solo in the morning. He seemed confident and was enjoying the acclaim from his friends, and I hoped that things went well for him in the air. I decided to keep quiet about my solo flight until after it was over and reconciled myself that going solo first was not necessarily a measure of a pilot's overall ability. I resolved that I would revise from the pilots' manual and be ready for anything Thursday might bring. I also decided that if my solo flight were successful, I would apply for the weekend leave pass for the fourth weekend but would not confirm it to Ruby until it was approved.

On Thursday morning, I briefed Sgt Maj Parry on my mission, he made some amendments to my flight plan, and we decided that I would take off and join the circuit around the airfield, line up and approach to land but pull up before landing to go round the circuit again, then land on the second approach. He said he would watch me through binoculars all the way but was certain I was ready to take this step, and that he may have some constructive comments to make after I had landed. It felt strange sitting in the aircraft on my own but as soon as the engine caught and the familiar smells, sounds and vibrations came alive to my senses I calmed down and was ready to go. I taxied out from the hangar, and I saw Parry giving me the thumbs up as I rolled past him, stood on the edge of the peri-track with a good view of the grass runway and his binoculars in hand, and I waved back at him. There were two aircraft ahead of me and I rolled slowly behind them towards the runway threshold and waited for each to be given the flashing light as permission to go from the control tower. The tension was rising in me as my eyes swept round over the control dials and I listened to the engine for any abnormalities, checking off in my mind what could go wrong. Then it was my turn to line up and wait, ready to go, for what seemed an interminable age, which was probably less than thirty seconds, for the two flashes that meant I could go.

I released the brakes, opened the throttle and immediately the aircraft leapt forward with a great surge of power. I felt the tail come up and then the lift pushing the nose as I pulled back and climbed into the sky smoothly and started my ascent to the airfield circuit, which was at 1,200 feet. I kept a good look-out for other aircraft already in the circuit and chose a suitable gap to insert myself safely without causing any threat to others. Once joined in the circuit, I moderated my speed a little to keep the distance between us stable. I was able to have a good look around – I could see the vastness of Salisbury Plain laid out below me and caught a glimpse of the megaliths at Stonehenge towards the east, and Salisbury Cathedral to the south-west. I did not have too much time for sightseeing, however, as I needed to keep a close watch on the preceding aircraft as it turned west into the next leg of the circuit and I followed at a discrete distance. I paid attention to the effects of the wind as we were now going downwind, and I adjusted the throttle slightly to moderate my progress to avoid overrunning the aircraft ahead of me. On the next turn into the southerly leg, I hung back for a few seconds to give the man in front time to select the point for his final approach as I looked around to pick up the water tower that I used to line up on for the best approach. As soon as the aircraft before me touched down, I started to line up ready for my first run in.

I knew I had to judge this right to just let the wheels brush the grass as I pulled back on the stick and opened the power to climb back to join the circuit. If I touched down proper the aircraft would not have enough power to lift off before the end of the grass track and I would look foolish. I lined up on the water tower and was confident that this would bring me in a central position over the runway and far enough clear of the threshold markers to make a clean landing. I leaned my head out of the cockpit to judge my descent to the grass but keeping my eye on the altitude and heading too. Everything seemed in line and as I just felt the undercarriage wheels gently whisk across the grass, I pulled the stick back hard into my stomach, opened the throttle wide and we soared back into the sky. I felt great because I had done a circuit and bump solo and my confidence was sky-high, but I almost veered too much to port and was in danger of missing joining the circuit cleanly. Fortunately, instinct played a part in dragging my attention back to the job in hand, I made a gentle correction and was able to slip into the circuit as easily as before. I knew that my instructor would have noticed my slight error, but I hoped he was in a forgiving mood. I flew the rest of the circuit carefully and with one hundred per cent attention so when I lined up on the water tower again, I was certain of a good clean landing to finish off.

Taxiing back, I hoped I had done enough as I swung the biplane onto the pan in front of the hangar, I could see from the look on my instructor's face that things were alright. We debriefed in the corner of the crew room where he gave me some criticisms, which he said were minor. He did mention my slight veering to port on my climb away but said he was satisfied because I had become aware of it quickly and took remedial action straight away. He said he would write up a full report and my logbook would be certified with my first solo flight today. Tomorrow would be the start of more detailed flying and I must work out a plan to get as much flying time as possible by 12:00 tomorrow. "You should also plan a couple of point-to-point cross-country flights within a thirty-mile radius of South Cerney to last about one hour duration, and if I approve your flying plan, you will start flying them on Monday next."

The rest of the day was spent in the classroom and when we were dismissed, I could not wait to write to Ruby and to Mum and Dad to tell them about going solo. I worked all morning in the crew room on my solo flying plan as requested by Mr Parry, submitted it by the allotted time. He read it through and then suggested some amendments to the point-to-points to include flying over the city of Southampton and Portsmouth for sortie one and west over the plain towards Bath for the second. I agreed to these changes and I had plenty of time to write the detailed flight plan for these flights. After lunch I submitted my leave pass application at the CFI's office and made a start on the flight planning.

Later that afternoon the peace and quiet of the crew room was shattered by the raucous blasts of the siren going off and although we all knew that this meant fire, an aircraft crash or surprise attack, we had never experienced it before. I joined all the others running out onto the pan to see what was going on and to ascertain whether it was a drill or for real. It was hard to tell but we could see the fire cart and two ambulances charging across the airfield at high speed. Somebody shouted and pointed towards the approach path and we could all see the Aero biplane staggering to stay in the sky as flames and smoke billowed from its engine. I wondered whether this was one of our crowd on his solo, then put it out of my mind as I reckoned that two ambulances meant there were two up. We were too far away to see the aircraft numbers but even if we could see them, we probably would not know who was flying that aircraft this afternoon. The pilot tried valiantly to keep the aircraft up high enough to cross the perimeter fence so he could affect a crash landing on the airfield, but the engine was rapidly losing power and was dropping fast. They just managed to cross the runway fence, the pilot slewed the aircraft to starboard so as not to churn up the grass track too much and to keep it away from the hangar and buildings.

He fought bravely but could not get her down safely, hit the ground hard and tipped forward upside down and the flames engulfed the aircraft in an inferno of burning fuel. It did not look likely that there were any survivors and we watched transfixed as the fire party and medic rushed in to try to save the pilot and trainee. The aircraft was almost burned completely within a couple of minutes and the rescuers could see that there was a body in the rear seat of the aircraft, horribly burned to a crisp. There was no sign of the trainee pilot, who must have been thrown out of the crashing aircraft as it hit the ground. We joined in the search party walking in line across the airfield looking for the other pilot, and five minutes or so later he was found lying unconscious in the long grass. He had sustained a broken leg and collarbone in the impact and his flying clothing was severely burnt, but later it was discovered that the survivor had few burns on his body because he was protected by the flying coat, helmet, goggles, and gloves. He was extremely lucky to have survived with so few major injuries and was identified as Cadet William Spencer, who would make a full recovery and return to qualify as a pilot in a later course. The instructor pilot was dead; he was Captain Ferguson with service as a pilot with the Royal Engineers Air Battalion before the formation of the RFC.

The chief instructor immediately issued orders that all flying was to be suspended for the rest of today and the following morning that the funeral of Captain Ferguson would be with full military honours, held on the following Friday in the parish church in South Cerney village. All flying school personnel would parade, and medals were to be worn. Weekend leave passes would be granted from 14:00 hrs on Friday until 23:59 on Sunday for those who had applied for them. I was so excited as this meant I could get two nights at home and would be able to spend plenty of time with Ruby. I pored over the railway timetable from Salisbury and found a train for Bristol via Bath leaving at 15:05 with a connection to Cardiff at 17:00. I reckoned I would be at home by early evening. I thought that if I wrote to Ruby this evening and told her what time my train came in, I could spend time with her before going home to Mum and Dad and arrange what we would do on Saturday and Sunday before I had to leave again. I felt that Mum and Dad would understand what my priorities were with only such a short time at home. I was also hoping that I might get a drink in with the boys from the rugby club, but I had told my brother not to book me in to play this weekend, as time with Ruby was more precious and I hoped to get her alone to myself instead of sharing her company at the rugby.

The flying programme went well the following week and I managed to get seven and a half hours of solo flying in by Thursday afternoon. I was gaining in confidence and was eager to pass to the advanced flying school, as I felt that I was ready to learn more operational skills. However, I was brought to earth with a bump quite literally on Wednesday afternoon with a couple of poor landings, one bouncing like a kangaroo down the runway for a hundred yards and the other almost smashing the undercarriage by hitting the ground too fast. Some stern words from Mr Parry sent me back up to practice circuits and bumps for the rest of the afternoon and this seemed to iron out the problem. On Thursday, my flying was much better as I finished the week feeling good and satisfied with the progress I had made so far. I knew that I still had a way to go before I would qualify to wear the Army Preliminary Pilot badge on my uniform and I was spending all my spare time preparing the flight plans for the two point-to-point sorties, one for next week and one the week after.

The funeral of Captain Ferguson was a sad affair but also uplifting and proud because the flying school and comrades from other units he had served with attended as well as members of his family. The parade was in best military tradition with the Cadets forming a guard of honour with reversed arms for his coffin as it was carried by six of his fellow flying instructors to the graveside whilst the band played a sad refrain with muffled drums. The army padre said the funeral words over the graveside, the guard of honour fired three volleys into the air over the grave and his coffin was lowered slowly into the ground and an Aero biplane piloted by Mr Parry, flew low and slow over the cemetery in tribute to Captain Ferguson. The immediate family and senior officers repaired to the officers' mess for lunch whilst the parade marched back to barracks behind the band. We all felt that this was a good send off and were doubly pleased because we were released for leave from 14:00. There was a bus from the guardroom at 14:15 direct to Salisbury railway station that I intended to be on, as it would enable me to catch the first train to Bristol that afternoon. My weekend kitbag was packed so I managed to catch a quick lunch at the servery in the sergeants' mess and then make for the bus in good time. I was glad that I had done so when I saw the crowd waiting to board the bus, but I was lucky to get a seat, and it departed on time leaving some cadets waiting for the bus to return from Salisbury for the second run into town.

ELEVEN

Ruby

As the valley train rattled up the line towards home, I was feeling a mix of emotions. A sense of anticipation in seeing Ruby again after nine months away from home; apprehension too in case she was not there to meet me at the platform when the train pulled in. I had a dryness in my throat and a tightening in my chest as this went round inside of me. I had received frequent letters from Ruby giving me all the news about things happening at home containing full accounts of the blossoming romance between Dai Rees and Freda Watkins and the interesting news that my brother Gwyn had taken up with Mair Davis, who was a clerk in the post office. This was particularly interesting because there was no mention of this in any of the family letters I had received from Mum and Dad and I resolved not to mention this at home until I had spoken with Gwyn first, to avoid causing him any embarrassment.

Ruby had never given any impression that she was tiring of me or had an interest in someone else, but I kept thinking that nine months away was a long time for her to wait and maybe she had forgotten me. At last, the train had completed its long climb and chugged into the last bend that led into our village station and my heart was in my mouth as the train screeched into the platform in a cloud of steam and smoke. I collected my kitbag and stepped down onto the platform, which was busy with miners returning to the villages up the valley after the evening shift change at the colliery. When they had boarded, I could see that the platform was deserted; my heart sank into my boots and wondered why she had not told me that she wouldn't be here to meet me. Slowly I climbed over the footbridge and descended the stairs to the downside platform and turned into the booking hall, where there was a great commotion as Ruby, accompanied by her mum and dad, was there to greet me. Ruby let out a great shriek when she saw me and rushed into my arms planting kisses all over my face and crying with happiness, then her father shook my hand and slapped my back, welcoming me back and congratulating me on my promotion all at the same time and then Mrs Thomas gave me a huge hug which made me think I was her son it was so all-embracing. She immediately grabbed one arm and Ruby the other, and I was frogmarched into the Station House for some tea with poor Mr Thomas left to rescue my cap and kitbag and follow behind.

The dining table was covered with sandwiches, cake, scones, and jam and plenty of Welsh cakes. Both mother and daughter fussed around me making sure I had plenty and my cup was always full. I felt like a king so much attention was lavished on me by all of them. After we had had our fill of good things from the table, we sat by the fire and Mr Thomas wanted to know about what it was like at the front and particularly how I had won the Military Medal. I tried to pass it off as less dangerous than it really was and said that the real bravery and courage was shown by my men, without whom the rescue could not have been affected. He smiled and said he was sure I was only being modest and held up newspaper cutting from the *South Wales Gazette*, which had published the citation and a detailed story of the events of the rescue obtained from Sapper Bryn Edwards who was wounded in the action and was also awarded the same medal for his bravery. Bryn Edwards had been interviewed by a reporter in the convalescent hospital in Monmouth and gave an accurate account of the events, also paying tribute to my leadership and courage in taking the brave action to rescue the wounded pilot and recover his stricken aircraft from the hands of the Germans and then without fear for my own safety to rescue him from certain capture when he was severely wounded, directly under heavy enemy fire. He said that he owed his life to my prompt and unselfish action.

I was humbled to have read Bryn's account and went a little silent and Mr Thomas realised that it was best to pass over this for the time being. I told them all about my flying training and what a wonderful experience it was to be free as a bird in command of the skies all around you, but I did not mention the recent sad demise of Captain Ferguson as I thought it might worry them. I wanted them to have an impression that flying was far less dangerous than operations on the ground. After two hours of chatter, I asked what plans Ruby had for the weekend, and Mr Thomas chipped in that Josh

Andrews did not need me to play this week because for once he had a full team and they were away at Treorche. I thought, perhaps, we could travel to Treorche for the match but realised that I would have to share Ruby with Freda and Dai and Gwyn and his new lady friend. Ruby said that she didn't want to go to the match and perhaps we could do something all day together as this was her Saturday off.

Immediately, I suggested that we took an excursion to Cardiff for the day and could visit the big shops and Cardiff Castle and enjoy being a young couple alone together. Mr Thomas thought that was a good idea, he looked up the times of the excursion trains in the morning and we agreed to leave before ten in the morning so we could enjoy all day in the big city. Just after eight, I made my excuses and said that I must go home because Mum and Dad would be waiting for me. After a quick kiss and cuddle in the hallway, I left the station and made my way up High Street and home where Mum and Dad were sitting by the fire waiting patiently for me to arrive. They were so excited to see me standing there smart in my best uniform with sergeant stripes on each arm and wanted to know everything. Dad wanted to see the medal and just looked at it in silent reverence when I took it out of its leather case... then he asked me if I had really done the things they said in the newspaper. I just nodded and he sighed; I thought I saw a slight trickle of a tear in his eye. Mum was not much interested in the war simply happy that I was home all in one piece and she made me feel quite morose when she started telling me who from the village had fallen in the most recent action in France and Belgium. I knew some of the names but was sad to hear that Staff Sergeant Billy Matthews from our street had been killed in the fighting near Arras in June. I remembered his large frame and smiling face, the way his boys looked up to him the last time I saw him when he shepherded me from Cardiff to Rochester on the day I joined up.

At nine-thirty, Dad got up from his chair, put on his jacket and cap and said that we would go and have a pint with Gwyn in the Miners' Welfare. He handed me the medal and asked if I would wear it so he could show me off to his mates in the club. I was reluctant because I am not a boastful person, but I could see that this meant a lot to him, so I agreed, and we left the house and strolled up to the club together. I had no trouble gaining entrance on this night because my siege company antecedents gave me honorary membership and when I walked through the door with Dad, there was a cheer and some clapping from the lads at the bar and Dad's workmates. Gwyn was in his usual place at the end of the bar but rushed forward, gave me a bear hug and then the drinks started coming. I noticed Dai Rees was missing and Gwyn just said one word, Freda, and sighed for the loss of his friend. Dad settled down at a table with his friends, started to play dominoes and Gwyn and I were able to talk at the end of the bar. It was difficult to talk too much because we were frequently interrupted by well-wishers who wanted to shake my hand and welcome me home, but I did broach the subject of Mair Davis. Gwyn went quiet, then with his voice in a whisper, said Mum and Dad must not know about Mair as it would break their hearts and cause a scandal. I asked what he meant and why would it cause a scandal, and he spat back at me that she was a married woman; her husband was a stoker in the navy serving on board ship on the China Station.

"Her husband has been away for almost two years, and she is the most beautiful and lovely woman you could hope to meet. We have been seeing each other now for seven months but in secret. No one must know." I told him that his secret was out because Ruby wrote to me mentioning you and Mair were seeing each other so it must be gossip amongst the young village girls already. He cursed, "This must have come from Freda Watkins who lived three doors from Mair. Even though we have been very discreet she must have caught on to what was going on. I am totally in love with her, I can't help myself." I reassured him that Mum and Dad would not hear about his affair with Mair from me, but he should be extra careful. My advice was to end the relationship as soon as possible for both their sakes but I could see from his expression that it was unlikely that he would take this course of action, so I resolved to say no more. We talked about other things and drank more beer until closing time. That night I found that I was worried for my brother for the first time in my life. He had always seemed so confident, in control and being taller, thinner, and better looking than me he never had any problems attracting the attention of girls. I really hoped that he had not got himself in too deeply and this would not destroy his life and future in this village. If he were discovered to be an adulterer this would break my parent's hearts and they would be so ashamed to show their faces at chapel and around the village. Welsh valley people were quite narrow-minded when it came to sex, marriage, and adultery and although they were very Christian people, were slow to forgive offences of this nature. I kept to my word and did not say anything to my parents about what I knew.

Ruby looked lovely when I collected her from her house in plenty of time for the Cardiff train. She was wearing another fashionable day dress made by her mother with matching hat, a medium weight coat and black leather gloves and handbag. She looked a pretty picture, and I was so proud that she was walking out with me. She looked so pretty and happy in her new outfit and the red tinges in her hair stood out in the sunshine. We sat in a double seat together and chattered like excited schoolchildren on a Sunday school excursion, oblivious to the scenery passing the window and with no care that this was a slow train stopping at every station for we only had time for each other. Although this was now the middle of October, the weather was still mild, and the winter rain had not yet started so Cardiff looked bright and busy in the autumn sunshine, and it was perfectly warm enough to walk about without being wrapped up too much. We went first to a coffee house and ice cream parlour, enjoyed some homemade ice cream with exotic flavours and sat together and chatted some more. After an hour, I thought I saw the waitress looking at the clock and thought, perhaps, we had probably sat at the table too long. We left the ice cream parlour, headed to the big departmental stores, and enjoyed window shopping, looking at the fine clothes on display and marvelling at the prices they were asking. I was certain that the dresses that Mrs Thomas fashioned for Ruby were worth equally as much as some of the dresses and gowns on display. We trawled through several ladies' dress shops and then looked at some jewellery displays until our feet were sore from too much walking.

On the next corner was a small restaurant with a fixed lunch menu, which looked wholesome and was a reasonable price, so we went in to see if there was a vacant table. The waiter guided us to a small table at the back of the room, but this suited us as it was intimate and secluded, and we ordered our food and continued talking happily until the food came. I was so happy to be so alone with Ruby and we talked about anything and everything non-stop except when we were eating. Eventually after we had eaten each course, we knew we could not sit in the restaurant any longer, I paid the bill and we went out, hand in hand into the city crowds again. We decided to walk to Cardiff Castle and to wander in the gardens down to the banks of the Taff and enjoy the remains of the day. The castle was impressive and the gardens beautiful as we wandered arm in arm slowly towards the riverbank where there was a footpath and park benches to relax on. The crowds were disappearing as the day was drawing in, but we were happy to sit close to each other and enjoy that closeness of being together. As it got darker, we started to kiss more deeply, and I slipped my hand under her coat and felt the swelling of her breast gently with my hand. I had never done this before but the reaction from Ruby encouraged me to keep going as my fingers traced out what lay underneath the material of her dress, I felt her nipple stiffen and little moaning sighs came from her mouth. It was difficult to see how we could go much further than this in such a public place although the stirrings I was feeling made me want to. I dearly wanted to explore her body with my fingers and tongue but knew that was not possible in the Castle Gardens.

Eventually, we broke off and headed back to the station for the trip home. We both had enjoyed the first sexual encounter but knew that we had to be patient until we could be properly alone together. It was almost dreamlike as we sauntered back to the station and on the ride home, we did not say too much but just clung to each other in a silent communion. The journey ended soon enough, and we were catapulted back into reality as we climbed on to the platform and across the footbridge to the Station House, hand in hand. I was happy and sad all in one complex emotion; happy because I knew Ruby wanted me and I was certain that I wanted her, but sad because I knew that I would have to leave early tomorrow afternoon to get back to South Cerney on time. I knew we would be able to snatch a few minutes together after chapel in the morning but only in the full gaze of our families and chapel congregation. We lingered on the doorstep for as long as we dared and then Ruby went in. I walked back up the hill in a kind of daze but could not resist the temptation to go into the tap room of the Railway Tavern and sink a few pints with the local boys. I would not be able to have a drink from tomorrow for the rest of the week because of my flying duties so I thought I would have a few tonight.

The bar was strangely quiet this evening and I guessed this was because the rugby team and supporters were not yet back from the away game in Treorche. Anyway, I found this suited me well as I was able to chat with the old regulars and sip my beer slowly instead of gulping it down with the boys. It was a leisurely hour and helped me calm my mind before I walked the last few hundred yards home. Mum and Dad were making tea before bed and I joined them and told them all about our trip to Cardiff, leaving out the more intimate bits, of course. They went up to bed about eleven, but I stayed down for another hour thinking quietly about Ruby, the war and flying before falling asleep in the armchair. Sometime later I was woken up by sounds in the back kitchen and I thought we were being broken into as I could see from my pocket watch that it was after three. I rushed into the back kitchen to find Gwyn with his boots in his hand, creeping softly across the room. When he saw me, his hand went to his mouth, and he whispered, 'Shhh, shhh'. I whispered and asked where he had been until this time because I knew they would have been back from Treorche by ten-thirty or so, then I realised that I knew where he had been and with whom. He was cutting things a bit too fine because he had to report for his shift underground at six, so there was barely a couple of hours to sleep. We both crept silently upstairs to bed and when I awoke in the morning Gwyn's bed was empty and I presumed he had gone to work. Dad was on the same shift and Mum said they had gone off together as usual.

It was just Mum and I for chapel but now we sat together in the pew with Mrs Thomas and Ruby and I was pleased that I could sit next to Ruby during the service. I chose to make the most of sitting close to her whilst the long sermon was on, knowing that it might be a few weeks before I got to be close to her again. I was hoping to get weekend leave before joining the advanced flying school in two weeks' time, but it was not yet certain that leave would be granted and I wasn't even sure which AFS I would be assigned to, Gosport or Croydon? Finally, the Reverend Lewis came to an end, announced the last hymn and we all stood, all the men sang with extra gusto as they knew the service was nearly over. The old minister had embarrassed me again as he drew attention to me, the award of the Military Medal for gallantry in action, my promotion to sergeant and again I had to endure the attention of the congregation with congratulations, pats on the back and handshaking when what I really wanted was to have a few quiet last words with Ruby. I managed to tell her that I was in love with her and would be thinking about her all the time I was away, and she just pressed into my hand a small, furry, hand-sewn rabbit about two inches high and said it was for good luck to bring me back safe to her. I was almost moved to tears and said I would cherish it and slipped it into my tunic pocket so that no one could see what she had given me. I knew that I would wear this under my flying clothing every time that I went up and in my pocket on the ground. Our time was all too short as I had to make it to the station for two o'clock for the Cardiff train but a quick kiss and hug and a hug for Mrs Thomas and Mum and I was off down the street to collect my kit. Mum had packed some sandwiches wrapped in paper and put them into the side pouch of my kitbag, and I was off to catch the train. The Cardiff train was on time and Ruby was waving and shouting from her bedroom window as we pulled out of the platform on the way to Cardiff.

Flying training resumed on Monday morning. I had booked three flying sorties for the day, had the flight plans approved by Mr Parry and logged with control before each one. My idea was to gently stretch out the length of each sortie in the air so that I could leave and rejoin the network over the airfield but only after flying a few miles further out independently. I was trying to improve my skills in flying by compass and map reading in preparation for the first of the longer flights that I was going to undertake on Friday. The flight plan was to take me from South Cerney towards Devizes and then turn north to Swindon, west to Bath, south to Salisbury and return to South Cerney. I had calculated the round trip distance as approximately eighty-five miles and the flying time as one hour, ten minutes. This was to be the longest flight that I was going to make during this training programme, and I knew that these estimates might change a bit when the weather conditions, visibility, wind direction and speed were known on Friday morning. This would be a more difficult flight because it would be largely over open countryside with fewer man-made landmarks to navigate by and it meant that I was going to have to look more carefully at the physical features of the landscape as well as the compass to keep on track. I was also going to fly at higher altitude to avoid training networks around airfields I might overfly so I chose to fly at 4,000ft, which could mean reduced visibility if there was cloud cover. My flying schedule enabled me to acquire six more flying hours in my logbook before the cross-country flight on Friday.

I spent many hours studying, looking over the charts to identify what salient features would help to identify suitable way points to keep me on track during the flight. I needed to be able to recognise when I had reached Devizes or Swindon or any other of the towns or cities I might pass over and to be able to pinpoint with some reasonable accuracy where I was in relation to the ground. I made detailed notes that I would carry with me in the cockpit alongside my maps and had also noted diversion airfields if it proved necessary to abort the mission through engine failure or worsening weather. When Friday morning came, I felt as prepared as I could be and spent the first half an hour after breakfast studying the weather reports for the duration of the flight where I could see that visibility was going to be good but reducing to fair towards the west and the winds were light but variable from the south-west, but this shouldn't have too great an adverse effect on my flight. Cloud cover was about 3/10 but was expected to increase from the English Channel in the Southampton area, spreading inland in a northerly direction around midday. My biggest concern was the ground temperature, which was only two degrees above freezing, meaning that it would probably be twenty degrees colder than the ground in the cockpit at 4,000ft. I knew that I needed to dress with my warmest clothes, gloves, and helmet so as not to feel the effects on such a long flight. I boiled some water to make some coffee but let it stand until it was at the right temperature to drink and put it into a small flask that I would carry with me. The lukewarm drink would send the reassuring messages to my body to keep it at a steady temperature, for I had learned on freezing nights in the trenches that a boiling hot drink just sends a false message to the body core that everything is alright, and the body stops working to keep warm. The flask was small and easy to handle in the cockpit so I would be able to drink small gulps from it during the flight to keep my core temperature stable. I made sure that my lucky rabbit was in my tunic pocket and I was ready to go.

I checked over the aircraft on the pan in front of the hangar, signed the service record and read the pilot's notes for any peculiarities I should look for in the running of this aircraft, but there were none. After some final words with Mr Parry, I climbed into the cockpit and settled myself in the seat whilst the airman tightened my straps before stepping backwards on the rear of the wing. I primed the magneto and fuel and gave a thumbs up as the airman swung the propeller, which caught on the third attempt and the engine rumbled into life. I was almost ready to go, and I realised that I was getting used to piloting the Aero biplane as this would be my fourteenth hour of flying solo in this type. I cautioned myself on becoming over-confident and remembered that this would be a gruelling initiation into long-distance flying, and I would have to concentrate hard to ensure that I kept on track and returned to base by the ETA. At 10:50, I released the brakes and started to taxi slowly across the grass to join the line of aircraft waiting for permission to take off. This was a busy flying day with at least six cadets from my entry flying their point-to-points today and the entry behind us were busy with circuits and bumps. It was 11:05 before I lined up on the runway waiting for the flashlight from the control hut and although it seemed ages before it came, it was probably less than twenty seconds before I was off.

As I rose into the air, I felt much of the tension in my body ease as I snapped into the flying routine, I had been preparing for all week; climbing steadily and entering the circuit at 1,200 feet; flying the northerly leg until I could safely pull out of the circuit and start to climb again in an easterly direction towards Devizes. I knew the climb would take about eight to ten minutes before I reached my operational height for the sortie and I was glad that I was wearing thermal underwear and woolly socks under my uniform. I had wrapped a thick scarf around my neck and had forsaken my leather gloves for woollen ones for warmth and had my helmet buttoned up and goggles down. I levelled out and found I had already covered most of the distance over the ground to Devizes. I could see the towers of the Norman castle in the centre of the town and the Vale of Pewsey stretching away to the east, so it was relatively easy to fix my position and find the new heading for Swindon. As the aircraft rolled over in the left turn, I could see over my left shoulder the vast extent of Salisbury Plain before I levelled out for Swindon. Again, Swindon was easy to recognise because it was a major east/west railway junction and the main lines from London to the South-West and Wales were huge landmarks to follow. I passed to the west of Swindon and found it remarkably simple to follow the mainline railway towards Bath and again, there were so many landmarks on the ground with the river Avon running through the city and the distinctive Georgian crescents easily spotted from the air. I kept well to the south of the city and was able to pick up a heading towards Melksham, which took me clear of the outskirts of Bath.

I could see ahead that the cloud cover was increasing, and I was heading into the base of some big cumulus clouds rolling in from the coast. I realised that I might have to reduce my altitude a little to keep underneath the cloud base but thought I could continue at 4,000ft until it became difficult to see the ground. I estimated I still had about twenty-three miles to run before turning into the final approach for South Cerney. Whilst the visibility was still passable, I took a few swigs of my warm coffee to keep my body temperature stable and checked my pocket watch. I had been flying for fifty-three minutes and estimated that it was twenty-two minutes before I was back on the ground at base indicating that I was slightly behind schedule and would be eight minutes beyond my estimated time of arrival. As I closed on the city of Salisbury, the cloud cover was down to 3,500ft and I had to swoop down to get below the cloud base so that I could make the turn to the east for the South Cerney approach. The flight was nearly over, and I was feeling satisfied and confident that I had proved that I could make a good pilot. The change in altitude increased the aircraft speed a little as I levelled out at 3,200ft and began my run into the airfield. I was hoping that by now the airfield circuit would be relatively quiet as instructors and cadets broke for lunch, and that I would not be delayed too much by having to join a busy circuit waiting for a slot to land. As I descended, I could see very few aircraft in the circuit so at 1,200ft I slipped in behind the one aircraft who was landing before me. As soon as he made the turn to begin his landing, I was already lining up to begin my approach as soon as he was down. Thirty seconds later and I began the slow and level descent to the grass runway stretched out in front of me. I would like to say that my landing was textbook, but I managed a little kangaroo hop on touchdown although I quickly corrected it and taxied off the runway and back to the hangar. I wondered why there had been a temporary lapse of concentration at the last minute but as I climbed out of the cockpit and jumped down to the ground, I found the answer as the great sense of exhilaration I had felt at achieving my first long-distance flight successfully was suddenly overcome by a wave of tiredness brought on by the intensive concentration, the cold and tension that I had unknowingly felt on the flight. I went into the crew room, collapsed in an armchair, and felt I could fall asleep for ever.

Mr Parry left me for half an hour and then we held a de-briefing session when I had overcome the first wave of tiredness. He was complimentary about my performance and asked me to describe, in as much detail as I could remember, the progress of the flight and particularly to reference the things that I had learned or were unexpected and any actions I had to take that were not included in my flight planning. He listened carefully and noted down some of the comments and observations I had made and stressed that being able to recall what had happened on a flight was an important skill for a combat pilot so he could report back significant intelligence to HQ on the ground about enemy troop movements; describe engagements with enemy aircraft and the number of their aircraft we destroyed and by whom; to confirm any of our aircraft lost and location if possible and where the concentrations of enemy high-angle batteries were situated.

He asked me to assess my performance and to describe what I had achieved from the flight today.

This personal assessment was the hardest thing to do. I was not yet confident enough to recognise what good meant in terms of pilot ability so tended to underrate my performance as improving but not quite there yet. He congratulated me on my ability to be self-critical but stressed that if I was going to survive in combat against skilful German pilots, I must be fully confident in my own ability as a pilot if I were to take them on in combat. He finished his assessment by saying all good pilots feel the same weariness after a long flight or a combat mission and it told him that I had put my whole self into the sortie both, physically and mentally. He told me not to worry about the six and half minutes that I was over the ETA as this was well within normal tolerance, which was only an estimate after all, and that he felt that I was more than ready for the advanced flying course. He congratulated me and recommended that I used every day of the next week to get as many flying hours in my logbook as I could to prepare for my second point-to-point (Salisbury–Southampton–Portsmouth–Winchester–Salisbury) on the following Thursday. There would be no flying for our entry on the Friday as it was the graduation day, and we would pass out to go on to the advanced flying school.

I was now finished for the day and I headed back to my room to relax and write to Ruby all about today's flight. Around five o'clock, I woke up lying on my bed having slept for three hours and no letters written. But I had a leisurely weekend ahead of me and with no flying scheduled for Saturday, I knew I could enjoy a drink in the mess bar after supper and would have plenty of time to write my letters home and get them in the post for Monday morning.

My last week at South Cerney passed so fast that I can only really remember being sat in the cockpit most of the time. I clocked up six hours of flying time in my logbook, which took me to twenty-one hours, with the last point-to-point to add on Thursday afternoon. I should graduate from basic flying school with twenty-two hours in the Aero biplane that I hoped would be a solid foundation for flying the scout aircraft which were faster and more aerobatic. My point-to-point flight over the built-up areas was an anti-climax and went smoothly with settled weather, good visibility, and a multitude of landmarks on the ground to navigate by. The round-trip distance was about half of my previous sortie, so I was only in the air for forty-six minutes. The only difficult thing about it though was having to keep a lookout for other aircraft, flying so close to the vicinity of so many military airfields, but I felt that this was good experience for me when I began to fly combat patrols in the future.

Friday morning was to be our passing-out parade and we were honoured that General Trenchard came himself to present us with our Army Preliminary Flying Badge to be worn on our left breast, just above the medal ribbons. Those who were cadets were to be commissioned as second lieutenants in the Royal Flying Corps and were permitted to wear the distinctive RFC uniform with jodhpurs and riding boots, whilst those of us who were secondees just removed the white band from our caps and continued to wear our normal ranks and regimental uniform. I had cleaned and pressed my best uniform and was proud that I still wore the Monmouthshire Siege Company flash on my shoulder and the Royal Engineers badges on my collar.

The entry had practised the parade and march past every evening under the direction of an elderly drill sergeant who had fought in the South African wars. He was a grand chap and took great pride in ensuring that we were as smart as could be for our big day, particularly with so many guests from the headquarters of the Flying Corps and the army more generally. The other cadet entries were paraded on the day but only the graduating class would march past. We had not lost anyone from our flight due to dropouts or accidents in the air, but we were shocked to find that two of our number had failed the basic flying course and were to be returned to their unit. They left South Cerney on Thursday evening. The parade marshals began marching the four junior entries on to the parade square, their officers took post and Captain Douglas had control as the parade adjutant. The Corps HQ band from Middle Wallop were halted to the left of the parade and played martial music quietly whilst the parade stood at ease. Our flight formed up in the entrance to the hangar under the command of Mr Parry, we waited for the chief flying instructor to take over command of the main parade and for the order to march on. Ten minutes before eleven, the CFI marched on the parade square, the adjutant handed over command of the main parade to him and then when the parade was called back to attention, this was the signal for Mr Parry to call us to attention. We marched out on to the parade square behind the colours of the Royal Flying Corps and the band playing the regimental march. The four flights were arraigned with two flights either side of the centre, leaving a large enough space for the graduating flight to complete the line with the RFC colour and escort in the centre in front of the saluting base.

The important guests and the directing staff who were not on parade were sat in a small stand behind the saluting base waiting for the arrival of the general in a staff car accompanied by the flying school commandant. The CFI called the parade to attention and to present arms for the arrival of the commanding general and when they were seated, he ordered arms and stood the parade at ease. The next phase was to call the graduating flight and escort to the colour to attention and give the order to quick march, eighteen paces forward. The band played 'British Grenadiers' as we marched forward and halted in front of the saluting base, where we were put at open order, made ready for inspection and to receive our preliminary wings from General Trenchard. The band played quietly whilst the general, our commandant and the CFI passed along the ranks stopping at each man to have a few words of congratulations and then to pin the badge on to our chests. The general seemed proud of us and genuinely pleased to be performing the awarding duty today. I was so happy and satisfied with my achievement so far and when he stopped in front of me, he could see from the beam on my face that I was pleased to have come this far. He remarked on my Military Medal and then asked me what my unit flash was, and I was proud to tell him I was from the Monmouthshire Siege Company. He prompted me to apply for a transfer immediately I received the RFC wings as the Flying Corps was in such a great need of more brave fellows like me. He then passed on to the next man and left me with many thoughts going round in my head about my future.

After the presentations, the CFI called the main parade to attention and asked permission for the graduates to march past and then gave the orders for our flight and the RFC colour and escort to march past first in slow time, then in quick time. The general took the salute on each occasion and the graduating flight took up a position at the right of the parade to lead the parade off. It all went extremely well, and I truly wished Mum and Dad and Ruby could have been here to see it. The graduates were to be guests at lunch in the officers' dining room where General Trenchard would address us. We were instructed that in the forty-five minutes before the reception we should sew the preliminary wings on to our uniforms. I was already a dab hand with a needle and cotton, so I quickly sewed my flying badge on and helped a couple of others who were not so adept with the needle to get ready for the reception.

The officers' mess was a little grander than the sergeants' mess, but the main difference was that there were stewards everywhere serving food and drinks and generally looking after the officers' every need. The food was like the fare in our mess, except that it was silver service at the table and not self-service from the servery. I was so excited that I did not eat very much and was eager to hear what the commanding general was going to say and to finally hear where I was to go for advanced flying training. Trenchard was frank and blunt in his talk when he told us that the failures in training had led to the loss of over 15,000 young pilots through a lack of proper training for combat operations. He stressed that the new training system that had been in operation since the start of 1917 – although slower to graduate pilots – was turning out more accomplished and able combat pilots who were able to hold their own against the enemy in the air. It was not enough just to fly; you must go on to learn how to fight when your aircraft was in the air. He wished us all good luck and then surprised me by going on to say that today he had met a lot of eager young talent but also some soldiers with experience at the front, and that he was especially drawn to a young Royal Engineer sergeant who had served in Belgium on the front line with a siege company, holder of the Military Medal and this impressed him very much. I was embarrassed as all eyes seemed to be on me and I could feel the heat reddening up my cheeks, but then it dawned on me that this was praise indeed and nothing for me to be ashamed of, and I smiled in acknowledgement of his kind words.

We all stood as the general and his party left the dining room and then the CFI asked all the graduates to sit whilst he read out the postings. The entry had been evenly split between Gosport and Croydon, with three from the north of England being sent to Woodvale near Liverpool. My name was read out for Croydon and we were told we could collect our joining instructions from the clerks in the command hut immediately we were dismissed from lunch. I discovered that those going to Gosport had to report for Monday morning start next week and Tuesday for Woodvale, but Croydon did not start their advanced course until Wednesday morning next week. Croydon Advanced Flying School was based at Kenley on the outskirts of London and was the second of the new Gosport system training schools to be set up. The joining instructions included rail warrants that I could exchange for tickets to go home for four days before reporting for training and if it had not been for Ruby at home, I might have been tempted to spend these days enjoying the sights in London. I decided to stay for the night in the sergeants' mess and to enjoy a celebration with some of the other SNCO graduates and set off for home early in the morning.

The mess manager was from Newport, and he told me that there was a bus from South Cerney at 07:30 in the morning to Bath, which he was sure would take about two hours but connected with the mainline trains from London to Cardiff. I thought this to be a good idea and resolved to do this. We started drinking at four-thirty but by eight-ish, I had had enough and decided to sneak off to bed. I slept well, was up for an early breakfast at six and walked to the centre of the village to catch the bus at seven-thirty. The bus was a single decker and quite busy, but I managed to find a seat in the rear, stowed my kitbag and slept all the way to Bath station. I had only fifteen minutes to wait until the Red Dragon Express pulled in, I scrambled aboard and found a seat in a compartment containing a smartly dressed elderly couple and a younger man in civilian clothes, but who walked with a stick and had burns on his face and hands. I settled my kitbag in the luggage rack and sat down with my back to the engine, the old lady smiled and then her husband asked me if I was pilot. I told him I was a Royal Engineer but had qualified as a preliminary pilot and would go on to train as a military pilot in time. They were kind and said I was brave but then lapsed into silence. The young man addressed me as sergeant and said, "I can see from your medal ribbons that you have been in action on the ground with some distinction," and then with some sadness he said that he just had his wounds to show for his service and he told me that he had been gassed in the battle at the Somme, his lungs were burnt away inside and the flash from an exploding shell had burnt his face and hands as he tried to shield his eyes. He was a poor sight because he was only about my age, but the war had robbed him of his youth. At Bristol, he got up and awkwardly lumbered out of the compartment into the corridor to get down from the train. The brief acquaintance with this anonymous young man certainly made me think about the huge cost to my generation of this war.

As the train hurtled under the Severn and into Wales some ideas were forming in my head. I had accumulated quite a lot of money saved from my pay at the front and the enhanced flying pay at the training school. As a trainee pilot, I was receiving eight shillings and sixpence a day; this amounted to over £5 a week and when I added it to the savings from nine months at the front, I had over one hundred and five pounds saved up. I knew that the award of the preliminary flying badge would increase my daily pay another two shillings, taking my pay to £6 a week. I had always been taught to be careful with my money and I did intend to save it carefully for the future, but I decided that I would stop off in Cardiff and buy an eternity ring for Ruby from one of the jewellers in the main shopping thoroughfare. I wasted nearly an hour surveying the rings on display but the ones I liked the most were always more than I could afford to spend.

In the end I came to a shop called Wooldridges, plucked up courage to go in and I told the elderly shop assistant my budget and what I was looking for and she called the jeweller from the backroom. He asked me again what I was looking for and I said I was looking for an eternity ring as a token of my love for a young lady and he asked me what my budget was and when I told him, he asked me to be kind enough to wait a minute, he would see what he could offer me. After a few minutes he brought a tray with half a dozen rings and showed each one to me. I liked them all, suspecting that they would be more than I could afford but selected a simple gold ring with a diamond cluster on the top. He congratulated me on my good taste and how I had chosen the best ring on the tray because of its simple beauty and quality. I was fearful that the price would be far more than I wanted to pay and when he turned over the ticket, I just caught a glimpse of a number over fifty; he must have noted my expression because he smiled and said, "We always give a discount for our boys at the front, and I will make a deal with you. If the young lady accepts your proposal of marriage, you will promise to come back to me to buy your wedding rings, I will let you have this ring for twenty-five pounds." I was amazed because this was at least half of the full price on the ticket, but without a hesitation agreed. Twenty minutes later, I was sat on the valley train with the ring in my pocket in a brown leather box, rehearsing in my head what I would say to Ruby when I gave her the ring. I had to think fast and even though I had gone over what I would say to her many times my mind was unusually blank today, which I guessed was just nerves and the fear that she would turn me down.

It was the rugby club annual dinner at the Bedwas Hotel that evening and as a playing member, I was entitled to get two tickets for Ruby and I. Mr and Mrs Thomas were also going, as well as Gwyn, Dai Rees, and Freda. I wondered whether Gwyn would be bold enough to bring Mair Davis as his partner, but I hoped not because he would risk everything if he did so, for all would be out in the open and common knowledge. I spent the afternoon sprucing up my best uniform, Mum gave me a haircut so I would look my best; when I was dressed, I looked at myself in the mirror and thought I looked presentable enough in my uniform with my sergeant stripes, flying badge and the Military Medal. I walked down to the Station House at six-thirty, making sure that I had got the ring and my lucky rabbit in my pocket to collect Ruby and to walk with Mr and Mrs Thomas the 500 yards to the hotel. It was a fine night, so it was not necessary to wear heavy overcoats and we were happy and light-hearted as we walked to the Bedwas Hotel.

Ruby looked absolutely stunning in a pale blue gown specially made for her by her mother, which made her look more like a society lady than the station master's daughter and I was totally besotted with her all over again. She was so beautiful, and I knew everyone would be looking at us tonight in admiration. Mr Thomas was wearing a black suit with a bow tie; Mrs Thomas was wearing another of her creations and both women carried shawls in case it got colder during the evening. The reception was for seven, dinner at seven-thirty; the bar lounge was already filling up when we arrived and there was a happy buzz of chatter from the assembled guests. This was the biggest rugby club event of the year and was guaranteed to attract a good crowd of supporters who would help swell the club funds to support the teams throughout the year. Player members were subsidised by the social members from the village so they could afford to attend.

I was so happy to see the attention that Ruby attracted as we circulated the room which made it easier for me when I was drawn away from her side into conversations with local dignitaries about my medal, flying wings and promotion. When we were called to dinner, Ruby and I were seated on the players' table and were separated from her mum and dad. We were both a little relieved as we were seated amongst our friends and could relax a little more. I was seated next to Freda Watkins and opposite Ruby, which I did not mind at all because it meant I could feast my eyes on her beauty throughout the dinner and Ruby had Dai Rees next to her, who was opposite Freda. I found that I was growing to like Freda more as she had certainly matured and quietened down since she had met Dai. I could see that behind the gossipy façade she was an attractive young woman. On the other side of me was Gladys Llewellyn, and her partner, George Talbot, who played in the back row, was next to Ruby. This was a happy table to be on as the jokes and banter were lively and we all got on so well together.

The dinner was good and served smartly and efficiently by the hotel staff, and then we toasted the King and went to the speeches. Josh Andrews spoke about the club's achievements over the past season, mentioning the famous victories, some defeats and highlighting performances by the star players before inviting the club president to present the President's Cup for the Player of the Year, elected by the members to Dai Rees. We cheered and applauded, some of Freda's old noisy exuberance came pouring out and we all joined in because it was obvious that Dai was not expecting to receive this award, being usually quite shy and happier out of the limelight. He finally got up and made his way to the top table to receive the cup from the hands of Albert Tunstall, the club president, and then he was asked to say a few words. Dai was a collier, not used to speaking to crowds of people, but he surprised us all, rose to the occasion and delivered a short but confident speech thanking the club members for their support. We applauded and cheered and loved him more because he had only spoken for two minutes. We were anxious to get up from the tables and dance to the music of a small band who were reputed to be able to play all the latest dance music. I noticed that there was an empty seat at the end of the players' table, and I could not see Gwyn anywhere, so I guessed he had chosen not to come to the dinner after all.

The six of us with the addition of two more couples commandeered a table at the edge of the dance floor, Dai and I went through to the bar to order drinks and there was Gwyn, stood at the end of the bar, looking very glum. Dai and I came each side of him so he would not run away and asked why he was not at the dinner table. He just groaned; his eyes were red from crying as he whispered, "She let me down at the last minute... she wouldn't come, too frightened what people would say." We tried to persuade him to join us at the table, but he refused, and I suspected that he would rather get drunk alone than sit in misery whilst we were enjoying ourselves. Dai and I left him to his pool of misery and woe and went back into the waiting girls, determined to enjoy ourselves this evening. I was not a great dancer, but I had mastered the rudiments of the slow foxtrot and waltz so I could hold Ruby tight as we moved as gracefully as we could around the dance floor to the music of the five-piece orchestra.

We were losing ourselves into the lure of the romantic music and each other, and only the occasional bump into another couple as we twirled around brought us back to reality. The little leather case with the ring inside was burning a hole in my pocket, I was searching for an opportune time to give the ring to her but in the ballroom it seemed impossible. The evening passed too quickly and when the orchestra leader announced the last waltz, we knew it was ending soon. The wartime licensing laws introduced to restrict drinking by factory workers meant that all licensed premises had to close by eleven at night unless they had a special licence for later hours, which was rare outside of the big cities. At about eleven-twenty we were collecting ourselves together and heading for the main exit of the hotel. Ruby's parents had been offered a ride in the car of Mr Jones-Daly, the manager of the woodyard and timber merchants, but we preferred to walk home so we could be alone together. Dai and Freda walked with us for a couple of hundred yards and then broke off towards Freda's parents' house and we continued toward the station.

With the Station House in sight, I gently pulled Ruby into a quiet corner, brought the ring case out of my pocket and as romantically as I could told her how much I loved her and wanted to share my life with her after the war was over. I then, without much finesse, placed the leather case into her hand and asked her to marry me, clumsily trying to get on one knee as the romantic stories tell you all proposals should be done. My attempt at the Prince Charming characterisation did not seem to matter much to Ruby, whose eyes lit up when she saw the shiny diamond engagement ring, and I slid it gently on her finger. She wrapped her arms around my neck and kissed me so deeply and whispered, "Yes," into my ear. I could have leapt across the street as if I were a ballet dancer on the stage, so full of exuberance and joy that Ruby had accepted my proposal, and she grabbed my hand and said we must tell her mum and dad before they went to bed.

The rest of the evening was a whirlwind as we swept into the Station House to find her parents enjoying a nightcap with their friends Mr and Mrs Jones-Daly. Ruby burst through the door flashing her ring hand towards her mother, shouting," Derfal has asked me to marry him, and I have accepted." I was a little embarrassed because I supposed I should have spoken to Mr Thomas first, but being away from home had made this difficult to do. He did not seem to be all that bothered about the protocol and very quickly I had a large whisky in my hand and Ruby a sweet sherry, and he proposed a toast to us both. I stayed there drinking and chatting with my prospective in-laws and their friends, all the time holding Ruby's hand in mine for about an hour and then I thought I had better go. I shook hands with the men and kissed the hands of both the older women, kissed Ruby more deeply in the entrance hall and set off for home with a real spring in my step.

Mum and Dad were fast asleep when I got home but I was worried when I saw that Gwyn was not in his bed. I was tempted to go back out and look for him but had no idea where to start and was not even sure which house Mair Davis lived in, so I could not go knocking on doors at random at this time of the morning. I thought it would be better to wait until the morning, I knew which street Mair lived in so I could find out if he was there. I woke early but Gwyn's bed was not slept in. I was kicking myself for not doing more to stop him from drowning his sorrows alone, but I was too wrapped up in my own happiness to care that much about Gwyn's troubles. I put on some civilian clothes and was just about to go out and look for him when I saw Constable

Mervyn approaching our door through the back-kitchen window. I opened the door quietly and invited him out of the cold and, very apologetically, he told me that Gwyn was in custody in the cells at the police station. Apparently, he had been involved in a scuffle with the staff at the Bedwas Hotel last night after closing time when he refused to leave and there was a little pushing and shoving, during which a window was broken.

'Sergeant Williams has sent me over to ask whether you can help Gwyn pay to get the glass repaired, he thinks he can get the hotel manager to drop the charges because Gwyn's behaviour last night was out of character, and he ought to be allowed one lapse without ruining his reputation.'

I knew that Sergeant Williams was a good chapel man and was thinking about the good standing of Mum and Dad as much as Gwyn's welfare. I asked how much it would cost to repair the window and he said it would be about ten shillings, but Gwyn did not have this much on him when he was arrested. I thanked him and said I would come to the police station within an hour to pay the money and speak with Sergeant Williams. After the constable left, I heated some water, shaved, and washed and as I went back into the parlour to go upstairs to dress in my uniform for the day, Dad was sat in his chair. He looked at me and asked who I was talking to in the back kitchen. I was tempted to dissemble and hide the truth, but Dad looked me in the eye as he said he thought it was the constable. I wondered how long he had been there and what he had heard, so I just told him the truth and what I was going to do. He looked sad and said that he knew something like this would happen when Gwyn became besotted with that woman. I was surprised and asked him how long he had known.

Sergeant William's was sympathetic and happily accepted my ten shillings to repair the hotel window and released Gwyn from the cells with no charge. When they brought him out from the rear of the police station, he looked rather sheepish when he saw me; he was rather dishevelled after sleeping in his best suit but largely remained silent as we walked to his lodgings. I tried not to lecture him too much but suggested that he needed to find a solution to this problem before it destroyed him and the reputation of his family too. However much, he was in love with Mair Davis she was a married woman with a husband serving in the Navy so until that situation was sorted out and she was free he would win no friends buy committing adultery with her. He just shrugged his shoulders and went into his lodgings leaving me standing in the street without an answer.

I wondered whether it was too early to call on Ruby but a glance at my watch showed me that she would be getting ready for chapel at this time so I returned home hoping that I would be in time for some breakfast before accompanying Mum to the service. After the service Ruby told me that Freda had invited us to have some lunch at her house that afternoon and then whispered that her parents were away at a family wedding in Swansea.

Freda had not made a great effort in preparing food but there were some sandwiches and cake laid out on the parlour table. I could see straight away that she and Dai were completely besotted although we were surprised when they excused themselves and left us in the parlour whilst they climbed the stairs to the front bedroom over the parlour. We could hear the creaking of the floor-boards as they crossed the floor above us and then the squeaking of the bed springs as they settled in the bed. There was the faint sound of Freda's giggling followed by the sound of the regular motion of their passionate lovemaking immediately above our heads. Ruby seemed as surprised as I was, and I am sure that this was not what she had expected for our lunch this afternoon, but I reckoned Freda and Dai wanted to give us a chance to be alone together away from the eyes of our respective parents and this was our opportunity. We were already sitting on a large sofa, so it was easy to gently pull Ruby towards me and begin deep kissing and running my hands over her body on top of her clothes. She began to squirm and respond passionately and guided my eager fingers under her blouse on onto her firm breasts encouraging me to play with her nipples until they were standing erect, and she was making little gasps at the back of her throat. I could feel my trousers taut with the pressure of my rising manhood and wanted nothing more in the world at that moment to put it inside her as quickly as possible. Ruby held me back a little and slid down the seat so that she could lift her skirts up to around her waist exposing her underwear to my view and she guided my right hand to between her legs to pull her drawers to one side to expose her labia and the entrance to her vaginal canal. I gently parted her labial lips and my fingers played gently until she pushed them inside her to feel her velvety wetness and then she prompted me to loosen my trousers and reveal my penis which was by now fit to burst and she guided me into that warm and lovely womanly orifice so I could thrust as deep as I could into her. She gave a little cry as I entered her; held on to me tight and pulled me in tighter and as the contractions of her vaginal walls squeezed my penis, I let out a shout as my semen burst forth into her. Disappointed that I could not last longer than a minute and had ejaculated far too early and had not satisfied Ruby I was ashamed of my inadequacy and hoped that I would get better the next time. I was about to pull out of her vagina when she wriggled her bottom closer and thrust into me which seemed to reawaken my member and we made love again this time lasting much longer and only ending when Ruby had enjoyed an orgasm. I had not expected to being enjoying sex with Ruby this afternoon, but it would send me back to the training school with a yearning that my next trip home would not be too far away. We cleaned ourselves up and rearranged our clothing and we could still hear Dai and Freda enjoying themselves upstairs we quietly let ourselves out of the front door and set off home.

PART TWO:

The Royal Flying Corps

TWELVE

Wings

The Croydon Advanced Flying School was located at Kenley on the Hill just three miles or so from the western edge of Croydon, where a large patch of level ground had been acquired to develop as an airfield close to London which was large enough to act as a base for scout aircraft for the defence of the capital as well as accommodate the advanced flying school. The AFS was located at the extreme west of the airfield with its own hangar and support and functioned much like an operational squadron in terms of its organisation and structure. It was equipped with Sopwith Camels, SE5 and Bristol scout aircraft. The main object was to give the trainee pilots as many flying hours as possible in types commonly used by operational squadrons and to train them as combat pilots. My posting from South Cerney, basic flying to Croydon advanced flying training was promulgated by the RFC Training Brigade to which I was seconded by the RE. The AFS was better equipped than the BFS and was staffed entirely by veterans of the air war, who brought to the classroom and the cockpit a high degree of expert knowledge backed up by real experience of flying in combat.

The pace of this training was far more intensive, and our days were packed with a full classroom schedule of lessons and testing plus long hours of flying with the intention of getting us at least thirty-five additional hours of solo flying in a type of aircraft we were likely to be using in the operational squadron we would be joining. Classroom work was more complex than before and I found myself learning new things like wireless signalling, Morse code, photography, the principles of artillery and infantry cooperation, reconnaissance, bombing, aircraft recognition and maritime operations. In the air we were taught air fighting, bombing, combat formation flying and night flying, which involved hours of dual flying with our instructors followed by solo practice. Although there were specialist instructors for each area of the flying curriculum, we were all assigned to a personal supervisor who coordinated our training and monitored our progress. We were expected to work six days a week from 06:00–16:00 and to undertake private study in the evenings after supper. Our progress was monitored closely and failing any part of the course meant a delay in qualifying or being chopped from the programme.

I was assigned to Major Coate-Barnes as my supervisor, who was also one of the senior air fighting instructors and had an impressive record in the air. He was an ace, credited with eleven kills as a scout pilot and had been awarded the Distinguished Flying Cross twice. He was tall and good-looking, about twenty-seven years old and many of the trainees and junior officers looked up to him. I found him difficult to warm to and thought he was rather cold and detached. I felt that he was over critical but as the time went on, I realised that he was trying to make his students realise the reality of what war in the air was really like, to debunk the many popular theories of the glory of aerial combat by describing the terrifying fear that lurks in the clouds over the battlefield. He taught us that flying was a dangerous enough business without a determined enemy trying to shoot us down or set our aircraft on fire. He showed us how to overcome our fears, to fly with skills that would save our lives in difficult situations and maybe strike back at the enemy too. We were to be constantly on the alert and had to be competent pilots to fly the aircraft whilst constantly searching the sky for potential threats. He often surprised trainees in the air by ambushing them from out of the sun or through the clouds to teach that lack of vigilance could cost your lives. Those who spotted him in time to take evasive action often found themselves in protracted aerial chases spiralling over the sky with Major Coate-Barnes hot on their tail. I soon learned that he was a natural predator and was constantly hunting for his next victim when on combat patrols. There were only a couple of times when he jumped me, we went into a long dogfights over the Surrey countryside where he really put me through my paces before I managed to escape his attention. When I landed the back of my shirt, under my uniform and flying jacket, was soaking wet from the exertion of throwing my aircraft around the sky to evade him. I promised myself that I would try to devise a strategy to jump him sometime when he was not expecting it and try to shoot him down if I could. The underlying principle behind the flying training was to get us to fly our aircraft to the limits of its performance, so that we were prepared for anything that we might come across in the air when we were on operations.

In one of our debrief sessions, after attempting to surprise him by diving on him from altitude through light cloud cover over Guildford, he praised me for my courage and determination, and he said he could see the qualities that earned me the Military Medal. He told me that I was resolute, completely focused and would have been successful if he had not just glanced to starboard at the right second, I would have caught him completely by surprise. "Once I knew you were there, however, I was able to use my experience to keep out of the trajectory of your guns enough to save my skin. Never under-estimate that little bit of luck that saves your life because a lucky pilot lives to fight another day." He went on to say that I had made rapid progress in air fighting and that he was sending me to the Hythe Air Gunnery School on the Kent coast for a week to perfect my shooting skills.

"You will take your aircraft and set out a flight plan to fly to Hythe tomorrow morning," he explained, "and report to Warrant Officer Drury who will be your gunnery instructor when you land at Hythe airfield.'" I was excited because I felt that I had passed an important milestone and I thanked him for his confidence but as I turned to go, he called me back. 'Sergeant Morgan, you have the makings of a good scout pilot and I sense that you have leadership skills too. The RFC needs people like you, and you will be wasted as a sergeant pilot in an operational squadron.' He urged me to think again about a transfer from the REs rather than secondment because if the transfer was approved, I would be commissioned on award of my RFC wings. I did not know what to make of this suggestion but was elated that the hardest taskmaster amongst the instructors thought that I was good enough to be a combat pilot and an officer. The only officers who came from our village were the sons of the middle-class and the closest they came to the colliery was as managers or owners. I wondered what Ruby would think or my mum and dad, but I hoped they would be proud and approve of my decision.

My week at Hythe taught me the rudiments of aerial gunnery and the hours that I was able to practise over the sea chasing moving targets towed by other aircraft were invaluable. I learnt how to conserve my ammunition by firing in short bursts and to offset my aim to allow for the movement of the target and deflection caused by the wind. WO1 Drury was an excellent teacher and like me came from the Royal Engineers. We talked about Lidsing camp which was his first posting with the Engineers nearly forty years ago, when he was a sapper in the No 1 Ballooning Battalion and then later served in both RE Air Battalions before becoming an instructor when the Hythe Air Gunnery School was set up at the start of the war. He was not a pilot but a qualified Air Observer and Gunner and wore the Observer's brevet on his uniform, but he had spent so many hours in the air in so many aircraft, there was little he did not know about flying. He was a patient teacher and sat in the rear seat of my aircraft as we flew over the ranges and coached me on aiming and firing for maximum effect. The machine guns were synchronised with the propeller so we could fire through the prop whilst it was rotating without hitting the props and damaging them severely. We were firing live rounds and I also loaded a tracer to light up and mark the trajectory of our shots to check for accuracy. I had always enjoyed shooting and qualified for my marksman with .303 rifle at the first attempt as a recruit, so I hoped I would have an equally good eye with the machine guns. Aiming was not as easy as with the Lee Enfield as there was no sights to line up to zero in the rifle. Sighting was only achieved by lining the whole aircraft up with the target in such a way that you have accurately estimated where the target will be in the seconds it takes from squeezing the trigger to hitting the target, considering that both are moving. I discovered that I still had a good eye for shooting and as I became more familiar with the machine guns, the more accurate I was. My only worry was that chasing a canvas trailer that was reasonably static in the sky would not be a good test when faced with an enemy aircraft with an experienced pilot doing everything in his power to escape the power of my guns.

After seven days, Mr Drury attested that I had reached a satisfactory level of aerial marksmanship and I was able to fly back to the AFS at Croydon at the end of the day to go straight in to four days of intensive training for combat formation flying, which almost made me collapse with exhaustion. I had been flying continuously now for eleven days without a break and was hoping to be stood down for a day to catch up with some sleep. Fortunately, the following week was made up of written and practical tests, so there was to be no flying and I was able to recharge the batteries somewhat. I passed most of the written tests satisfactorily but was struggling a bit with wireless signalling and particularly flashing messages by Morse code. I was OK at receiving the messages but too slow at sending them. The instructor had only awarded me fifty per cent; I was the lowest score of my class, and he suggested that I retook the test in two weeks. This was a blow to me, I did not think it was serious enough to fail the advanced flying course, but I spent several hours each evening after supper flashing messages on the wall in my darkened room to increase my speed. I retook the test two weeks later and passed with sixty-five per cent, so I had no need to worry about a poor score.

I still managed to fire off frequent letters to Ruby and got all the news from home less frequently from Mum and Dad. Things had not been going too well with Gwyn, who was still seeing Mair Davis, had left my parents' house and taken lodgings with a widow in School Lane. There were lots of rumours going round that Mair's husband knew about her affair with Gwyn from an anonymous letter that had found its way to him on board his ship off the Chinese coast, and Gwyn had been threatened with a severe beating by some of his relatives if he did not leave her alone. Gwyn was particularly worried because some of those who threatened him were miners in the same pit as him and he knew how easy it could be to arrange an accident underground which might leave him seriously or fatally injured. Gwyn had applied for a transfer to another colliery but was keeping quiet about where he was going for his own safety. Mum was distraught but Dad was more phlegmatic and said it was his own fault as he had the opportunity to stop the affair and walk away but he chose not to.

Ruby told me that Freda had asked her to be her bridesmaid at her wedding to Dai Rees, which was being scheduled for Easter Saturday in the village chapel. Ruby said she suspected that Freda was pregnant although she had kept quiet about it, but she suspected that she was, and they wanted to tie the knot before she was showing too much to avoid any scandal. This made me think about that Sunday afternoon in Freda's front parlour and she and Dai going hammer and tongs in the bedroom upstairs. Ruby was certain they were keeping quiet because if old Reverend Lewis got wind that Freda was pregnant, he would refuse to marry them. I smiled to myself. I wished them every happiness and hoped that we would be as happy as them when we got married. Ruby and I had discussed a possible wedding date but we both agreed that we should wait until the end of the war so that I could come home, and we could be together all the time. I was earning nearly ten shillings a day now and with flying pay this was increased by two shillings, but I knew if I took a commission my pay would almost double, which would allow me to continue saving to secure a decent nest egg for our wedding. I still had £85 saved after buying the engagement ring and I was adding to this total every week. I guessed that expenses would be a little higher as an officer, but I still reckoned to be able to save steadily and hoped to have over £200 available to pay for the wedding and get us a house before we started thinking of a family.

I wondered what Freda and Dai would do when the little baby arrived and how they would survive on only a miner's income if Freda had to give up work to look after the child. I thought that Freda's parents might help so that Freda could keep her job at the gas company, but that might not be possible. Ruby wrote that Freda and Dai were incredibly happy about the baby even though they were not able to share the good news too widely just yet. I wished them both well and wondered whether they would have a boy who would grow up to be a useful outside half like his father. I received a letter from my brother, Wesley, which was a surprise because he was not the writing kind, in which he told me that he had been promoted to a detective sergeant in the Criminal Investigation Department and had been posted to Swansea Police Station. I immediately wrote back congratulating him and giving him the news about my progress at the AFS. I heard no further word from Gwyn other than he had been transferred to another pit where he was not known; nobody knew where he had gone. Ruby had heard rumours that he may have gone to a pit near Cross Keys and was living in Magor, but nobody could confirm it.

It was early December and I had completed nearly six of the eight-week programme and if all went well, I should graduate before Christmas. I thought about how much had passed since last December when I had just joined the regiment in Chepstow and was under training to join the siege company in January. I had now clocked up forty-two solo flying hours and needed to acquire at least fifty in my logbook before graduation. Major Coate-Barnes advised me that he was recommending me for deployment as a scout pilot to an operational squadron unless I had strong feelings about bombing or reconnaissance work. I told him that scout flying was what I wanted to do above all other types of flying and he said he would plan a schedule to get me in the air as much as possible in the SE5 in the next few weeks. He promised that he would find a couple of days to fly with me and let me test the SE5 to its operational limits aerobatically and mechanically. He stressed it was vital that scout pilots knew the limits they could push their aircraft to in aerial combat as this could be the difference between life and death over the battlefield. I was calculating in my head how many hours of solo flying I could get completed before qualifying and I set myself the target of sixty hours before Christmas.

I left his office exhilarated that things were going my way, although I had not yet had a reply from my regiment concerning my request to transfer to the RFC as a pilot.

The flying programme was hectic as he had promised, and he did find a couple of days to devote to teaching me how to push the SE5 to its limits and bring it back safely. I learnt, under his tutelage, the aerobatic capability of the aircraft and how to recover from a spin, and how to make an emergency landing without power or major rigging failure. After the second day of flying together he got out of the aircraft and said, 'You fly alone tomorrow and practise what you have learnt over and over until it becomes second nature. You are as good a pilot as I can make you, so everything is up to you to prove me right.'

With barely eight hours daylight each day I was starting early and flying as many sorties as I could get accepted into the flying schedule by flying control. I was getting quite confident that I would achieve my flying hours target comfortably. I still hadn't heard from my regiment about transfer, and it was into the penultimate week of training before the signal effecting my transfer from the Royal Engineers to the Royal Flying Corps on the 20th of December, 1917 as a flying officer in the rank of lieutenant (acting paid). There was a note attached to the signal, which said that I could meet a representative of a reputed military tailors from London to get fitted out with my new uniforms before graduation day. The tailor was very experienced and most of the young officers already had the correct uniforms, having been commissioned as second lieutenants after basic flying training, so only needed alterations to be made to their rank badges. However, those of us being commissioned from the ranks and transferring from other regiments needed a complete set of kit.

He measured me for the flying officer's distinctive double-breasted Hussars-style tunic in khaki and for the jodhpurs, riding boots and a forage cap. He said that he understood that this was a big expense and that they would offer credit terms so that I could pay over a period that was convenient to me, rather than all at once. This was attractive as the costs were high and the uniform grant of £20 on commissioning was hardly enough. He also drew my attention to a rail where second-hand uniform jackets and jodhpurs were hanging and rummaged along the rail and showed me a tunic of the finest quality, but it had been pre-worn. I scrutinised it carefully and could not find any marks or blemishes or broken stitches, and when I tried it on and looked in the mirror it fitted perfectly. The rank badges were for a lieutenant, so no alteration needed to be made and the price was less than half of a new garment, so I took it. He said that he would stitch my flying wings and medal ribbon on to the tunic. Unfortunately, he did not have a second-hand pair of boots that would fit so I was forced to buy new ones, which were awfully expensive, but I bought two pairs of jodhpurs from the second-hand rail and ordered a forage cap and a Sam Browne belt. The total cost was £42, but I calculated if I had to buy all new items it would have been over £100. I made an initial payment of £5 to open my account, the balance was debited, and I agreed to make monthly payments of £2. The tailor said that I would need a sword; most officers on a temporary wartime commission did not go to the expense of buying their own sword but rented one on occasions when a sword is needed for special parades etc. He said that he would rent a sword to me for the passing out for three shillings for the day and I agreed. I was feeling contented and looking forward to showing it off to Ruby and her family and Mum and Dad when I got home. He said that he would deliver the alterations and new items by Wednesday before the passing-out parade.

Daily orders were asking for names of guests to be invited to the parade, as each graduate was entitled to have two guests each. I knew that Mum and Dad would not be able to come but I wondered whether Ruby would like to come with her mother or Freda as a chaperone and wrote immediately to invite her to see me pass out as a flying officer and lieutenant. I was by no means certain that Ruby would come, but I could only hope that she would. She replied by return of post that her parents had agreed that she could come to the passing-out parade, provided she was accompanied by Freda. I was so excited and happy with this news, I read the letter through again and realised that it would not be possible for Ruby and Freda to travel from Wales to Kenley and return all in one day if they were to attend the parade and the luncheon afterwards in the mess. The rail connection for London Waterloo from Kenley Station was nearly an hour and then the crossing of London by the Underground to Paddington, three hours to Cardiff and just under an hour to our village on the valley line meant that it made sense for them to stay overnight at Kenley and travel back in the morning. Even so they would have to leave home on an early train on Friday morning to make it to Kenley in time for the parade. I went into the library, checked the railway timetables, and picked out the 05:40 to Cardiff, 06:40 to London Paddington, 10:45 from Waterloo to Kenley and I would arrange for a taxi to meet them at the station and bring them to the airfield. I had found decent accommodation for them in the Kenley Arms Hotel in a double bedroom that I would pay for, because there was no overnight accommodation for guests at the camp. The hotel was close to the station and would be convenient for our return home together on Saturday morning and Ruby, Freda and I could have dinner together in the evening.

The week passed extremely rapidly with all of us attempting to get as much flying time in our logbooks as we could before the end of the course. Two hours every evening was spent rehearsing the parade and ceremony in the hangar away from public gaze, particularly as we were learning the sword drill for the first time, which for me anyway replaced the rifle drill I had hitherto been used to. The late December weather was cold and damp, so the ceremony and parade were going to be held indoors for the comfort of the guests. Each day after practice we could see the progress in making the hangar an attractive place to hold the event. We heard that Lord Trenchard, our Commanding General, was to present the wings and commissioning scrolls written on vellum and signed personally by the King. I wondered if General Trenchard would remember me from South Cerney but I doubted that he would. I knew that it would be different from the basic flying badge which we sewed on after the parade because now we were officers, the military tailors had made all alterations and sewn in place the RFC wings, our medal ribbons and rank badges on to our uniforms professionally. The drill instructor explained to us that Lord Trenchard would present each of us with a silver replica of the RFC wings and a certificate of qualification as a Category B pilot. He did not doubt that some of us would go on to qualify as Category C pilots when we became qualified flying instructors in the future. The sword drill was difficult at first because I was unaware of the weight in the sword itself and how difficult it was to hold it perfectly upright without any wobbling until I managed to master the trick of locking my wrist to keep it still. I am sure that if we had not been at open order when we practiced the various sword drills, we might have done each other fatal injuries before we got near to flying against the enemy in earnest.

Ruby's reply came promptly, and I was able to book the room at the hotel, the taxi at the station, two places in the stand and seats for lunch after the ceremony. I wrote back saying that I could not wait to see her on Friday, even if I had to share the experience with Freda but explained that I would not be able to meet her at the station because I would be getting ready for the ceremony. The taxi driver was well briefed and would give them the tickets, which would admit them at the main gate and the taxi would drop them at the hangar in time for the parade.

On Wednesday morning, I received a signal addressed to Lieutenant Derfal Morgan MM RFC which contained a cutting taken from the *London Gazette* of today's date which promulgated in the temporary wartime only commissions column... *Morgan, Derfal Ieuan 0209616 Sergeant South Monmouthshire Regiment, Royal Engineers formerly of the Monmouthshire Siege Company, Territorial Army to be commissioned as a Flying Officer in the rank of Lieutenant Royal Flying Corps with effect from Friday 20th December 1917.*

Later that day, I received a second signal posting me to No. 354 Squadron Royal Flying Corps at La Coupole Airfield, near St Omer, Northern France by 28th December 1917 at the latest. I wondered if Major Harcourt and Captain Moss had worked some magic to get me posted to them or was it a lucky coincidence? I felt blessed because I was going to be a scout pilot and I would get a week at home over Christmas before I had to leave for France. I felt so fortunate getting two Christmases at home when many boys at the front barely got two weeks' leave in a year, or like Mair Davis's husband who had been away from home over two years on his ship with no chance of home leave. I wrote to Mum and Dad to tell them the good news about my Christmas at home and dropped a short note to my brother Wesley, hoping that we could get together for a day whilst I was at home.

On Friday morning I packed away the RE sergeant's uniform for the last time and dressed in my new clothes, which were certainly much finer and better tailored than anything I had worn before. The jodhpurs and riding boots took some getting used to but were comfortable and the tailors had adjusted the seat and waist of the trouser to give a more comfortable fit. The boots were new, so I had worn them for a couple of nights in my room to get used to them before Friday. I did not want to have blisters on my heel for the big day, but I was impressed because the leather was soft and supple and a perfect fit. When I put on my tunic, I began to feel rather different as I felt the Hussar jacket made me look quite dashing. I buttoned up the tunic to the neck, affixed the Military Medal to the ribbon on my chest underneath the gold wire RFC wings and belted up the Sam Browne from which I would attach the sword scabbard on the left side. I felt quite transformed as here I was, the son of coal miner brought up in modest circumstances, standing here as an officer in the British Army. I was anxious that the parade would go well, and I would not let myself down, but I was more anxious that Ruby and Freda would be collected from the railway station by the taxi and arrive here on time. The graduates were assembling to the side of the hangar and where we could not be seen by the guests inside the hangar, we had a view of those arriving by car and I was gratified to catch a glimpse of Ruby looking radiant, every inch an officer's lady and Freda, who looked equally lovely. I felt proud that I would have two such lovely ladies to watch me graduate and to help me celebrate.

At five minutes to go, the staff cars pulled into the pan at the entrance of the hangar. The general and his staff and the directing staff from the advanced flying school went in to take their seats. We were called to attention, given the order to march on, we quickly formed the flight, Major Coate-Barnes took command of the flight and gave the order by the centre quick march as the band struck up the regimental march. He halted the parade in front of the saluting dais, and I recognised General Trenchard immediately at his seat in the centre of the important guests. The major marched forward and invited the general to inspect the flight and accompanied the reviewing officer as he passed down the line, speaking to each man individually. I was in the middle of the front rank. I had a clear view of our guests sat in the stand to the left and right of the dais and could see Ruby and Freda in the second row. The general was presenting each man with the silver insignia of the RFC wings and the qualifying certificate, which were immediately passed to the squadron adjutant when the general passed along to the next man, for safekeeping. When Lord Trenchard stopped in front of me, looked me squarely in the face and said, 'Well done, Sergeant, you will make an excellent lieutenant,' he shook my hand, leaned closer to me, spoke quietly just for my hearing and said," he had not forgotten me from the last time we met". The band played throughout the inspection and then when the general had resumed his seat, we returned to close order and the parade commander asked for permission to march past. When the band struck up a traditional slow march for the first pass and a rousing quick march to follow, to which we saluted again and marched around the hangar and back out on to the pan where we started.

We were dismissed so that we could mingle with our guests and then wander across to the officers' mess for a reception before lunch at 13:15. Ruby and Freda greeted me exuberantly and both kissed me as they were so excited by the whole ceremony. I was pleased when I noticed the envious looks, I was getting from some of my classmates who had only their parents to celebrate with. I think they were hoping that I might introduce them later in the proceedings, but I did not think I was in the mood to share today. I was so grateful to both for making the long journey to share this day together and I was going to keep them to myself. Ruby's outfit was, as always, a home-grown creation made by her mother, and I found out that she had made Freda's as well. They were both divine and even though I knew that Freda was pregnant, she looked as slim as ever in this dress. Major Coate-Barnes came across to offer his congratulations and I introduced him to both girls. I could see that he had an eye for a pretty girl from the little smile that crept across his face. We circulated the room and met most people, until Lord Trenchard appeared at my shoulder and asked me where I had been hiding these beautiful young women. I introduced Ruby and Freda and they both blushed at meeting the general and his flattering words. As he passed on, he whispered to me that I should marry them both as they are equally delightful. Lunch was excellent, accompanied by some fine wines, and the speeches from the commandant of the flying school and Lord Trenchard were light and amusing.

Around three-thirty I summoned the taxi to take us to the Kenley Hotel where I was in for another pleasant surprise. On entering the hotel reception, I signed in Ruby and Freda and paid for their room and then went up with them to the second floor. When we reached Ruby and Freda's door the one opposite opened, and Dai Rees was standing there bold as brass. I did not catch on but quickly realised that Dai had booked a room in his name for the both of us and I had booked one for Ruby and Freda, but of course he and I would swap rooms. Freda kissed me and Ruby on the cheek and said that they would meet us for dinner at seven, went into the room across the hall with Dai and shut the door. I stood aghast and could not believe what was happening, as Ruby just took my hand and led me into our bedroom. I went to speak but she clamped her lips on mine and stifled any words from me. Eventually, we came up for air and she explained that this was Freda's idea to get away with Dai, and she thought it would kill two birds with one stone so to speak. I was in a quandary because on one hand I was so pleased to be alone with Ruby for a whole night, but I did not like the subterfuge and lies, especially to the people we loved back home. I have never been a great dissembler and I would have to be careful in the future not to inadvertently give away what we had done. My plans were now changed, I had to return to the airfield to collect my kit and return to the hotel in time for dinner so we could leave together in the morning after breakfast.

The hotel reception called a cab, and I was able to go to the camp and return in just over an hour. I was now free to enjoy my time alone with Ruby until we were to meet Dai and Freda. In my absence Ruby had bathed and was dressed in a bathrobe over her underwear and was relaxing on the bed waiting for my return. I could hardly contain my excitement when I saw her, and my instant desire was to tear off her undergarments and feast upon the sight of her naked body for the first time, but I restrained myself. I would savour that pleasure until after dinner when we had the whole night to enjoy being together. We just sat close, talked dreamily about ourselves and our future, how Ruby had been impressed by the ceremony and parade and was so proud of me for achieving so much. The time passed so quickly that we did not see it was almost time to meet Freda and Dai in the dining room and I had to hurry to dress in my uniform again for dinner.

We were only five minutes late into the dining room, where Freda and Dai were already seated at a table for four in the bay window. Dai was looking very smart in his Sunday best suit and Freda was wearing the dress that Ruby's mother had made for the occasion. They both gave us banter about what we had been doing to be late and even though I tried to explain about having to collect my kit from the airfield, they did not seem to believe us. Anyway, they stopped when the waiter approached with the menus and we pretended to be serious whilst we ordered our dinner and a bottle of wine to go with it. The dining room was beginning to fill up now and Freda and Dai had to contain themselves unless they would attract the attention of the other diners to our table. Dai told me that he had travelled on a later train, arriving at the hotel at about two-thirty and had taken a day's holiday from work to be here. Ironically, he said that getting time off work was no problem but telling Josh Andrews that he could not play for the rugby team on Saturday was a major concern. He had told him that he had to visit a friend who had been taken ill in hospital in Cardiff and would miss the game. He also filled me in on what he knew about Gwyn, which was not a great deal more than I already knew, but he did tell us a new snippet of gossip that we did not know. Mair Davis's house was empty, and she seemed to have done a moonlight flit in secret. Nobody had any idea where she had gone although many suspected that if we found where Gwyn was now living, we might find Mair too. I did not approve of Gwyn's behaviour because Mair was a married woman, but on reflection I thought that in the light of our behaviour who were we to judge him. The dinner was passably good, we enjoyed the wine, took coffee in the drawing room after our meal and then the four of us made our way upstairs arm in arm about nine forty-five. We lingered in the corridor saying our goodnights until we were sure that the hallway was empty and then quickly entered our respective rooms and locked the doors.

The night was now ours without distraction. I removed my boots, hung up my uniform, stripped to my underwear, reclined against the bed head and watched entranced as Ruby lasciviously did an erotic dance in which she stripped off her clothing, piece by piece. I had never experienced anything like this before and found it very stimulating. Finally, she was completely naked, standing before me. I sat transfixed by her beauty until I gently folded her into my arms and drew her down into the cold sheets with me. We started to kiss with a passion that only true lovers possess. She pulled my shirt and vest over my head, pressed her body against mine and I could feel her firm and full breasts and her distended nipples pressing hard against my naked chest as she snaked her hand further down my body and underneath the waistband of my drawers to feel my erect member struggling for release. I did not have to wait long before Ruby had manipulated my drawers down my thighs to my knees and I was able to wriggle out of them.

We were both completely naked now and as if by magic, the sheets were nice and warm as Ruby squirreled herself down the bed under the sheet, took my penis into her mouth and began to move her head up and down, sliding its length in and out of her mouth so deliciously. Her hands were cupping my testicles gently as she worked on my penis until I could feel the tension gradually rising in my loins. Ruby threw back the bedclothes and sat astride of me and worked me deep into her with just the movement of her hips, faster and faster until she let out a low scream and climaxed which caused me to ejaculate inside her with a gush and a wonderful feeling inside. The release of sexual energy was only temporary for my member recovered its stiffness within minutes and Ruby was eager for more. She laid on her back and I knelt between her legs, gently opening the way to her vagina with my fingers and pushed them inside her until I could feel the wetness again, when I knelt closer into her, lifted her legs up and back towards her shoulders and entered her from the front. I slipped in easily and could feel each thrust I made deep inside her as she wriggled and moaned each time I pushed and begged me to go faster. I built up the speed and the strength of each push until I could feel her shuddering and squealing as she felt the explosion of each orgasm between her legs, and I kept up this pace going faster and faster until I felt the climax rising and the sperm flooded into her again. Ruby did not want me to stop so I tried to keep going for as long as my penis remained stiff, but gradually it subsided. I moved back down the bed, kissed her vagina, and tasted the mixed juices of our ejaculations and gently manipulated her clitoris with my tongue until Ruby slipped out of bed and went over to the wash basin, filled it with water and washed out her vagina of my sperm to avoid pregnancy she said. Then she came over and washed my penis and testicles as well. We were both exhausted and lay back cuddled together to sleep and I lay my face upon her breast and took the nipple in my mouth and suckled like a new-born as I drifted to sleep. We woke early in the morning and made love in a slow and leisurely way, before getting up and ready for our breakfast with a fine appetite.

That morning I could sense that our relationship was different than yesterday. We had become one spirit in two bodies, joined thoroughly through sexual union. We were lovers properly, not just a courting couple anymore and I was certain than Ruby felt the same way. I felt a glow inside me telling the world that I was now a man, and Ruby was my woman. Freda and Dai looked equally aglow when we met them in the hallway to go down for breakfast and I could tell by their appetite that they had enjoyed an exhausting night like us. Dai explained that he would travel with us as far as Cardiff, he would not catch the same valley train but wait in Cardiff for a later train so as not to cause any suspicion. After breakfast we left the hotel, walked the 200 yards to the station and caught the next train to Waterloo, where we boarded the Underground to Paddington to board the Red Dragon. We caught the 11:15 that was due in Cardiff at 14:10, settled into an empty second-class compartment and made ourselves comfortable for the journey back home. The ticket collector was a little perturbed because I had a first-class ticket and could be travelling in a better compartment if I wished. I told him that I wished to travel with my friends and was perfectly happy where I was. Ruby sat against the window and after a while I noticed she had drifted off to sleep. I left her to nap whilst Freda and Dai just chatted quietly in the opposite corner, and I marvelled at what a miraculous effect Dai had made on Freda who was quiet, serene, and almost as beautiful as Ruby.

Arriving home, everyone wanted to know all about their trip and my passing-out parade and commissioning. Mrs Thomas scrutinised the tailoring of my uniform and passed it with flying colours as real quality work, and Mum and Dad were so proud to see me smart in my officer's uniform and wanted to show me off to friends and neighbours, but not everyone in the village expressed pleasure and some of the boys in the Railway Tavern and the Miners' Welfare thought that I had sold out my working-class heritage and crossed a line to become one of the bosses. I did not see it like that and my elevation as they put it was only temporary until the end of the war and then I would be looking for work again, just like the hundreds of thousands of returning soldiers. The reception from Reverend Lewis and the chapel congregation was warm and full of praise and congratulations; once again I was embarrassed as the minister led the prayers for the safety of the boys at the front linking my name to them. I received many handshakes and congratulations after the service and was glad that now Ruby was wearing an engagement ring that I could hold her hand in public.

Ruby was unable to get a second day off for Monday, so I only saw her briefly for lunch and we spent the evening together with my mum and dad. Mum acted typically like so many Welsh matriarchs, a little reticent of the girl who was going to take away her youngest son from her, but as the weeks and months had gone on, she was warming to Ruby which I thought was probably much to do with the burgeoning friendship between Mum and Mrs Thomas. Dad accepted Ruby right away and I think was as transfixed by her beauty and lively personality as I was, which I sometimes resented because he tended to monopolise the conversation when Ruby was around. I knew that I could rely on Dad to look after Ruby and ensure a welcome at our fireside whilst I was away in France. The preparations for Christmas were well under way and there was some festive spirit, even in the dark days of the fourth year of the war. The South Wales valley communities had suffered less with casualties and wounded than other areas because a higher percentage of their men were serving in the mines and associated industries instead of as soldiers in the army or navy. Fewer families were split apart at Christmas than in other parts of the country, where not so many men were employed in vital occupations to the war effort. There were Christmas social events in the village and Ruby and I attended carols, the nativity and bazaar at the chapel to raise money for the poor, so much of our free time that week was taken up with these social gatherings. I had taken off my uniform and had found a suit that still fitted me from my days at the office and took to wearing civilian clothes so as not to upset those who thought I had defected to the upper class. This was a happy episode of normality, peace, and tranquillity, a kind of lull before the storm of returning to the front so shortly after the Christmas festivities were over.

We agreed to spend Christmas Eve with Freda and Dai at the rugby club, which had opened to celebrate Christmas with a festive social evening with food and drinks for players and members. When we heard that Wesley was coming to spend Christmas Day and Boxing Day at home, we all kind of hoped that Gwyn might get in touch and come home too. Mum and Dad had not heard a word from him for over six weeks and still did not know where he was living. However, there were rumours in the village that Wyn Davis's ship had hit a mine and sunk off the Chinese coast but there was no word whether he was alive or dead. Ruby and I were wondering how we could please both sets of parents on Christmas Day but without cutting ourselves into two pieces we could not see how we could achieve this without upsetting somebody. However, luckily for us fate played a part because Mr Thomas decided he would work on Christmas Day because there were trains running until six in the evening. He had given all but a skeleton staff of volunteers the day off; he would run the station on Christmas Day and Mrs Thomas would cook a Christmas supper for him in the evening. Ruby and I would spend Christmas Day with Mum and Dad and then go to Ruby's parents for the evening.

This worked out well and Mum had acquired a lovely big chicken and two rabbits for our Christmas lunch, which made a good spread indeed. Wesley arrived about eleven o'clock, driving a motor car which was essential now that he was a detective, and he looked smart in a suit rather than a constable's uniform. He was in good form and immediately started chatting happily to Ruby, pretending to let her into my secrets, giving her a full account of all my faults and enjoying my apparent discomfiture. In the end they were laughing so much at my expense that I felt that I ought to put a stop to this and thought I would rather have Dad hogging the conversation with Ruby than all these scurrilous lies about me from my brother. Wesley had changed since he had joined the detective branch and he seemed more confident, assured and in control than last time I met him. He liked his new job in Swansea, where he worked in a team that worked secretly to uncover spies and traitors. He enjoyed the work very much and had decided to make the police service his permanent career after the war. He had passed the sergeant's examination already and was waiting for the opportunity to study for the Inspector's examination as soon as possible.

After lunch, Mum and Ruby sat in the parlour whilst Wesley and I cleared the table and washed up, which was our traditional annual contribution to

Christmas Day. Wesley was impressed with how well I had made progress in the army and trained as a pilot already, and we talked together about our aspirations and expectations after the war was over. I talked about marriage, settling down with Ruby, having a family of my own and that I would probably seek senior clerk jobs in the civil service or local council. Wesley also talked about a wife and children – but not yet, as his ambition was to become a detective inspector first so that he would have a position that people would look up to. This was all a bit serious for Christmas Day and we resolved to get this job done as quickly as we could and return to the parlour for a few more glasses of beer and some fun and laughter. As we fell through the door into the parlour, we were stunned to see all three of them, Mum, Dad and Ruby fast asleep in front of the fire. We tiptoed to get a quart bottle of beer, poured out two glasses and tiptoed back into the kitchen where we could talk without waking them up. Our conversation turned to Gwyn; Wesley was sure that he could find out where Gwyn was living now through his police sources, and he would go and find him and bring to his senses. I was doubtful that this would work as it had been going on for so long. Gwyn had been prepared to give up everything in his old life – home, family, job, reputation, and his rugby – through his infatuation with Mair Davis. Wesley said he would try for Mum's sake and I agreed.

Ruby was the first to wake up, she joined us in the back kitchen and eventually Mum and Dad resurfaced, and we made a pot of tea and sat at the table again to play some card games. Around four o'clock, just as it was getting dark, our peaceful and happy evening was rudely interrupted by a loud hammering and shouting at our front door. We hardly used the front entrance as everyone came through the back entry into the kitchen, but this hammering was loud and persistent and was not going to go away. Wesley and I got up to answer the door and went into the small hallway, closing the parlour door to keep the warmth in, undid the bolts and opened the door to come face to face with a man in a naval rating's uniform who was obviously drunk. He rushed at me, it took all my strength supported by Wesley to push him back into the street and he almost fell on his backside he was so drunk. Wes and I stepped out of the house, closed the door, faced him shoulder to shoulder and I demanded to know who he was and what was his business here. I had never seen him before, but I was beginning to get an inkling that this might be Able Seaman Wyn Davis saved from a watery grave. We calmed him down and ascertained that he was Davis and he lurched again into us trying to reach the front door. He was convinced that Mair was inside with Gwyn and however much we tried to convince him that this was not the case, he did not seem to believe us.

Eventually a fist swung in my direction which I was able to fend off without too much trouble, but Wesley immediately leapt into action as a policeman, not just my brother. Davis was turned around, and his hands handcuffed behind his back. I heard him say,"Able Seaman Davis, you have just struck an officer, Lieutenant Derfal Morgan RFC, I am arresting you pending court martial, and you will be held in cells at the local police station until the Naval Regulators in Swansea come to collect you." He stepped further into the street, produced a police whistle, and blew three loud blasts, which were answered by a single blast from a distance. Wesley said that help was coming and then turned his attention back to Davis, questioning him about what had brought this about. Davis was incoherent, but we were able to surmise that after receiving letters from home naming Morgan as his wife's lover, he had applied for home leave to sort it out. He obviously did not know that his ship had been sunk because he had taken passage home in a fast destroyer some weeks earlier. He found his family home empty and his wife gone when he reached the village and had been on a rampage of drinking and affray ever since. He was certain that Gwyn and Mair would be here celebrating Christmas and came here to sort things with his fists. Wesley told him that he was a detective from Swansea CID, and he was now his prisoner. A few minutes later two uniformed constables appeared around the corner and took Davis to the police station to be charged. Wesley told them that he would be along in the morning to complete the necessary paperwork because it was useless trying to get a statement from Davis whilst he was still drunk.

We went back inside and recounted what had just happened at the front door. Mum and Dad were frightened, but Ruby was glad that they had Derfal and Wesley to protect them. Our cheery Christmas mood was now somewhat deflated, and we tried half-heartedly to pick up the cards where we had left off although no one had their hearts set on it any longer. The clock on the mantelpiece struck five and I thought that Ruby and I should be thinking of making our way to the Station House to spend the evening with her parents when more knocking became apparent, but this time from the back door. Both Wesley and I made for the back kitchen but did not really believe that Davis could have broken away from custody so easily. I opened the back door and saw two figures huddled there in a poor state; one was Gwyn and the other person I did not know. We pulled them into the kitchen and could see that the woman was dishevelled and had blood on her face and two black eyes shining up nicely, she was holding her side as if her ribs were injured but even through the injuries, I could see she was beautiful. I guessed this was Mair Davis and quickly pulled out a chair for her to sit down, calling Mum and Ruby to tend to her injuries.

Gwyn looked dishevelled too, he did not seem to have any injuries, but we questioned him about what had happened. He told us that he and Mair were sharing a house together in Magor but he worked the night shift last night at the pit at Cross Keys and when he got home this morning he found Mair in this state. Apparently, her husband had called the night before about ten o'clock, pushed his way into the house, set about assaulting her badly and then left her lying in a pool of blood, unconscious. 'He told her that he would be back to do the same to me today so I thought it would be best to find a safer place for Mair to stay while I go and look for Davis and settle this once and for all.' Wesley stepped in and said that would be a foolish thing to do as we already had Davis in custody at the local police station for attempting to push his way in to this house only about an hour and a half ago. 'He threw a punch at Derfal and was drunk, I have arrested him for striking an officer and being drunk and disorderly and he is sleeping it off until the morning. If Mrs Davis will bring charges against him, she can make statements in the morning but if not, he will be collected by the Naval Regulators tomorrow and taken into military custody.'

Mum and Ruby had shooed Dad out of the parlour, and he had gone upstairs whilst they stripped off Mair's clothes so they could wash her cuts and bruises and strap up her ribs tightly to ease the pain. Most of the cuts were superficial but she had taken quite a battering to her head, especially around her eyes as if her deranged husband tried to mask her beauty with his punches. The bruising around the eyes would fade in a couple of days and her sight did not seem to be seriously affected, although one of her teeth was loose and may fall out in time. The worst injuries were to her ribcage, now badly bruised and swollen although none seemed to have been broken which probably meant that she would have to endure some stiffness and pain but would be back to full fitness within three to four weeks. They took her upstairs and put Mair into Gwyn's bed, covered her over and she was asleep within a few minutes. Mum came into the back kitchen and broke the good news that Wesley, Gwyn and I would be sleeping in the parlour tonight as

Mrs Davis was using our room. There would be no statements taken tonight as she was already asleep and needed rest to restart her recovery. Ruby and I had to say farewell as we had promised to be at the Station House by six-thirty.

Mrs Thomas had served an excellent roast beef supper and Mr Thomas had invited his friends from the woodyard, Josh Andrews and his wife and Dai Rees and Freda to join us for supper. Even though Ruby and I were not feeling particularly jolly anymore, we settled into the happy mood of the company and forgot about the troubles of the afternoon a little bit. I think Ruby confided in Freda about the events with Davis judging by the heavily whispered conversation they had in the corner, and I hoped that this didn't mean that it would-be all-over town in a couple of days. I found that I was able to let myself go and forget about our family troubles and enjoy the evening. Boxing Day was my last day before returning to active service and I hoped to be able to spend at least some of the day with Ruby rather than sorting out events at the police station. In the morning I was relieved to see that Mair Davis looked a lot better after a good night's sleep and although she was stiff and sore, she seemed to be on the mend. She was reluctant to press charges against her husband, but Wesley explained to her that whatever guilt she might feel about her adulterous relationship with Gwyn the law did not allow Wyn Davis to inflict these injuries upon her. If she did not press charges, he would be let out and probably beat her again. Eventually, she agreed and Wesley, Gwyn, Mair and I went to the police station, in Wesley's car, to make our statements and Davis was charged with striking an officer, assault and battery and drunken and disorderly behaviour. The Navy Regulators came for him later in the day and he was taken to the naval detention centre near Swansea. They were sure that the charge of drunk and disorderly would be dropped but entered in his record, although he would stand court martial for the other two charges and would probably be sentenced to at least five years' hard labour in the naval prison at Portsmouth.

After the police station Ruby and I managed to spend a quiet evening together for my last hours at home. I was sure that I would miss her so much when I was back in France, but I was also looking forward to becoming the ace combat pilot defeating the German fliers in honourable combat in the air. Mr and Mrs Thomas were glad to leave us alone in their dining room together so that we could ease our parting without their interference. When it was time to go, Mrs Thomas hugged me tight begging me to come home in one piece and Mr Thomas also hugged me, shook my hand and whispered," stay safe". Early next morning I was off by train to London, first class on the Red Dragon to Paddington and then across London by taxi to catch the express to Dover from Victoria and the ferry to Dunkerque. I was to be billeted in the Dover Marine Hotel and my ship sailed in the morning at 10:00. At Dunkerque the squadron had sent a car with a driver to meet me as I came ashore and whisk me off to La Coupole to rejoin the squadron.

THIRTEEN

Passchendaele Stalemate

Corporal Smith had volunteered to meet me from the port and was waiting on the dockside with a small staff car to drive me back to La Coupole; I was pleased to see him and to know that he was now feeling comfortable and happy in his role in charge of the engine bays. He filled me in on some of the background to autumn and winter in the Ypres and Passchendaele sector of the front. The squadron had carried out regular patrolling every day but had not engaged in a great deal of aerial fighting as the enemy largely kept out of their way. Most of the missions were reconnaissance-based focusing on charting how the enemy were building up their forces and the strength of their positions. He said that there was much comment amongst soldiers on the ground enduring the terrible conditions in the trenches about the incompetence of our own generals who had failed to build on the early success of the first attacks in the summer. This lack of decision meant that we had failed to press home our advantage before the winter weather which had turned the whole of the battle front into a water-logged quagmire where conditions were terrible, and disease was rife. The Germans were given a vital breathing space which allowed them to regroup and rebuild their defences untroubled by actions from the enemy.

He also filled me in on changes in the squadron and not least that Major Harcourt had been promoted to lieutenant colonel and posted to Brigade HQ, and Captain Moss had been promoted to major and taken over command of the squadron. I had massive admiration and respect for both officers who had played no small part in organising my transfer to the RFC and without whom I would not be a pilot today. I knew Moss to be an excellent pilot, first-class instructor and was sure he would be a good commander to serve with. Several squadron pilots had been posted to other squadrons and their replacements, of which I was one, were joining. One pilot, Lieutenant Rabey, was shot down over enemy territory and was now a prisoner of war. Smith reassured me that my friend, Mr Dalrymple, was still on the squadron and as jolly as ever. The journey from the port took about an hour and a half and by the time we pulled in at the main gate I felt as if I had never been away so up to date with all the news I seemed to be. It was strange when the guards at the gate saluted me as I had not yet got used to being addressed as, "Sir'" or being saluted by other ranks.

As I glanced around, I could see that some obvious changes had taken place during the five months I had been away; the most obvious being the construction of a second and third big hangar to accommodate two more squadrons operating from this airfield. I could see much activity around the new hangars and Smith confirmed that the new squadrons were moving in this week and would be operational within seven days. I could see that the old command hut of 354 Squadron was demolished and replaced by a much larger temporary building which had been constructed to serve as the wing commander's office and control for the three scout squadrons operating from this field. The whole place seemed much more bustling and was taking on a greater sense of purpose than was evident before. The354 command hut had moved much nearer to the squadron hangar alongside the airfield and Corporal Smith dropped me there. I went into the new hut, which was considerably larger than the old one because it now had an open office for the administrative staff, a small private office for the adjutant, a briefing room large enough to accommodate all the squadron pilots and a larger office for the CO.

I knocked on the adjutant's door post and could see through the open door an officer who I did not know but who smiled and beckoned me in. I came to attention, saluted, presented my joining instructions and he pointed to a seat whilst he read my documents. When he looked up, I could see that he only had one hand and some signs of burns on the side of his face. He introduced himself as Charles Forbes and I could see he was a captain and a pilot too. Forbes looked at me and said, "I can see from your face that you are wondering how on earth can I fly a plane in combat with only one hand and the answer is that I can't which why I am the adjutant of this squadron." I learnt later that he was a promising young pilot who had been shot down when he was returning from a solo mission behind enemy lines and ambushed by three enemy aircraft who shot him down in flames. He was taken prisoner, but the Germans took him to hospital and managed to save his mangled arm at the expense of his hand. When he had recovered sufficiently to travel the Germans sent him home thinking his wounds meant he was no longer able to be a flier. They were right but it was his left hand that was missing, and he was right-handed, so there was not much he could not do provided it could be done one-handed. He was a warm and friendly character and while looking at my papers he asked me if I had served on this squadron before on secondment from the RE and I said that this was me. "I have heard the CO talk about you, he is expecting you and I will take you in to see him shortly."

Major Moss was all business when I met him a little later that afternoon, talking to me about the new role that the squadron would have as part of a new fighter wing being set up here at La Coupole. A number of these new fighter wings were being created and located just behind the front line to increase the harrying of enemy supply lines and weaken their defences and communications in preparation for a big push as the weather ease into spring. We had been flying patrols every day over their territory, but the German air force had stayed on the ground and hardly engaged with us over the winter. The new strategy was to create a superior force over the battlefield and actively attack and harry their capacity to challenge us in the air in preparation for the breakout from our positions which was going to come in the spring. He said that I was assigned to B flight, whose flight commander was Captain Dalrymple, and the squadron was now part of No. 2 Fighter Wing commanded by Lieutenant Colonel Harcourt from his new headquarters on this airfield.

"We will be working with No.380 and 404 Squadrons and will have the capacity to put over fifty aircraft up at any one time against the enemy. We willl attack their command-and-control communications, supply lines and troop movements and will work in cooperation with No. 46 Squadron to escort their bombers to targets deeper behind the enemy lines to destroy enemy airfield and rail and road hubs. Jamie Dalrymple is a new flight commander which is why I have allocated you to his flight because he will need support from pilots who have a heightened sense of airmanship and experience on the battlefield to mould the flight into an effective unit." He called the corporal orderly from the main office to take me to Captain Dalrymple and to arrange for my baggage to be taken to my room in the flight hut.

Jamie Dalrymple was as exuberant as ever when he saw me and gave me a bear hug that almost squashed the life out of me which showed how glad he was to see me again. He said that I was flying as his number two and Staff Sergeant Knowles was to fly as my wingman. "Lieutenant Bradby who arrived mid-December is still struggling to adjust to combat flying although he is a competent enough pilot, he lacks the aggressive edge required in the air, will fly as my wingman." He said, "The CO has read your reports from the advanced flying school and combined with his experience of flying with you previously is certain you are the right man to back me up." He explained that we would fly most of our patrols in flight formation fighting as one unit and it was essential that the No.2 was a fearless and watchful pilot to keep the flight safe whilst engaged in any attack. We also know that you have proven courage and experience of managing men as a corporal and sergeant and have already served in this sector earlier this year." B flight now occupied a large wooden hut, which had a crew room and office at the front and four bedrooms and a bathroom for the pilots behind which was a big improvement on the tented accommodation that we lived in earlier in the year. There was a large wood burner in the middle of the crew room which kept the temperature at a steady and comfortable level even though it was a cold December day. In the crew room we met the others in the flight; Terence Bradby I recognised from South Cerney but he hadn't been at Croydon for his advanced flying training. He was young, having come directly from OCTU into the RFC Training Brigade and qualified as a pilot before which he was a schoolboy. He seemed likeable and friendly enough, but this was his first experience of active service, and he did seem a little too gentle for this work as Jamie had suggested but Charlie Knowles was twenty-three and had served two years in the infantry before volunteering for flying training. He was a northerner from Huddersfield and spoke with a bluff Yorkshire accent and had a no-nonsense manner exuding a confidence that suggested he would soon become an excellent combat pilot. I liked him straight away and felt we would be friends in a relatively short time. I could tell that Jamie thought we were strange bedfellows as a flight led by the honourable third son of a baronet, two grammar schoolboys risen through the ranks and a minor public-school boy from the home counties. How we communicated was a mystery with Jamie's upper-class drawl, my Welsh lilt, Charlie's broad Yorkshire and Terence with his London middleclass accent. But we found that we managed reasonably well.

Charlie took me through to the sleeping quarters where there were four single rooms and directed me to the farthest one on the left. The room was just big enough for a single bed, armchair, bedside cabinet, wardrobe, and desk but it was private and a lot better than living in a tent. The bed was not made up but there were sheets, pillowcases, and a bed pack of two blankets and two pillows laid out. He then showed me the ablutions, where we met Airman Spragg who was mopping the floor and was to be batman to Mr Bradby and myself, who would lay out our clothes, do our laundry and clean our rooms for us. Spragg was a general duties airman and split his time between the guardroom and looking after us. Charlie explained that it was convention for subalterns to share a batman, but captains had a batman allocated to them personally. We were expected to tip Spragg ten shillings a week and any out-of-pocket expenses to augment his pay. I was a bit uncomfortable about this because I did not really believe in servants but realised that I had no choice as this was an established military custom. Spragg had been an assistant in a gentleman's outfitters until he was called up and seemed totally unsuited for any kind of martial pursuit except that he was an excellent batman, keeping all my uniforms and my boots in perfect condition and always knew the protocol of what to do, what to wear or how to behave in any situation. His one fault was that he was a terrible gossip so one had to be careful what was discussed within his hearing as you would often hear a garbled version of what you said on the grapevine a few days later. He also had that unusual knack of making himself indispensable and very soon he was an integral part of my life a La Coupole.

Jamie was in good spirits and proposed that we all went to St Omer for dinner that evening to get to know each other better, as we were not rostered for flying the following day. Jamie would drive us in his touring car, which he had driven back after his last leave, and we were to be ready at six-thirty in front of the hut. Jamie's car was an open-top Bentley and we had to wrap up in our flying coats and gloves against the cold and set off in high spirits for St Omer. Jamie knew where he was taking us and after a hair-raising dash through the French countryside we arrived in the central square at St Omer. Jamie took us down a narrow side street and parked in an alley to the side of a small restaurant bar called Suzette's Jamie led us through the front door, and it was immediately obvious that he had been here before judging by the warm welcome he received from Madame Suzette and Anton the chef who was also her husband. She led us to a table in the middle of the room and looking round I could see that almost all the tables were full of officers accompanied by many ladies who I guessed were all local girls. The uniforms indicated officers from all branches of the British, French, and Canadian forces and a sprinkling of RFC from other squadrons too. I was self-conscious, being such a new officer, and I wondered if Charlie Knowles felt out of place being an SNCO but watching him laughing and messing around it did not appear to bother him. Terence Bradby seemed overwhelmed by the noise, laughter, and the host of pretty girls all around us. Madame Suzette came with the menu card and told us that there were only two choices of main course which was duck or sole with soup or pate to start and a range of desserts to follow. Jamie took the wine list and ordered some champagne to be followed by bottles of red and white wine to drink with our food.

I was sipping my champagne and looking around when I thought I saw Vivian Craddock-Williams sat at one of the tables in the corner. I excused myself and wandered over to his table, but I did not want to burst in on him as he was fully engaged with a young woman who was sitting on his lap. I noticed that Vivian was now a captain and looked fit and well, certainly different from the young inexperienced subaltern I met a year previously. I coughed politely and he stared in dismay, jumped up with a start and nearly dropped the girl on the floor. He broke free and shook my hand profusely. He said, "You were the last person I expected to see when I walked in here tonight, and he was amazed that the man he had last seen promoted to sergeant and seconded to the RFC was now a commissioned pilot." I invited him to join our table and he agreed if he could bring his friends too, and Madame Suzette rearranged the tables so we could all sit together.

Our company had now swelled to six officers and four young and pretty French girls, and I was beginning to think that we were going to have a good evening. Jamie and Vivian had, of course, met before, remembered each other and were soon deep in conversation and more champagne was ordered. Vivian was now the permanent adjutant of the siege company, promoted to captain; his fellow officer was his cousin who was a captain in the South Wales Borderers and remembered my two older brothers who were killed at the Somme. As the champagne and wine flowed, we got progressively louder and louder and I noticed that two of the girls, Clara, and Yvette, were paying full attention to Terence Bradby and keeping his glass filled to the brim as they flirted outrageously with him. He was like a rabbit transfixed by the eyes of the weasel before it struck, and I wondered if he had ever kissed a girl before because he seemed to be getting plenty of practice tonight. Charlie Knowles had struck up a lively conversation with a striking lady who sat on the next table; they were oblivious to what was going on around them so engrossed were they in what they were saying. I was enjoying chatting with Ivor, Vivian's cousin, but I did notice Charlie disappearing upstairs with his newly met acquaintance from the next table and I realised that the serious conversation was probably the negotiation of terms of business.

Vivian renewed his attention to the girl who had been sat on his lap, Jamie made the acquaintance of the fourth girl, and I was left chatting with Ivor. Terence had become livelier, out of control the more drinks he consumed, and I began to think it would not be long before he was unconscious. He was pawing at the girls with all the finesse of a schoolboy; they were squealing and teasing him with delight as they managed to keep just out of reach. Finally, when I saw him turn a shade of green and the convulsions start in his throat with Ivor's help lifted him up and out of the door so he could vomit in the street. He could hardly stand up and his speech was incoherent, so we bundled him into the back seat of Jamie's Bentley and left him to sleep it off. The welcome we got from Clara and Yvette when we returned was momentous and they came and sat on our laps and pampered us with kisses of thanks for dealing with Terence. Yvette was around twenty with beautiful white skin, flame red hair and was most striking and I was quickly aware that she knew how to arouse a man and enflaming his passion easily. She could feel my manhood rising beneath her and she knew that her feminine wiles were working even more as she started to kiss me deeply, pushing her tongue into my throat and nibbling my ear. I was in heaven but also in hell for I wanted this woman so badly at this moment, but I was engaged to Ruby and knew the guilt I would feel in the morning. I tried to break away, but her sweet kisses drew me back and closer to her. I finally succumbed, and I followed Charlie up the stairs with Yvette to one of the private rooms.

Yvette had a beautiful body and was well versed in all the courtesan's tricks to make a man enjoy her and I certainly did release that tension within me through the act of love with her, but I did not really enjoy it much and I immediately regretted it afterwards. I vowed not to do this again and that I would remain true to my promise to Ruby. Ivor had relished the attentions of Clara and had enjoyed time with her in an upper room and later we all rejoined the company at our table and drank some more. My guilt was weighing heavily on me and I felt disappointed in my own weakness to resist temptation, but the good nature and bonhomie of my companions slowly began to cheer me up. At around two we piled back into Jamie's car for the ride back to camp, finding Terence snoring in a deep sleep, but we managed to push him into the corner of the back seat so that we could get in. He was certainly sleeping the sleep of the just as despite the pushing and shoving and our shouting and singing, he did not stir. We had arranged to meet Vivian and Ivor again soon and I promised to drive over to the siege company headquarters when I got a chance. It was three in the morning when we got back to the B flight hut. The three of us managed to manhandle Terence into his room and dump him on the bed but even then, he did not stir. I was glad to retire to my room, pull off my boots and uniform, get into bed and was fast asleep in seconds with all thoughts of Yvette out of my mind.

We were all slow to surface the following morning and considering the amount we had drunk it was surprising that we got up at all. I came out of my room around ten to find hot tea and breakfast prepared by Joe Spragg, which helped me come round no end. Jamie did not appear to be suffering any ill effects, but I was certainly feeling a sense of detachment and a kind of delay in real-time of a few seconds in everything I was saying and doing. After a couple of mugs of tea and some eggs and toast and marmalade I was beginning to feel a little better, but it was a good job that B flight was stood down from flying today. Jamie obviously had a greater capacity for alcohol than I as he was his usual bright and cheery self. Sergeant Knowles did not appear from his room until eleven with a rotten headache but there was no sound at all from Terence Bradby's room. Eventually, Joe Spragg ventured into the room and found Terence half-awake but feeling as though he was dying judging by the moaning and groaning that came from under the bedclothes that were thrown over his head. However hard Airman Spragg tried to coax him he could not tempt the young officer to get out of his bed until Jamie took direct action and picked up a fire bucket from the corridor and when Spragg threw back the bedclothes, tipped the contents over Terence's head. The cold water had the miraculous effect of pumping life into the dying corpse as he was able to leap out of bed with a certain alacrity which had seemed impossible just a few seconds before cursing his flight commander in language unbecoming an officer of the Flying Corps. Now he was up it was relatively straightforward to point him in the direction of the ablutions whilst the batman cleaned up his room and refilled the fire-bucket.

Half an hour later, he appeared in the crewroom looking better and clutching a mug of tea whilst waiting for Spragg to rustle up some more eggs for his breakfast. He said he could not remember everything about the night before but how marvellous it had been and that he was now in love with

Yvette, or was it, Clara? We egged him on and described how he had gone upstairs to a private room with both together, they were up there for three hours, and we had to wait for him to finish before we could drive back. We said we were in awe of his prowess with women and his endurance to satisfy two together for such a long time. He said he could not remember much about it and was disappointed because he could not remember the sensation of losing his virginity to two such wonderful girls. He admitted that he had never had any luck with girls before, they always thought he was rather wet, but these French girls were far more discerning and could see him for what he really was. We did not have the heart to tell him that Clara and Yvette were working girls who made their living entertaining officers at Suzette's place because he had such a look of contentment spread across his face. I felt concern that we were proceeding with this deception but more worried about the naivety and innocence shown by Terence and how that would transpire in the air. I needed him to have a proper sense of reality if he was going to watch my back and fly as my wingman when we engaged the enemy.

I quietly expressed my concerns to Jamie, and he agreed but said that was why he had put him with me in the hope that he would learn to be a better pilot and adopt the correct aggression and attitude for combat flying. He doubted that Terence would last long in combat but flying with me might prolong his life significantly. I reminded him that I was new to combat flying too but he laughed and said, "You have proven courage on the battlefield and are an excellent pilot and you are a fully mature adult man. These young boys they send us from the flying school are not ready for the fight over the battlefield when we can have experienced soldiers like you and Charlie Knowles instead. Every member of B flight will have to cosset young Terence and maybe he will develop into a passable pilot if he lives long enough."

In the afternoon, Jamie spent an hour discussing flight formations and the tricks of combat flying then went on to describe a series of upcoming sorties that we were rostered to fly over the following week in support of the bomber group attacks on the railway hub to the south of Brussels. Our role was to provide a high-level escort for the slow moving bombers en route to and from the targets to protect them from surprise attack from German aircraft as there were several fighter airfields in the vicinity of the railway junctions which could cause considerable disruption to the attack. The first wave of the bombers would mount attacks on two of the German airfields to attempt to destroy German aircraft on the ground or prevent them launching their aircraft in time to stop the raid on the railway. We were to be assigned to the bomber group whose target was the marshalling yards near Oudenarde about twenty miles west of Brussels deep into enemy territory, so it was imperative that we acted as mother hens to get them to the target and back safely and to drive off any potential enemy attack. The duration of these sorties would mean that an additional reserve fuel tank would have to be fitted temporarily to the SE5s to give us the range to complete the mission safely and he indicated that we would all need to practise flying with this extra fuel load over the next couple of days. The operations would be tricky the first time because it was a completely new strategy and the marshalling of such a large force of aircraft would take up time and burn a lot of additional fuel. We were excited about this mission and spent the rest of the day studying the maps of the route and going over the target making notes for the operational briefings when the date of the actual attack was known.

It was great to be back in the cockpit today as it was just over a week since I had last flown an SE5. I planned a formation flying sortie with Terence Bradby in the morning where I intended to practise flying as a pair in close formation, changing altitude, banking, and turning in quick succession. I needed to ensure that Terence was able to watch me and react with me whatever I had to do. We took off and I took us over an area of farmland several miles further east into France where I felt sure that there would not be many other aircraft in the vicinity. The first lesson was getting Terence to concentrate on staying in position on my wing in straight and level flight. Once I was certain I signalled that we were to start climbing and descending at high speed with a loop and several rolls and that he was to follow me whatever I did. He was reasonably good at first at the changing altitude but was unable to keep position when engaged in rolls so that after I had completed a massive loop followed by three rolls in quick succession, he had lost contact with me completely. I hunted around the sky looking for him, finally spotting him flying straight and level about 2,000ft below me. I immediately swooped down on him in what would have been a killing pass with a burst of machine-gun fire had I chosen to fire. I could tell that he was taken completely by surprise by the way he lurched almost out of control, unable to take effective evasive action. The first time that this happen in contact with the Germans he would be dead meat for sure. I circled round and took up my position in the lead, signalled a return to base and we flew straight back to La Coupole.

I was furious with him for his lack of concentration and his inability to keep a good lookout all around him as these were the basic tenets of a fighter pilot in combat and made me even more grateful for the excellent training, I received at the hands of Major Coate-Barnes at Croydon. By the time we got into the crewroom I had calmed down a bit and was able to conduct the debrief without losing my temper. Terence had done reasonably well at first but when our manoeuvres became more erratic and expansive in the sky as they would if we were engaged in aerial fighting, he lost the ability to keep up, disengaged from the wingman position and allowed himself to be detached completely from his leader so that he had no idea where I was in the sky. This would have been OK and a likely thing to happen in combat providing that he was able to take evasive action, keep safe and search the sky to affect a rejoining as a pair. Unfortunately, once he became detached from me, he was completely lost, and it was obvious that he was not navigating himself but simply following his leader. These were basic errors that should have been eradicated in training; he should not have been sent to an operational squadron at his state of readiness but the biggest fault of all is that he broke the combat pilots' number one rule to always search the sky all around you for possible danger. He had assumed that because we were twenty-five miles behind our front lines, he was totally safe and resumed straight and level flight whilst he tried to get his bearings. He was a sitting duck and could have been shot down by a roving enemy fighter here just as much as over the battlefield. I asked him what he would do if we became engaged with enemy aircraft as a pair and I got hit in the action; he did not venture an answer. I told him we would go up again this afternoon and repeat the sortie again and again until he could stick to me like glue whatever happen. He was a little sheepish and resentful but when I went through to my room to lay down for half an hour, I heard Charlie Knowles chiding him to snap out of it., "Derfal is trying to save your life over the battlefield and you should thank him for what he is doing, not resent him."

We repeated the sortie four times in two days and finally I was beginning to think that Terence was getting the idea more thoroughly although he was still totally reactive and had not yet caught on to the necessity to be proactive every second you were in the air. It was a hard transition for him because I think he thought that the Flying Corps was like a flying club in uniform. I would say he was a reasonable pilot but totally lacked what it takes to be a combat pilot. He had not come to terms with the fact that a combat pilot's sole job was to inflict casualties on his enemy; whether it was shooting him down in aerial combat or strafing him on the ground; nothing else mattered. By the end of this cycle of sorties I was able to report to Jamie that Bradby was just about capable of taking part in the bombing raid escort mission and that this would be a test of his potential in one way. Terence was now able to stick to me like glue, but I was not confident that if anything happened to me, he could get himself back to base safely. He agreed and said the mission was likely to be early the following week, but we would know a day beforehand when detailed briefings will be held for the whole squadron.

I received a whole crop of letters from home that day so after stripping off my flying clothing and brewing a pot of tea, I sat in the armchair and read all the news from home, saving Ruby's letter until the last. The first letter was from Wesley, filling in the details of the Wyn Davis case who had come up before a naval court martial and been sentenced to two years for striking an officer and a further year for assaulting his wife. There were considerable arguments in mitigation concerning Mair's adultery with several men during her husband's absence and the fact that he had an exemplary service record, so the court decided to suspend the sentence for three years and drafted him back to sea immediately on a battle cruiser. I thought that this was probably a good outcome for all concerned and went on to read the letter from Mum and Dad which gave me a different view of the Davis case as they felt he had been let off and had got away without any punishment. Mair was still staying with Mum and Dad, and they were growing to like her; Gwyn had gone back to Magor, returned to work, and was intending to visit at weekends. Wyn Davis had given notice that he was going to sue for divorce on the grounds of her adultery and in the light of this information, Gwyn had decided to keep his distance so that the divorce could go through unopposed, and he and Mair could get married. Ruby's letter was long and lovely full of her love for me and her aspirations for our future. I had only been away a few days and she was missing me desperately already. Then she told me the startling news that Freda was not pregnant after all, and her missed menstruation must have been because of another cause because they had started again normally. She and Dai were relieved but have decided to go ahead with the wedding anyway, as they are having sex so regularly, she was bound to fall pregnant at any time and they are both so in love with each other. Her mum and dad were in good health and the rugby club was doing well this season. I was so filled with remorse about Yvette when I read and reread this letter as I thought of the purity of Ruby waiting patiently at home for me.

Terence Bradby was keen to go into St Omer again on Friday night to get reacquainted with Yvette or Clara, but Jamie was reluctant to approve because of the closeness of the big raid and our need to be ready immediately when the date was fixed. We all had an inkling that it was most likely to be early Monday morning, but knew that at any time the weather report or aerial intelligence might determine an earlier or later start. The whole squadron was on standby and that included all the ground staff as well as the pilots to be ready at a moment's notice. Jamie suggested that we could all pay a visit to the small café bar in the village for a few drinks and a meal but would return by ten-thirty to get a good night's sleep in case the raid was brought forward. We all agreed but Bradby was disappointed not to be going to St Omer again. I was glad because as a good a pal that Jamie was, I did not have the resources to afford the high living that he could so easily pay for and probably more important was my fear of whether I could resist the charms of girls like Yvette and break my promise to Ruby again. My pay had gone up tremendously and I was now earning £9 a week which was three times what my father and brother were earning in the pit for all their hard graft. Here I was, nearly twenty-one, earning so well. I realised well enough that I was only a temporary gentleman, my commission would end at the end of the war, and I would be back into civilian life looking for work with so many other returning soldiers. I had always been brought up to be a saver; I was trying to build my capital for my marriage to Ruby and for buying a house to bring up our family together. To keep to my savings target I could not afford too many expensive nights in establishments like Suzette's which would also help me to keep temptation at bay.

Jamie drove us to the nearest village only five minutes from the airfield, where there were a couple of small bars and one slightly larger with a passable restaurant. It was to the larger restaurant that we were headed and on entering we found that the main bar area was already full of infantry men from the nearby rest camp, but the patron showed us through to the private dining room to the rear of the bar where we were able to sit in relative calm. A few other tables were occupied by officers from the infantry units at the rest camp, but it was not packed or noisy and when the menu came it was surprisingly diverse with many choices for hors d'oeuvres, entrees and desserts. Jamie ordered some local wines to drink at the table but said that we would save champagne for our next big night out. The young waitress was the patron's daughter and she charmed us by her attempts to speak English which she had been learning to communicate better with the soldiers who were now almost exclusively the restaurant's clientele. She was only about sixteen and was simply dressed but had a friendly personality and I felt that she worked hard to make our dinner an enjoyable experience. The food was excellent, simple fare but delicious and cooked to perfection and we all enjoyed it very much. I decided to be adventurous and selected escargots to start with a little trepidation as like for most British people, the idea of eating snails was abhorrent to me but when they came in a delicious sauce and with a pick to scoop out the juicy meat, I began to change my mind. Charlie chose frogs' legs being equally adventurous and he also found them quite palatable. We all chose the entrecote for main course and a selection of desserts and cheeses to finish. The local wines were a little dry but after a glass or two our palates became accustomed to the taste and we found them enjoyable enough.

We all relaxed around the table and conversation roved around what we had been doing in civilian life before the outbreak of war. Although we all assumed that Jamie had the most privileged and easy home background, being a member of the minor aristocracy, we were surprised to hear about the loneliness and rejection he felt being sent away to school at the age of seven and the years before that when he was brought up by a nanny and was somewhat estranged from his parents. His transition to a major public school meant more years spent away from home so that by the time he left school he found that he hardly knew his parents at all. His father wanted him to go up to Oxford to his old college, but Jamie decided that he would be better in the army, and he was commissioned in the Royal Horse Artillery in 1915 and transferred to flying training later in the year. He envied us all but especially Charlie and I for the close family life we had enjoyed growing up. Despite the obvious lack of money in our households we did not want for love and support which turned us into the men we had become. He described how the only tangible things that his parents gave him were through money and the nanny, school and public school were just things they could buy so that they did not have to deal with their three sons themselves.

His father was a big landowner in middle England and had also invested heavily in munitions and small arms so was extraordinarily rich. Although he was only really interested in his first-born son who would inherit the title and take over the businesses, he did settle generous capital sums on his two younger sons on their twenty-first birthdays so they could live as independent gentlemen of means. His eldest brother, Jerome, was managing director of the munitions business whilst his father had taken a step back to manage his estates. His second brother, Oliver, had joined the Royal Navy and was serving as a commander of a destroyer in the Home Fleet and had determined to make his career in the navy. He was now becoming melancholy as he talked, drank another red wine, and said he was certain that the future of our country would be in the hands of people like Charlie and I who have worked hard to get where they are today. He said that he was just another member of the upper class with few practical skills to contribute to building a new future for the hundreds of thousands of young men fighting this terrible war. We tried to cheer him up and to tell him he was wrong, because we much preferred the ebullient Jamie Dalrymple who was a good friend and excellent flight commander but realised that if you scratch beneath the surface, he suffered the same as we did despite his wealth. We returned to camp somewhat chastened but with a better understanding of each other than before. I realised that although Terence had kept quiet during most of the conversation his own upbringing mirrored some of the loneliness and pressures felt by Jamie. I decided I would try to get to know Terence more and to help him overcome his shortcomings.

Saturday morning the signal came for the briefings to begin at 14:00 and for the raid to be launched at 04:30 on Sunday morning. Yet again Jamie had shown good judgement and we were ready for detailed briefings that afternoon.

FOURTEEN

Oudenarde Bombing Raid

Saturday was a day of intense activity for the whole squadron as the ground crews prepared all the squadron aircraft including the reserve machines in preparation for the raid. The engine fitters and riggers were checking that all machines were in serviceable condition and the refuellers replenished the fuel tanks, including the reserve tanks that had been specially fitted to provide additional range for this mission specifically. The armourers were checking the machine guns and loading the belts of ammunition so that each pilot had the reassurance of a full load if he had to engage the enemy. The pilots slept late but then spent four hours in detailed briefings, first at squadron level and then each flight on its individual task. The briefings were detailed and complex because this would be the first time that the RFC had attempted to assemble such a massive strike force in the air and the task of marrying up the large bomber force with its fighter escort was key to the success of the mission. Our first task was to get the whole squadron airborne and to climb to the south of the airfield to the operational altitude of 6,000 ft which would take approximately twenty minutes to achieve. Each flight would take off together and climb in formation to assemble at the agreed altitude two miles to the west of Armentieres where the squadron would arrange itself in echelon by flight to sweep in from the south to a position 2,000 ft above the bomber formation assembled ten miles inland from the port of Dunkerque to the north-east of Ypres.

The bomber force was split into four sub-groups within the formation with each assigned toone of the four targets. Force A was attacking the signal boxes at Waregem, Force B the marshalling yards at Oudenarde, C the junction and points at Zottegem and D the railway viaduct at Ninove.

If the mission were successful, it would deal a massive blow to the railway capacity of the enemy to supply their troops at the Ypres Salient. Each of the bomber group was colour coded with their distinguishing colour in luminescent paint on their tails so that they were easily identified in the air. B flight was allocated to escort the B Force attacking the marshalling yards at Oudenarde, which were identified by bright blue tails. It was estimated that it would take another hour from take-off to achieve complete preparation to launch the attack. The lead bomber pilot would fire a white flare when the bomber and escort were in position and Force A with its escort would turn onto the prescribed heading for their target to be followed at two-minute intervals by each of the succeeding bomber groups on the headings for their targets. Takeoff was set for 04:30, the commencement of the attacks at around 06:00 and the targets hit by 06:55 if everything went to plan. It should still be dark when the first attacks struck, and our intention was to create complete surprise and confusion amongst the enemy just as they were turning to in the morning. We estimated that there would be little or no resistance from the enemy as we approached the target but anticipated that we would be chased by enemy fighters on the return leg. This meant that 354 Squadron would have to fight a strong rear-guard action to prevent the enemy from penetrating our defensive screen and shooting down the slow-moving bombers.

There was some tension in the flight hut as we all came to terms with the enormity of the task facing us early next morning. For all of us it was the first time flying in such proximity to lots of other aircraft and for Jamie it was his first test as our flight leader. Charlie and I had been through battles on the ground and kind of knew what to expect but poor Terence had no idea. I think we all felt a little afraid and I spent an hour before sleeping writing letters to Ruby and Mum and Dad in case I did not come back. We all knew that anyone who pretended to have no fear before action was lying or a fool, but we were a little concerned about Terence who had gone noticeably quiet and retreated within himself. He had come on well with the additional training, and although I would not be confident in sending him on a solo patrol, I hoped he should be able to perform his duty tomorrow without any problems. As soon as it got dark on Saturday afternoon, we took our evening meal and headed for bed by 18:00 to rest adequately before the 03:00 start in the morning.

Sunday morning was cold, and we all took time to ensure that we were wrapped up in our warmest underwear and socks because it was going to be even colder at at 6,000 feet. I put on thermal underwear and heavy-duty woollen socks under my uniform and pulled on my boots which felt tight because of the extra-thick socks I was wearing. I had my greatcoat, two scarves to wrap round my neck. my flying gloves and helmet so I should be warm enough even though I did not take a flask up with me this time because it would not be safe to be drinking from it whilst in the combat zone. At 03:45 we had a final squadron briefing where Major Moss went over the headlines of the attack plan again wished us all the best of luck and we walked out over the whiteencrusted frosty grass to our aircraft at 04:15 climbed aboard and strapped in. Jamie was in his usual ebullient mood and said, "How about a trip to Suzette's tonight to celebrate the success today and our first blood as a flight?" I hoped that this was not bad luck to be planning to celebrate a victory we had not yet won, but we all cheered and said OK. It was nerve-wracking sitting in the dark cockpit waiting for the signal for starting the engines and to move off; I could hear props being swung and engines coughing into life all around me until it was my turn. The engine caught on the fourth swing, roared into life and I gave the thumbs up sign to the ground crew and then kept my eyes firmly on Jamie for the signal for B flight to take off.

The airfield was a wide stretch of grass with a capacity for a whole flight to take off at once, so once Major Moss had got airborne followed by A flight, Jamie gave us the signal to start to roll. We climbed away from La Coupole, quickly got into flight formation, and turned onto a south-easterly heading for the squadron rendezvous over Armentières. At 04:50 we were reaching the assembly area and Jamie led us in a wide sweep to the north to take our position smartly behind A flight as we levelled out. Major Moss was leading us in a box circuit to allow C and D flights to join us promptly before turning with the whole squadron on to the heading for the Ypres rendezvous with the bomber force. It felt good to be flying with the whole squadron, you could feel the power of all seventeen aircraft flying together and it seemed to me to be a formidable fighting unit. The flight to the rendezvous would probably take about fifteen minutes and we settled into the steady progress, conserving our fuel as best we could. I guessed that the additional fuel load was the reason that my aircraft felt more cumbersome than usual, and I was glad that when we finally engaged with the enemy the fuel load would be substantially reduced and the aircraft's manouevrability returned to normal.

As we approached the city of Ypres, we skirted to the north-west and were amazed to see beneath us in the middle distance a massive force of aircraft milling around and forming up waiting for our arrival. I estimated that there had to be 150 aircraft in the bomber force below us and the noise from their engines could be heard even from our cockpits. Very soon, the white flare was sent up, A flight leader took his aircraft down and identified Bomber Force A with their bright red tails and signalled the rest of the flight to take post at 6,000 feet above this force as it moved away from the main force heading for its target. Jamie followed him down, this time looking for the bright blue tails and as the bomber force began to turn towards Oudenarde he signalled us to take post similarly and we left the main assembly area on our way to the target. The Oudenarde marshalling yards occupied fourteen hectares of land and I tried to work out how many rugby pitches could be fitted on a piece of land that big. I estimated about fifty or so but had no idea if this was right, but it reinforced in my mind the vast size of the target and why there were over forty bombers assigned to this task. Goods wagons from the whole Austro-German Empire funnelled supplies, weapons, and ammunition in vast quantities through the rail networks in Luxembourg, Holland, and Belgium to be unloaded in the marshalling yards built to serve the Belgian capital. This was a prize target and had the potential to starve the German armies of vital supplies and equipment just before the Allies made the next big attack. We were surprised that so far there appeared to be no response from the enemy.

As we approached the target, we were aware of the bombers descending as they intended to push home their attack from 2,000 ft whereas we were to provide overarching defensive patrol coverage in the event of enemy fighter attack. Our surprise was complete when we saw the marshalling yards below us still lit up like daylight and trains moving in and out of the loading and unloading bays. They were not expecting the RFC to come calling and as soon as the first bombs started to fall the lights were rapidly switched off, but by now the flashes from the explosions and flames from burning rolling stock and stockpiles of supplies provided the bomber pilots with enough light to see what they were doing very efficiently. We could see that there were some high-angle gun emplacements, but they did not seem to be firing and then one or two started began to open which suggested that the crews had probably been asleep and were caught on the hop. It appeared as if the complacency of the stalemate after the Passchendaele battle affected the enemy as well as our side in equal measure. We knew that any future raid like this would be much more difficult to mount with the German defences on alert with fighter screen in the air. By the time the guns had started firing and were beginning to get range and altitude over two-thirds of the bombers had completed their bombing runs and were turning for home whilst the last wave pressed home their attack. By now the gunners had improved their rate of fire and accuracy; two bombers were hit before they had delivered their bombs and exploded and crashed to earth in flames, landing on top of the wooden goods cars being unloaded setting the train on fire from end to end. A third bomber was hit as he climbed away after his bombing run but the pilot with great bravery deliberately crashed his aircraft on to the nearest gun emplacement and was engulfed in the flames fuelled by his fuel and exploding ammunition.

B flight was desperate to get into the action, but Jamie held us in check as we at 6,000ft as ordered. We kept our eyes peeled to spot enemy fighters that would inevitably appear sometime soon. Our surprise had been complete, and the Germans had not been expecting such an attack to be mounted before dawn by such a large force of aircraft. It appeared that no German fighters were in the air, but we were sure that once the signal for help was sent out by the authorities on the ground at Oudenarde, it would not be long before they started to arrive in some numbers. Once the German pilots took off, they would be vulnerable to attack whilst they were climbing to attack the receding bombers. It would take them twenty minutes or so to gain altitude and they would not have the benefit of a well worked plan, whilst we knew where the fighter airfield was located and that they would head for Oudenarde, which was where the British aircraft were last seen. We reckoned by the time they were approaching Oudenarde the fighter bombers would be twenty miles away heading for their home bases and they would find themselves facing the whole of 354 squadron providing the protective screen and blocking their way in a line from Ninove to Waregem.

The German response when it came appeared to be a little half-hearted and the aircraft were single or in pairs, suggesting that they were not able to put up a squadron to challenge us. The individual pilots were brave enough but were just too late to attack the retreating bombers who were already too far away on the journey home to be caught by them leaving them with little choice but to engage us even though we had the tactical advantage of altitude. Jamie led us on a sweep to the East where a pair of German fighters were desperately trying to gain altitude and as we gained speed in our rapid descent on to the approaching pair they split up and dived for the ground to escape from our guns. Jamie pulled a tight turn to the left to chase the first German, closely followed by Charlie whilst I banked sharply right and dived after the second one hoping that Terence was sticking to my tail. Our fugitive was a good pilot, and he did his best to shake us off by twisting and turning all over the sky, but we stuck to him like glue waiting patiently for him to make a fatal error and allow me to line up a deflection shot. I had tried several two-second bursts and although I thought I had hit him it did not seem to slow him down much, but I knew that if we pressed home our advantage, we would get him in the end. Finally, whether because of some damage inflicted by one of my earlier passing shots or not, his aircraft seemed to lose some of its responsiveness, and he was marginally slower than before, but I found that I was able to give him a four second burst from which larger pieces of wreckage appeared to break off and smoke billowed out of his engine. He was done for and was heading rapidly towards the ground to make a crash landing. I broke off the engagement and began to climb back up to 6,000 feet again when taking a few seconds to look for Terence, I could not see him on my wing. I was immediately worried that in selfishly pursuing my target I had neglected Terence, I desperately searched the sky for his aircraft when my attention was caught by an SE5 chasing the tail of a German fighter but with a second German on his tail.

As I got closer, I could see from the aircraft number that it was Terence who had broken off from flying as my wingman to go after a target himself. He was doing alright and had the first aircraft on the run although I thought he was flying too close to get in a good shot, but it was his closeness to his prey that was preventing the second German on his tail from firing for fear of hitting his compatriot at the same time. I hoped that I could catch them before the second German got lucky and hit Terence or damaged his aircraft enough for him to have to ditch in an emergency. I climbed 500 feet above the trio locked into an aerial combat dance to the death and used that extra height to dive down on to the second German with a passing shot as I crossed his tail. I did not think that this would shoot him down but would be sufficient for him to break off from Terence and to defend himself from further attack from me. I gave him a two-second burst as I swooped in at high speed, I could tell by his reactions that he had not known I was there, and I pulled a very tight turn to get behind him and line up for another burst of machine-gun fire as he tried to disengage himself from Terence's tail. I kept the pressure on and fired a second burst of fire which caused him to dive away sharply with flames licking up the side of the fuselage. I did not follow this one down either but turned to help Terence who had not lost his nerve and was pumping machine-gun rounds into the German aircraft in front of him. I made a note to have a word with him about wasting too many rounds as he carried on firing even though it was obvious his enemy was done for. I moved my aircraft alongside Terence and waved him off as the German headed for the ground and then exploded in mid-air in a fireball.

We resumed our patrol until we found Jamie and Charlie. Jamie recalled us to return to base. We were in such high spirits; I claimed two shot down, Terence one and Jamie got one kill, but Charlie was unlucky even though he fought a long dogfight with one persistent German who had managed to get away. The debrief said that intelligence reports suggested that the marshalling yards had been severely damaged but not completely put out of action. It was estimated that it would take a couple of weeks to clear the damage and get the yard functioning again but much longer to replace the thousands of tons of supplies and equipment destroyed on the ground. Bomber force B lost three aircraft over the target and one crashed on landing on return to base. B flight claimed four kills of enemy fighters. Overall, the bomber force lost twelve aircraft shot down and 354 Squadron lost one aircraft shot down over Ninove from D flight; the fate of the pilot Lieutenant Stevenson was unknown.

Even though I had come through my first aerial battle unscathed and had claimed two kills, which were later confirmed, I felt physically and emotionally drained. I had no energy and after the debrief I just needed to sleep. Terence was hyperactive yet to come down from the high level of excitement and anxiety he had experienced in the air and was all for setting off to Suzette's place right then, but I knew that when the euphoria passed over, he would come to earth with a bump when he realised the enormity of what we had just been part of. Jamie was still involved in deeper analysis with the squadron commander and the other flight commanders, and Charlie was fast asleep in an armchair in the crew room. I washed thoroughly to get the dirt off my face and to clear the taste and smell of the mix of engine fumes and cordite from my mouth and nose and within twenty minutes I was drifting off to a deep sleep. I could already feel the pressure in my neck and the ache in the back of my head lessening and a warm feeling came over me as I began to imagine what Ruby was doing this Sunday in Wales. I was vaguely aware of Joe Spragg taking my shirts and underwear for washing, tidying my room and then he left me in peace.

It was after five in the afternoon when I surfaced, washed, and shaved and went to meet the others. The lively exuberance of the early hours of the morning was gone and we were all in a more quiet and reflective mood than before. I for one did not want to go to Suzette's and suggested that we returned to the local village restaurant where we had enjoyed dinner a few days earlier. To my surprise, everyone agreed, and we set off in Jamie's car about six-thirty and managed to get a table. The restaurant was busier than our previous visit, but we were served by the same pretty young girl who welcomed us with an open smile as she directed us to our table. Jamie pointed out the three surviving members of D flight sat in the corner and went over to speak with them. They were holding a private wake for their friend, Peter Stevenson, but Jamie prevailed upon them to join us so we could honour the memory of a comrade together. The waiters moved the tables around so all seven of us were seated together and introductions were made because even though we all served in the same squadron, Terence, Charlie, and I were newcomers and had not yet got to know everyone. It turned out to be a good move on Jamie's part as it rescued us from a certain post-operational melancholy by acting as hosts to the D flight boys and it redirected their attention from solely concentrating on the loss of their comrade. Jamie and Captain John Beresford were fellow flight commanders and had served together for ten months already so got on well. Pinky Perkins and Albert Sissons were also quite new to the squadron although Albert, like Charlie and I, had served in a front-line infantry battalion. The meal was equally as good as the previous occasion and as the wine flowed the conversation became lighter and more animated as we discovered that Pinky was a natural raconteur and Albert a straight-faced comic. What had been the prospect of a dull and sad evening turned into a jolly mixture of laughter and good company, which was a more fitting tribute to Stevenson I thought.

In the morning, I went to the flight line to inspect my aircraft and was surprised to see the airframe riggers hard at work patching the bullet holes in my fuselage some of which seemed remarkably close to the cockpit. I was struck by how vulnerable the pilot was to stray rounds in the heat of battle and this was a salutary thought. All the control wires had been checked thoroughly and luckily no damage was sustained. The corporal rigger pointed out fourteen holes caused by machine bullets and confirmed that by the end of the day my aircraft would be airworthy again. Jamie's aircraft had taken hits too and a couple of his control wires had been damaged enough to need replacing but again, this was easily rectifiable within a few hours.

B flight was not rostered for flying for two more days and we were stood down at lunchtime. I decided to go over to the siege company, visit Vivian

Craddock-Williams and see some of my old mates from the transport section. I asked Jamie if he would like to come with me, he readily agreed, and we set off in his Bentley later that afternoon. Seven months had passed since I left the siege company but because of the lack of action over the winter the company headquarters was still located in the same place as before. It was a little more difficult to find because large numbers of new troop formations were billeted in around the village ready for the next spring offensive and the arrival of American forces who had occupied a vast swathe of formerly open land on the Canadian southerly flank. Eventually I spotted the siege company colours painted on a sign board and recognised the entrance to their company headquarters. I remembered the days I spent digging out the ground for the building of the new headquarters and Jamie and I both recognised the field where he had crash landed and where Bryn and I had been awarded medals for his rescue. Despite being only few months ago it seemed like an age and the company headquarters had taken on an atmosphere of permanence especially now that the whole company seemed to be billeted here. Jamie parked the Bentley, and we went in search of Vivian's office. I was keeping my eyes open to see if I could recognise any familiar faces but to no avail as no one seemed to take any notice of us. There was more interest in Jamie's car, however. We headed towards the company headquarters and met the CSM coming out who threw up a smart salute at Jamie and some sense of recognition spread across his face as he realised that Jamie was the wounded pilot rescued from the Germans by the transport section. When I spoke, he took a double take as he realised that it was me. His face split into a huge smile and he saluted me this time then shook my hand in congratulations on my commission He took us in and pointed out the adjutant's office.

We knocked, a voice called out to come in, we entered, saluted our friend, and then told him he was a lazy workshy oaf hiding behind a desk while others were out winning the war. He retorted that we were too stupid to have a desk job which kept everything running smoothly and, we were totally expendable and could be sacrificed in action flying a stupid aeroplane but when the war was over people like him would be kings and needed to rebuild the country in peacetime whilst we would be still playing with our toys. We fell about laughing as we were so happy to see each other again. He picked up his cap and said to follow him and as we rushed across the hallway, he said the CO was going to Second Army headquarters, but we would try to catch him before he left as he would be disappointed if he missed us. He knocked on the CO's door, flung it open and we went straight in. Major Rees-Evans was about to remonstrate with the intruders when he saw me, stepped forward and took my hand and said how glad he was to see me again and that I was doing something I really loved. He said that he knew from the first time we had met on our almost capture by the German patrol, "that you were quick-witted, bright and brave and would quickly outgrow your role with the transport section and you certainly did. He went on that he owed me several debts of gratitude, one that I had saved him from capture from the Germans, second you turned Vivian here from a schoolboy into a half-decent officer and lastly, you did not hold back Lewis who is now a sergeant chief clerk in headquarters. You recognise talent in people and bring them on to realise their potential. He apologised that he couldn't stay any longer but was called to Second Army to discuss the next task for the siege company before the next attack". I thanked him for his kind words and said I hoped that we would meet up in South Wales after the war was over.

When we got outside, Jamie turned on me and said, "We have you to blame for this excuse for an officer here," guffawed and we headed for the mess to get a sundowner. I just dropped out said I would join them in a few moments and went into the company main office where all the admin staff stood to attention as I came through the door, but I could see Ivan had his back to me. I called across the room that I wanted a word with him, and I thought he must have recognised my voice because he immediately spun round and stared at me in disbelief. So as not to embarrass him in front of his staff I suggested we took a walk outside in the fresh air. He grabbed his cap and followed me out of the building when he gave me a hug and said how glad he was to see me again. He filled me in on what had been happening in the siege company and particularly in the transport section. He talked with so much authority, I now knew the reason why Vivian had become a such an effective adjutant because of the support he had received from Ivan Lewis just as he had supported me from the first minutes, we met at Crickhowell Barracks when I was a brand new corporal. I was certain that my own success was largely because of his loyalty and support. I congratulated him on his three stripes, and he was modest as usual but was grateful for the extra pay, which helped at home. I told him I was engaged to be married, a little about Ruby and he seemed genuinely happy for me. He asked me if I were part of the big raid that went over in the early hours of Sunday, and I said that I could not say too much but told him that I was flying fighter escort to the bombers who attacked some strategic supply chain targets behind the German lines. He said they were just standing to for the morning alert and we heard and saw this huge aerial armada go over heading towards Brussels and it cheered the lads in the line no end to see that we could strike the enemy with such air power. He asked me if I saw any action and I told him that I shot down two German fighters during the battle and that my aircraft was hit but I suffered no injuries.

He had received several letters from Bryn Edwards who was now a corporal and returned to duty as a recruiting clerk as he was not fit enough for service at the front because of his injuries but the recruiting office was pleased to have him as he was decorated for gallantry and had a Military Medal to show for it. He was based in Chepstow at the Regimental Headquarters near to his family and seemingly was enjoying military life. My old classmate, George Smithers, had been promoted to corporal and posted to the vehicle maintenance unit in Arras, Sapper Davies had taken over his role as a lance corporal. He told me that he had heard through gossip that former Lieutenant Vaughan was released from prison after six months of hard labour, had the rest of his sentence suspended and was sent to the front to serve as a private in the infantry, but he was not sure whether this was true or not. I was glad to catch up with all the news and as we walked, I told him that I would be getting married at the end of the war and I would very much like him to attend the wedding if he could. When we reached the door to the officers' mess room he saluted and said it was great to see me. I went through the door to join Jamie and Vivian who were already starting their second drink. I recognised some of the sapper officers but there were some new faces I had not seen before. After the third drink, I managed to prise Jamie away from the mess so that he would be sober enough to drive us home, but not before he and Vivian had made plans to meet up at Suzette's in St Omer the next weekend.

Jamie was perfectly capable of driving, but I knew him well enough to know that the more drinks he had the harder it would be to get him to stop the drinking session. We made good progress and arrived back at La Coupole in time for dinner, shared a bottle of wine and reflected on a good afternoon visit to the siege company. Jamie pressed me for the details of how I had saved Major Rees-Evans from capture, and I told him about our breakneck motorbike escape from almost certain capture as we had been caught napping by the German patrol. He just laughed and said that was why he was glad to have chaps like Charlie and me in his flight and on that note, we turned in early as we were rostered for flying tomorrow and would be briefing by 08:00. The morning briefing was taken by Major Moss who had selected a pair from each flight to fly a sortie over the four recent targets to gather as much intelligence as possible regarding the actual damage that we had inflicted in the raid on Sunday. The photo reconnaissance planes had flown over the targets, but the cloud cover was too thick to take good pictures. It was urgent to get damage assessments immediately and the task fell to us to go in underneath the cloud at low level and fast to take the required pictures. Remote cameras were being fitted to the underneath of the lead aircraft of each pair and all we needed to do was to activate the cameras at the start of our run and switch off after each pass. The second aircraft was to provide cover for the lead aircraft as it flew fast, straight, and level over the target and to drive off any potential threats. The mission's success, like before, depended entirely on surprise and speed; it was estimated that the time over the target would be less than 120 seconds. The pair selected was to be me and Terence. Although I would have preferred that Terence was flying the lead aircraft to take the photographs so that I could fly the close protection, I had no choice but to accept the mission as it was. The taking of the photographs and getting them back to base was the most imperative outcome of this sortie so if Terence got into trouble, I would just have to leave him to extricate himself as best he could. I went out on the flight pan, inspected the camera arrangement under my aircraft and was pleasantly surprised that it was smaller than I had imagined. The corporal rigger said it was no heavier than a metal ammunition box and should not affect the handling of the aircraft at all. It was mounted centrally so as not to affect the balance of the aircraft too much but meant that I would have to fly directly over the top of the areas to be filmed as the camera was fixed, which would be a more hazardous than using a hand-held camera.

The weather forecast was grey, overcast with almost complete cloud cover with a ceiling around 800ft which would allow us to fly low, hidden in the clouds until we were over the target when it should be possible to swoop down to 500ft for the photo run if the forecasters were correct. I stressed to Terence that he must stick to my tail like glue because if we got separated in the low cloud, he would be on his own twenty-five miles into enemy territory. We spent an hour with the air charts, mapped out the compass headings we should follow and the way points to the target and back. It reminded me of planning my first cross-country over Salisbury Plain at the basic flying school. I made sure that we both copied the detail exactly in our flying notes, wished him good luck and we were ready to take off at 11:15. There was no need for the extra fuel tanks on this mission as we were going directly to and from the target without the stooging around the sky meeting up with the bomber group this time. The A flight pair had already gone about fifteen minutes before us and there were no other movements over the airfield, so when we received the signal to go immediately, accelerated together into the sky in echelon and turned on to the first heading to cross over the front lines near to the village of Passchendaele. I hoped that this time our passing over their lines was not noticed by the boys in the siege company, who were immediately below us.

We were flying at 1,500ft and completely immersed in the low cloud, which was damp and cold but with sufficient visibility for Terence to stay on my tail about 60 ft to my rear. Although I kept sweeping around the sky for potential danger the cloud was impenetrable, and I felt relatively safe for the moment that any enemy would have to get in remarkably close before they were aware that we were there. After Passchendaele, we made a second course change to come on to the heading for the Oudenarde railway marshalling yards but kept at the same altitude. There were no breaks in the cloud, so we were flying blind using our dead reckoning skills with compass only. The map was useless at this moment because we could not see the ground. I estimated eighteen minutes running time should bring us over the marshalling yards and when we had run down seventeen, I signalled to Terence that we were going down for a looksee. We cautiously descended through the cloud until we broke into daylight at about 700ft and I quickly tried to orientate us in terms of our run into the marshalling yards. I could see that we were approximately a mile and a half to the east of the target, and I estimated that two runs across the target would be sufficient to get the intelligence required. Again, I signalled to Terence that we were beginning our run in over the target but staying at this altitude until we were almost crossing the perimeter fence of the yard, when we would level at 500feet for the photo passes. Terence gave me the thumbs up that he understood, we went in, and I could see the whole area mapped out below me. Although there was some movement of vehicles and lorries there were no railway movements within the yard itself. I crept down from the cloud base to 500 ft and felt exposed because up until now we had been difficult to see against the clouds. It did not take long for the two dots hanging in the sky to be identified as enemy aircraft and I could hear the sirens going off on the ground below me. I could see the Belgian workers abandoning their vehicles and running for cover, and machine guns were beginning to open fire, but the high-angle guns could not fire as we were too low for them to be brought to bear. Luckily for us our surprise had given us the advantage and the machine gunners had not managed to get the range accurately, but I knew that the return pass would be more deadly as they would know where we were coming from and what our intention was. I surmised that by now the commander on the ground would have got a signal off to the German fighter airfields nearby, so I expected company for the return leg of the mission if we made it across the marshalling yards a second time. I gave Terence the hand signal for the second pass and we banked and turned in full view of the enemy gunners and lined up for the second pass. I could feel the sweat on my brow and the icy fear in my stomach as I held steady and begun the second photo run.

The machine guns opened with a massive barrage, which was much closer to us and I could feel some hits on the fuselage but kept straight on filming as I went. I had lost track of Terence and hoped he was sticking close to my tail but was suddenly aware of his aircraft diving beneath my wing and his machine guns rattling away as he strafed the line of machine gunners on the ground below. I could have cheered out loud and hoped to heaven that Terence was able to avoid being hit, he was so low to the ground. I kept my attention on my mission and flew straight and level with my eyes focused on the perimeter fence in front of me as I counted off the seconds until I crossed it and could climb back to the safety in the clouds. I did not want to climb away without knowing Terence's fate so instead of climbing I swung around as if I was going to make a third pass and was relieved to see Terence about 400 yards to my left coming fast. I made a sweeping turn to the right climbing all the time and I became aware that Terence had rejoined me. I gave him the thumbs up and we both headed for the clouds and safety. I estimated that we spent less than three minutes over the target making the two photo runs and once again we had caught the German fighter squadrons on the hop, as the weather conditions had kept them firmly on the ground.

Our return flight was uneventful in terms of enemy action but harrowing, particularly when the visibility closed in as darkness came down and turned into ground fog. We had a hard job to find the La Coupole airfield, I was already thinking of diverting to an alternative landing ground but was aware that our fuel was now getting low, and our options were limited. I knew that we were on the correct heading for the airfield but only caught glimpses of the ground below us through the swirling of the fog, but my eye was caught by bright lights flickering in roughly the right direction for La Coupole and I realised that these were in a pattern and were beacons fuelled by petrol which indicated the way to the runway. I was glad to have spotted them and followed them down for the pair of us to land safely on the grass together. We taxied over to the hard standing and cut the engines as I was aware of the photo recon people unclipping the camera from its mounting in their hurry to get the film developed. I climbed down from the cockpit, walked over to Terence and for the first time I thought of him as my equal as a pilot. I clapped him on the back, told him, "Well done," and we walked arm in arm to the briefing room for the debriefing. Major Moss was anxious to hear about the progress of the mission. I was frank and honest and said that if it had not been for the low cloud the mission would have been suicide. The element of surprise was great and enabled us to make the first pass before the defence was organised, but the second pass was against a hail of bullets that would have ripped us to pieces if it had not been for my wingman who without fear for his safety went down extremely low to destroy some of the machine-gunfire. His brave action split the enemy barrage and allowed me to complete the second run unscathed. We later heard that the photographs gave much greater detail than the high-altitude ones and had been passed to the battle damage assessment team at Second Army air group for detailed analysis.

FIFTEEN

Terence Bradby

Suzette's place was packed out and we were fortunate to be able to get a table for the four of us plus Vivian. When we entered the atmosphere was already loud, electric, and smoky. Our table was in a secluded corner but from my seat I commanded a good view over the whole of the dining room in front of me and I enjoyed watching the antics of the young, and not so young, officers trying to attract the attention of the hostesses who were liberally spread all over the room meeting and greeting the customers as they came into the restaurant. Some of my brother officers were transfixed by the beauty of the girls and staring like dogs with their tongues hanging out in anticipation of a treat. I hope that we had more sense and did not behave like this but then I thought back to our last visit to this place, and how we had behaved then. I realised that we were just as eaten up with animal lust as all the rest, and I vowed in my head that I would resist temptation and be true to Ruby and just enjoy my dinner, the good company and plenty of champagne and wine.

Vivian was a little late arriving but brought with him two of the sapper officers from the siege company. When he came in, he brushed off the attention of the girls near the door made a beeline for us in the corner and introductions were made all round. One of Vivian's companions, Gareth Lloyd, was known to me from my time in the company but the second, Carwyn Roberts, had only recently joined from Chepstow. We seated him next to Terence and Gareth sat next to me. Gareth was from Brecon and knew the valley pits well because he worked as a mining engineer before the war; he was also a keen rugby player, so we had much in common and chatted freely as the wine flowed. Terence was much calmer than our last visit and

217

seemed to be getting on well with Carwyn, but I noticed he kept his eyes roving the room probably looking for Clara or Yvette, who had yet to make an appearance. I was glad too as I did not want to see Yvette again, because I knew it would be hard to trust myself if she was there.

The menu was as limited as before with only two choices of hors d'oeuvres and entrées and a selection of desserts and cheese to end the meal. I selected anchovies to begin with and a delicious pork and calvados casserole dish, whilst Gareth chose liver paté and a veal escalope. The food was as good as we were expecting, and I enjoyed mine very much. The champagne was going down well, and I was ready to switch to red wine to drink with my pork. We were all feeling relaxed and as our tongues loosened, we became louder and louder and added to the cacophony in the dining room. I noted that we were the only flying officers in the restaurant and some of the infantry officers from the surrounding tables started baiting us with good-natured jibes about living charmed lives miles behind the lines safe from enemy action. There was one young infantry man, however, who went further than his companions and was becoming personal and rude. I resolved it was the drink and tried to keep my temper in check but could not hold it in any longer when they decided to pick on Terence, who for all his growing confidence, was the least robust of the four of us. This particularly oafish lieutenant, who had all characteristics of a schoolyard bully, could see that his barbs were striking home on Terence who was looking confused and about to collapse into tears. As I stood up and challenged the red-faced oaf, I was aware that the room had suddenly fallen silent in anticipation of a confrontation. I raised my voice so all could hear my firm rebuke in front of his friends. I suggested to him that his behaviour was unbecoming for an officer, even from the infantry. I asked him if he knew who he was addressing, and whether he knew anything about any of us other than we were flying officers. He began to speak but I cut him off and continued that his behaviour was crass and reminiscent of a spoiled schoolboy bully who has just met his match. I pointed at the space on his left breast.

"There are no campaign medals on your left breast on view to testify to your worth whereas among my friends here we have several who have been mentioned in despatches, our flight commander has shot down six enemy fighters and is a holder of the Distinguished Flying Cross and four of us have served on the ground in frontline regiments for more than a year. I think you owe these gallant officers your humble apology and then, if they accept, you will remove yourself from this restaurant so as not to embarrass yourself further. If you haven't the guts to apologise the only solution for a gentleman is to step outside with me and we will settle this like men"

His friends tried to pull him away and were pushing him to apologise. One of them said to him to stop being a fool and pointed at the ribbon of the Military Medal indicating gallantry in action at the front before joining the RFC. The oaf shrugged himself violently out of the arms of his companions and still shouting insults at us rushed out of the doorway. After his departure, several of his friends came over to our table to apologise further for his behaviour. I introduced them around the table and made it clear to them that Terence was a fearless and brave soldier who had saved my life only a few days before. By now we had the five infantry officers joining our table and the wine was flowing even more freely. Suzette must have directed more girls into the room as were suddenly surrounded by a bevy of beautiful women all vying with each other for our attentions. Our inhibitions were down and soon there were as many women as men in our group. I could see Clara and the older woman who Charlie had been with before made a beeline for him and sat on his lap; they were soon in deep conversation. Terence and Carwyn seemed happy in the company of two younger girls I had not seen before and were laughing and joking together. The rest of us just took our pick and indulged ourselves in sensual fun and games with the girls. I had no intention of going upstairs with any of them, but I was happy to join in the teasing fun and drinking around the table and I felt that I was not breaking my promise to Ruby.

The evening continued long after midnight and by now some of our company had sloped away up the stairs with their partners, but Gareth and I stayed put and continued drinking until it was time to go. I had enjoyed myself very much and had proved to myself I could resist temptation. On the drive back Terence, who was no longer in love with Clara and Yvette but was now swearing undying love to Minette the girl who had sat on his lap and kissed him tonight, asked me if I really would have fought with the rude infantry officer. I told him that I probably would not have stooped to his level, but he did not know that because he was the worst kind of bully who crumbles as soon as somebody stood up to him firmly. Jamie laughed out loud and said I had sounded just like his old housemaster at school giving him a good wigging in his study and that he was going to call me 'the housemaster' from now on. We all laughed and headed back to La Coupole happy and contented and ready for a good night's sleep. Sunday was going to be a slow day as we all slept until late in the afternoon, and relaxed ready for the new week of flying combat patrols over the Ypres Salient.

A and B flight were rostered to fly patrols on Monday and Wednesday and Friday with C and D covering Tuesday, Thursday, and Saturday. Each flight covered a sector of the front overlapping with the other flight and a section would fly a patrol every two hours, which meant we would spend at least four hours in the air each day. The object was to observe any enemy troop movements, changes to their defences, to challenge any enemy aircraft that encroached over our airspace and to shoot them down. We would take off and fly an hour patrol and then return to base to refuel and rearm ready for the next patrol. It was a strenuous routine, which is why we only flew every other day to enable pilots to rest and be fit before each patrol. Our patrol sector was from Poperinge along the lines of the salient towards Menen and then south-west towards Armentieres and back to St Omer. We all knew that the build-up was beginning for another attempt to breakout from Ypres along the line to Lille, and the bomber raids the previous week were an opening salvo in this campaign.

The weather had moderated since the depths of the winter, the quagmire of mud and floods had largely dried up and the armies could move more freely again. It appeared that the generals had decided that their caution of the previous summer had contributed to the long stalemate with nothing moving in either direction. The arrival of the Americans had allowed for the massive reinforcement of Allied troops along the Western Front and an increasing confidence that one more decisive victory would break the German Army once and for all. It sounded plausible enough, but we had all heard such optimistic claims before. The Germans did not seem to follow the same way of thinking as us and despite the common stories that there were now only old men and boys in their frontline, they managed to hold us back with great ferocity. The only area of undisputed superiority was in the air where the new training regime in the RFC had produced a cadre of better-trained and more professional combat pilots who had turned the tide against the German air force over the battlefield. Jamie and Charlie were flying the first patrol at 08:00 we were to follow at 10:00 and every other two-hour slot throughout the day. Terence and I studied the maps again and noted our headings, altitude and patrol schedule into our note pads and were sitting in our cockpits, strapped in waiting for the order to swing props and taxi to take-off.

At 09:50 we started our engines and taxied out from the hardstanding to the edge of the airfield to await the signal from the control tower. We received an amber light to proceed to the end of the runway and lined up abreast ready for take-off waiting for the green light which came within fifteen seconds. We opened the throttles and both aircraft roared away down the grass strip together until we reached take-off speed and climbed away turning to the east to begin our patrol. Visibility was good with the cloud base at about 5,000 ft which meant we had an excellent view of the battlefield stretched out below us but also it meant that we were clearly visible to the enemy, and we may well expect some contact with enemy fighters during the patrol. Before we began our patrol routine, I signalled Terence that we would test fire our guns to ensure there were no jams and we both fired a one second burst to ensure that they were working perfectly should we need them to fight off or attack an enemy fighter.

We turned together on to a south-easterly heading over Poperinge and began to patrol slow and steady along the line of the salient towards Ypres at 3,000ft at eighty miles an hour. I was studying what I could see on the ground and making notes on my pad whilst Terence was keeping his eyes on the sky around us for potential enemy aircraft. I was first quite struck by how dramatically the landscape had been churned up over the winter and the patchwork of fields was now a brown mud-coloured desert. It was easy to see the reinforcement of the Second Army by the sprouting up of tented encampments a mile or so behind the forward trenches and I was hoping to be able to see something similar of the German side of the lines. The German lines seemed less busy than ours, but it was clear to see that concentrations of men and materials were engaged in considerable rebuilding work around the command and communication centres in their line. I guessed that these command posts which had proved vulnerable in the 1917 battle when they were undermined by the moles were being reinforced and strengthened from attack on the surface and underground.

I began to pay more attention to the location of the machine-gun positions and making rough sketches of the position of the firing points on my pad. What I could see was suggesting to me that the Germans had changed their tactics since the last battle when the subways allowed the first wave of the attack to outflank the machine gunners by coming up behind them. I was not sure about this as it was only an impression in my mind, but it looked to my untrained eye that the Germans had placed additional machine guns so that they covered an arc of fire which included the immediate front of their parapets exactly where the first wave of infantry emerged from the subway tunnels. To confirm my suspicions, I attempted to mark the positions of the machinegun posts as best I could.I would recommend that a series of photo-reconnaissance sorties should be able to provide the necessary evidence if required. We turned south again over Passchendaele and followed the line where I had taken part in the battle last year, I looked closely again at the machine-gun positions when I became aware of Terence creeping up alongside me and waving frantically at me from his cockpit.

When I looked at him, I could see he was pointing up towards his right at two enemy fighters who were crossing in front of us and did not appear to have seen us yet. I immediately broke off the line patrol and signalled Terence that we would attack and led him into a sharp bank to the right and then a steep climb to get above and behind our prey. The German pilots appeared to be still unaware of our presence and I hoped to keep it that way until we were able to fire the first shots as we dived on them from behind. At 4,000ft we had sufficient altitude to begin our attack and banked hard left to line us up on the same heading as the unsuspecting Germans and increased our speed to overhaul them as quickly as we could. As we got closer, I could see that the first aircraft was a two-seater reconnaissance aircraft with heavy-duty cameras fixed underneath with a gun position mounted in the rear cockpit and the second was the fighter escort. I reckoned we should attack together, and our priority would be to destroy the fighter escort first because he posed the greatest danger to us. Once he was destroyed the slower two-seater would not be able to escape and we could attack from both directions at once to restrict the fire of the rear gunner. Terence was perfectly poised on my right wing and gave me the thumbs up that he understood our plan of attack.

We began our fast dive onto the German aircraft and our surprise was almost complete until about a hundred yards and just out of range the rear gunner spotted us, and we could see him frantically signalling the fighter pilot to warn him of our presence. The German fighter banked sharply to the right, and I altered course to follow him in a high-speed chase and Terence cleverly swooped down beneath the recon aircraft so that the rear gunner could not bring his weapon to bear and pumped two three-second bursts into the underside of their aircraft paying close attention to the camera housings. I was quickly on the fighter's tail and held back far enough to be able to fire whenever a shot was on. He was a skilful pilot and several times he almost slipped out of my grasp, but he was always at a disadvantage because he had so little warning of our presence before we pressed home our attack. He tried to dive for the ground and twist and turn but every movement he made was mirrored exactly by the SE5 which had been designed exactly for this kind of aerial fighting. I tried to anticipate his next movement perceiving that he was tiring as his twists and turns were becoming a little slower. I crept in closer and managed a three-second burst directly into his tail section, which to my surprise completely folded and broke away from the fuselage. I found myself now under threat as I had to take evasive action to avoid the pieces of wreckage breaking off the dying aircraft, which threatened my safety too. I managed to break away and circle around to see the front section of the German fighter plunging like a dead weight towards the ground to crash into a field on the edge of a Belgian village that I later identified from my map as probably Moorslede.

My attention now turned to rejoining Terence and destroying the recon aircraft. After thirty seconds or so of scanning the sky, I spotted the German aircraft staggering along on the same heading being harried by Terence who was keeping well out of the reach of the rear gunner. The weight of the heavy-duty cameras mounted under the cockpit had destroyed a great deal of the manoeuvrability the aircraft may have had when it was built, and it was now a lumbering flying carthorse. I increased my speed and caught up with the pair quite easily, Terence gave me the thumbs up and pointed to the damaged cameras hanging underneath the aircraft and I was sure that Terence had done enough to render the recon mission a total failure already. I indicated to him that I would circle round in front of the pair and come into attack from that direction. This should keep the gunner occupied whilst Terence could sit back and destroy the aircraft at leisure whilst he was engaged attacking me. It did not quite work out as we expected because the rear gunner having had a taste of Terence's shooting, already judged him to be the greater threat and every time Terence tried to get into a good firing position, the gunner gave him a steady stream of fire. However, he was gambling that I would not be able to shoot them down from my frontal approach, but he gambled wrong because without any hail of lead to distract me in my frontal run, I came straight towards them firing two-second bursts directly at the engine, propeller, and the pilot. My fourth burst struck home, and I saw the pilot's head slump forward and guessed he had been hit as the aircraft fell away left out of control and Terence raked the whole underneath of the aircraft as it rolled sideways and immediately the plane was on fire. The aircraft was out of control and on fire and I considered that there was no way it would survive. Terence and I resumed our flight formation scanning the sky for other threats before resuming our patrol over Menen and turning west for Armentieres where we turned for La Coupole.

We were debriefed on landing; I claimed one kill of a Storch fighter and Terence, and I jointly claimed the recon aircraft. I explained my theory about the relocation of machine-gun positions and showed all my sketches. I saw little evidence of any increased troop formations immediately behind the German front line to match our build up but on this patrol did not have time to fly deeper into enemy territory and agreed that we would attempt to penetrate deeper into enemy territory on subsequent patrols. Terence and I looked again at the maps and decided to fly a similar patrol line for the 14:00 sortie and this time to cross the German trenches near to Poperinge, then fly six miles deeper into the German-held territory and follow parallel to the frontlines as far as Menen, then reverse our heading, fly back to Poperinge three miles closer to the front line, observe troop movements and the locations of fuel, supply and dumps in particular.

After barely half an hour to rest Terence and I were strapped back into our aircraft and ready to go again at 14:00. The first stage of the sortie was like the previous sortie as we climbed as fast as we could to our operational altitude, but this time at Poperinge we did not turn south-east but continued easterly for approximately six miles when we made the turn to fly parallel to the front below us to the right. There was plenty of activity in this area immediately behind the German defences, mostly vehicles and small columns of marching men, nothing to suggest a building up of major reinforcements. When I looked to my left I could see in the distance, maybe ten or twelve miles back from the front. These areas looked like vast tented encampments and vehicle parks ready for a quick reinforcement of their line when necessary. I could also make out the railway lines from Brussels connecting into the inter-state railway networks which I surmised could move troops and equipment quickly from safe areas deep within Belgium, Holland, and Germany at truly short notice. I noted the positions of what I had seen on my note pad and estimated that the camps were situated near the town of Roeselare between the smaller villages of Staden and Zarren. As we started to turn to begin the reverse leg, over to the west of the town of Kortrijk I noticed hidden on the edge of woodland a conglomeration of armoured tanks in the process of moving into camouflage positions under the canopy of the trees. I could only estimate the total numbers, but I counted at least twenty in the open countryside waiting to hide among the trees. This build-up of armour would be of interest to the intelligence officers at Second Army in their planning for our attacks along this section of the line.

We completed our 180-degree turn and were now flying the reverse course three miles inside the German lines. Like before we could not see much sign of preparations for an attack on our lines other than the rebuilding of the command posts destroyed in the last battle that we had already noted in our earlier patrol. I adjusted our heading to pass over Moorslede and on to Langemark when suddenly my heart was caused to jump into my mouth by the chattering of machine-gun bullets that seemed to be spraying all around me, I was aware of two German fighters swooping fast over us in a pass that caught Terence and I by complete surprise. I immediately pulled the nose of my aircraft up into a climb and opened the throttles wider to give me greater thrust as I sought to get above our attackers who were still diving below us ready to climb up into the loop which would bring them in to a good position to press home their initial attack. My plan was to thwart them by climbing faster than them and to get ourselves into such a position where we could attack them whilst they were still in the loop and unable to return fire. These were Storch aircraft of the same marque that I had shot down earlier today, and I was confident that our SE5s could outmanoeuvre them at any time.

I frantically searched behind me and strained my neck to see if Terence was still there and I just caught a glimpse of his aircraft a little further back than normal but still in contact distance. I thrust my arm out of the cockpit with a thumbs up and hoped that he could see that I was aware that he was there. I now kept my eyes rooted on the lead German aircraft which had started its climb into the loop, I could already see that our rate of climb was greater than theirs and I was certain that we would be able to hit them at the apex of their loop when they would be inverted and unable to take evasive action. The German leader had made a fatal error in his initial attack plan in that he had assumed that he would destroy us both on his first pass because of his element of surprise. By choosing to dive on to us at high speed he continued downward until he could pull up and into the loop to make a second pass. His assumption had proved to be wrong as his shooting had not been sufficiently accurate to deal us anything other than superficial damage and he had handed the advantage back to us by giving us the altitude to strike him when he was most vulnerable.

I looked again over my right shoulder and I could see that Terence was much closer and he waggled his wings to show he was with me and understood what we were going to do. I turned my attention back to the lead German and could see that I had to judge the point of contact very carefully to hit him when he was powerless to hit back. He was just reaching the point in the loop when he was inverting, and his appreciation of our positions became more difficult to follow. I wondered why he did not try to spin out of the loop, but I guessed that he realised that would still put him at an altitude disadvantage which would be eradicated once he reached the top of the loop. I throttled back a little just to hold off to make the point of contact at exactly the right moment and was glad that I had judged it just right as when he passed right across my gunsights I gave him two three-second bursts that ripped along the whole length of the underside of his aircraft until I could see hot oil and smoke coming out of the side of his engine and he fell away into an uncontrollable spin that would end in a fiery crash below.

I continued climbing but searched around for Terence, who I could see was engaging the second German, but I guessed that Terence had attacked a little too early and although he had damaged his opponent, it was not enough to shoot him down. I could see that the German pilot was intending to go over the top of the loop, then break off to his left and run for safety deeper behind their lines hoping to shake off Terence as he dived for the safety of low altitude. I was convinced that the German was not aware of me, so I adjusted my course to place myself roughly in the path of where he was likely to break out of the loop and head for home. I hoped that he would have the shock of his life when he spun out of the loop straight into the path of my guns. I was gambling that he would be so preoccupied with evading Terence that he would be unaware of what I was doing. My tactic worked perfectly; as he came out of the loop and banked on to his heading for home, he was driven by Terence's guns directly into the path of mine. Our combined barrage was enough, his aircraft just seemed to crumble in the middle and collapsed and ceased to be a flying machine all at once.

Terence and I broke off and reformed flight formation. I dropped below Terence to check the underside of his aircraft for damage and could see some small oil leaks from his engine fairing, but it did not look too serious. He then did the same for me and apart from torn canvas everything seemed

OK but when Terence came up alongside to give me the thumbs up, I could see that he was covered in blood and that he must have been wounded in the action. I decided to abort the remainder of the mission gave the return to base signal to Terence and led us on the most direct heading back to base which would take us over Ypres, Steenvoorde and Arques and we should be on the ground within twenty minutes. I flew as fast as I could and kept a close eye on Terence to ensure that he was still with me and although he still seemed to be bleeding, he was coping well until I noticed that a wisp of smoke was coming from the base of his engine, which suggested that his time in the air was limited. Luckily, we were only five minutes from La Coupole and I prayed he would make it. As we turned into the final approach, I got hold of my flashlamp and hoped I could remember enough Morse code to send the distress code for a wounded pilot. I desperately flashed the distress message which was immediately acknowledged from the ground, and I could already see the fire cart and ambulance moving fast on the airfield. I led us in gently and we touched down on the north grass pulled out of the line of the active track as flames began to lick up the side of the engine compartment of Terence's aircraft. We rolled to a stop and I was fast out of the cockpit and running clumsily in my flying gear to pull Terence out of the burning aircraft. Nearer, I could feel the heat intensely and then felt strong hands pushing me back as two firemen grabbed hold of Terence and lifted him quickly out of the burning aircraft and rushed into the waiting ambulance, driven off to the safety of the military hospital at St Omer. I could not see very much because Terence's head and shoulders seemed to be covered in bloodthat masked his features, but I could hear him talking though so I knew he was not yet dead.

I decided that I would go to the hospital that evening and enquire about Terence's wounds and Jamie kindly lent me the use of his Bentley to make the trip. I arrived at the main entrance of the hospital just after seven and went into the busy entrance hall to ask about Terence's whereabouts. I was hoping that he was not too seriously wounded so that he would probably still be in the main hospital receiving first aid treatment. There was a crowd around the reception desk, which was manned by two young French women, who both seemed quite fluent in English, and were dealing with the barrage of requests quickly and politely. When my turn came, I enquired about Terence but the young lady who I spoke to said she was unable to help me and passed me over to her colleague, Monique, who compiled the lists of the latest arrivals in the hospital. She came over to me and asked for Terence's details and when she spoke, I thought I recognised her voice from somewhere else the only Frenchwomen I had had any contact with were at Suzette's place, but she did not look like any of those girls because she was demure and professional in the way she carried herself. She found Terence's location very easily and directed me toward the observation ward where he was being held overnight before being transferred to the convalescent hospital in Fruges in the morning for two weeks' recovery period before returning to duty.

I found my way to the observation ward, made my way to the nurses' desk, asked after Terence and the nursing sister pointed to the doors that were open to the terrace, saying that I would find my friend outside. Terence was sitting on a bench and was in conversation with another wounded soldier who seemed to have been blinded for his eyes were swathed in bandages but as I came nearer Terence spotted me and jumped up eagerly to greet me. He was extremely glad to see me, and I was happy to see that now the blood was washed away his injuries looked much less severe. Terence had been hit by a bullet that left a flesh wound across his face; neatly removed the bottom of his left earlobe and badly bruised his neck and shoulder blade on its passage through the cockpit. No serious harm had been done although he may be left with some small scarring on the side of his face, and he should be fit to return to flying duties in a couple of weeks. I was glad to hear that he was going to be fine, and we sat on the bench alongside the blinded soldier who Terence introduced as Herbert Clough, a lieutenant in the South Yorkshire Volunteers who had been caught in a gas attack this morning at Poperinge. Clough did not say much, but even with the bandages around his face he looked vaguely familiar, and his voice bore a distinct resemblance to that of the arrogant soldier who had been so boorishly rude to us at Suzette's a few weeks before. I did not say anything to Terence because I did not think he had realised yet and I didn't want to cause a scene at the hospital. Anyway, if this chap had lost his sight, I was not going to remind him of his past bad behaviour at this moment in time. I told Terence that Jamie, Charlie and I would come and see him tomorrow morning and I left about eight o'clock.

As I walked away from the observation ward my mind was trying to come to terms with two coincidences in such a short space of time, both connected to Suzette's. I was now pretty much certain in my own mind that the young lady, Monique, who I had met at the reception desk an hour or so earlier was Yvette who I had taken to bed the first time I visited Suzette's. Although she looked vastly different at work at the hospital than she did in the courtesan's finery she wore at Suzette's, she could not conceal her beauty especially her stunning eyes and complexion. I decided that I would try to speak to her again on my way out, but her colleague told me that I had just missed her as she had finished her shift. I wondered whether she had recognised me and was laying low so that her secret occupation could remain a secret a little longer. I walked slowly back to the car which was parked near the trees and as I approached, I saw a slender figure step out of the darkness and instantly I could see that it was Monique. She was still strikingly beautiful in her business attire, and I could see that she did not need heavy make-up and fancy clothes to make herself attractive to men. I could feel the same tingling running down my spine and the hairs on the back of my neck standing upright just at the sight of her. I knew that I wanted her very much, but I also wanted Ruby too. Although I was aware that some men would happily make love to both without a second thought, I knew that I was not that kind of man and that I had to make the hardest choice of one or the other.

Monique asked if we could go somewhere to talk away from the hospital, so we got into the car, and she directed me to drive to a small café tucked away in the back streets behind the main square where we sat at a table outside and drank coffee and a small brandy. She tried to explain the reason for all the secrecy and that she did not acknowledge me in front of her colleague at the hospital because she was trying to keep her second job as a hostess at Suzette's a secret. She was a war widow, her husband had been killed at the battle of Verdun and she was left with a meagre war pension, two young children and her elderly mother to keep. Her salary from the hospital barely paid for the rent of their apartment and food for the children so she had no choice but to take up a second job to make ends meet. There were so few jobs available and too many applicants for each. Not everyone had the attributes to work as a hostess at Suzette's place, "… but I am lucky that I am good at entertaining the customers which is why I use a different name when I am working there. I only work part-time but I can earn enough by working a few nights each month to make the lives of my mother and my children more comfortable. If the hospital authorities found out what I was doing at Suzette's I would lose my position at the hospital, just when I have been recommended for promotion to a higher grade which would enable me to reduce my hours at Suzette's even further." She went on to say that she hated prostituting herself, even though she did enjoy the attention from some of the officers, although others were quite unpleasant, but in these difficult times, difficult choices must be made. I said that I did understand her situation, that she could rely on my discretion and could trust me to keep her secret, and she acknowledged that I was one of the kind ones. With that she finished her brandy, stood and kissed me lightly on both cheeks, walked briskly away and seemed to disappear down a side alley behind the café. I could still smell her delicate fragrance although she was no longer there, and I wondered whether I would ever see her again. I ordered a second brandy and sat for another ten minutes or so musing over what had just transpired, before walking back to the car and returning to the airfield.

SIXTEEN

The Capture of the Deserter

I was so tired that I slept soundly all night and despite Spragg's excellent night-time breakfast, was ravenous for some more and ready to eat the same all over again. Although I had slept well, my mind kept whirling with images of Ruby, Yvette and Monique and I was no nearer to resolving my feelings than I was the night before. I had to admit that despite my resolution, my heart jumped when I realised that Monique was really Yvette and then I felt like a schoolboy with a first infatuation because I could not shut her out of my mind. The big problem for me was that now that I knew Yvette was only an alter ego of Monique forced into this line of work at Suzette's to support her mother and children, it was not so easy to shut her out of my thoughts. When I could dismiss her as a casual sexual acquaintance with no emotional attachment to me, it was easier to cope with but now that I had been introduced to her real persona, I was not so sure. Jamie and Charlie were still asleep and Spragg was waiting for them to cook breakfast for us together but brought me a pot of tea. I tried to write a letter to Ruby but found it difficult; I could not help thinking that my commitment to her was eroding even though it was only a couple of months since we were together. I knew that I loved her dearly when I was last with her but now, I was not so sure; even though I tried to list the reasons why I might think this, I could not find anything other than constancy and love exuding from Ruby's letters and the guilt increased again as I accused myself of despicable behaviour towards her. My dismal mood was broken by the arrival of Jamie and shortly after Charlie for breakfast and we ate together, making plans for our trip to St Omer to visit Terence in the hospital.

I soon forgot my troubles as the three of us set off to the hospital in a happy mood, very much looking forward to seeing Terence again and Jamie reminded us that, of course, Terence would be surrounded by pretty nurses which was a bonus for us who were well enough to take advantage. The guards on the gate remembered me, or perhaps the Bentley, as we drove up to the gate and the barrier was lifted immediately. I directed Jamie to the area where I had parked in the trees the night previously, we went into the hospital, and I took us straight to the observation ward without enquiring at the desk for I knew that there was a good chance that Jamie or Charlie would recognise Monique as Yvette and I had promised to keep her identity a secret. The observation ward was even more crowded than last night, but I drifted across to the French doors where I had last seen Terence. Charlie was the first to spot him in the middle of a group of provost officers and military policemen who appeared to be questioning him quite closely. We wondered what Terence had been up to overnight that would require the attention of all these provost officials, however, when he saw us, he waved quite cheerily, and we were reassured that perhaps he was only a witness and not the suspect.

We wandered out on the terrace and sat on one of the benches overlooking the garden, waiting for Terence to be finished with the provost department. After ten minutes or so he appeared on the terrace and made over to us. He looked much worse than when I had been with him the previous evening, he was looking a little grey and haggard and I asked if he was feeling worse or had seen the doctor. He replied that he was only tired, he had little sleep because Herbert Clough had gone missing; the hospital staff and some patients who were able had been searching for him all night. I said that I thought he could not have gone far because he was blinded so he must have gone missing with someone to guide him. Terence spilled out the whole story for us as apparently there was some doubt now that Herbert was ever blinded or even involved in a gas attack at all. There was a gas attack on one sector of the line but six miles from where Clough was at the time, so it seemed impossible for him to have been affected because the wind was blowing in the opposite direction. There were a few casualties from the gas attack, and it appeared that Clough absented himself and joined the wounded and ended up here passing himself off as blind. They suspect that he squirted drops into his eyes to dilate his pupils and blur his vision and was obviously a passably good actor to have fooled the medics that he was blinded temporarily at least. It was incredible that Clough had gone through this elaborate charade to get himself out of the front line, but he must have had terrific gall to brass it out with Terence and myself, because although we recognised him immediately, he did not give any sign that he recognised us at all. He must be some cool customer to carry off this deception knowing that we had recognised him. Terence told us he was being sent for convalescence at the nun's hospital near the village of Fruges, about ten miles south of La Coupole, and was waiting for transport. He was given a camp bed to sleep on last night and Herbert Clough was put into the camp bed next to him. "At two o'clock this morning I was awoken by much activity as Clough's bed was now empty and the bandages that had been wrapped around his eyes were laying on the bed, which suggested that he could see as he had disappeared on his own stealthily out of the French doors and out of the hospital grounds."

Later the military police found that a motorcycle had been stolen from the rear of the hospital and guessed that this was his escape route. If it proved to be so, then the whole blindness issue was probably a pre-meditated plan of action to desert. Jamie came up with a great idea and suggested to the sister in charge that instead of Terence just sitting and waiting for the transport to arrive, that we would take him there in our car and ensure he was safely delivered into their hands. She said this was irregular, but she asked the doctor anyway and he said if we were to wait to collect Terence's medical notes, he could come with us. We were delighted and within twenty minutes the doctor gave into our safe keeping the medical file for the Mother Superior in charge of the hospital, we bundled Terence out of the hospital, safely into the car and set off into the countryside south-west of St Omer. Terence was sitting in the back and was fast asleep within a few minutes of setting off. He was pleased to put his uniform jacket over his shoulders rather than the drab hospital issue dressing gown. We had to stop at the barrier and produce the patient release form to be stamped by the guard before we could exit the hospital grounds.

Jamie was sure that Fruges was about fifteen miles to the south-west of St Omer and headed in that direction, soon we were into French countryside less affected by the war, being far enough behind our lines to be untouched by the military. The farms were working as normal, and life seemed relatively untouched by the ravages of the war. Jamie headed towards Montreuil but knew that we would have to turn south at the Hucqueliers crossroads, which would take us off the main road into twisty lanes leading to Fruges itself. As we passed through Desvres we came upon a roadside hotel and bar and Jamie quickly turned in and parked in front of the door. We woke Terence and carried him into the restaurant protesting that he needed to get to the hospital, but we rebuked him by saying he needed to have some lunch first because hospital food was even worse than Spragg's cooking. The waiter came over quickly with the plat du jour menu, which was all that was available at this time. The casserole beef and vegetables seemed to be a good and filling choice and we ordered four cold beers to begin with and a bottle of red wine to have with our lunch.

The cold beers went down very quickly, and we ordered four more cold ones before the food and wine arrived. The lunch proved to be very tasty and after two beers and a large glass of red wine I was beginning to feel a bit lightheaded for in my upbringing, although drinking formed part of our heritage it was almost always confined to the evening and even in the rugby club we did not drink until after the game was over. Since joining the officers' mess, I had drunk much less beer than I was used to and taken to drinking champagne and wine more often. I think we all found the cold French beer refreshing and all of us enjoyed it. After two pleasant hours we finally thought we had better get Terence safely delivered to the Mother Superior at Fruges Priory Hospital. We were all so happy, fuelled by the good food and drink at our lunch that we were singing at the top of our voices as we arrived in Fruges and followed the military signs marking the way to the hospital. Jamie pulled into the main square, screeched to a halt, we lifted Terence out of the back of the car and carried him in a fireman's chair between Charlie and I into the front door. The peace and tranquillity hit us as soon as were we inside and we shut up immediately, feeling quite guilty at having disturbed the sanctity of this place. We looked around for someone to deliver Terence to but there was just silence, until we could hear the footsteps coming towards us with determined treads. We could not yet see who was coming but the steps were getting louder and nearer.

Finally, a smallish nun in a white habit, a white headdress and a large gold cross around her neck was approaching us from the end of the main corridor and it was the sound of the stomp of her leather boots that we could hear. From thirty feet or so away she looked rather small and sweet but as she came towards us with determined steps, we could see that she was a formidable woman despite her stature. With an icy edge to her voice, she addressed us; "Captain Dalrymple, I see that you must have got lost on the way and have finally delivered our patient to us over two hours overdue and you all seem to have been drinking." Jamie turned on the charm and said that we had indeed got lost in the country lanes and had stopped for some lunch on the way, but we had brought our companion safely to her. By this time, several other nuns dressed as nurses appeared, took charge of Terence, whisked him away from us and the Mother Superior dismissed us by telling us that we could visit on Sunday afternoon for one hour before evening prayers but there would be no alcohol, smoking or bad language. We hung our heads like schoolboys and then as we made it safely back outside, collapsed into fits of laughing that we had managed to escape without a thrashing.

Piling back in the car, Jamie headed into the centre of the village, found the hôtel de ville, parked outside and said, "After that wigging, I need another cold beer and a glass of brandy." We all knew that we were rostered for flying the next day so would not be able to drink after seven o'clock. The first café was small but cosy, we ordered three large beers and sat at a table in the entrance where we had a good view over the square to the parish church and the park. Charlie was the first to notice but pointed out to us that there was a military motorcycle on a stand outside the bar on the other side of the square, which he thought was unusual as there were no military units between here and St Omer. We understood where he was going with his idea, drunk up our beer and decided to take a short walk across the square and see if the rider was in the other café, which would explain the mystery. As we got closer Charlie suggested that he should go in and take a quick look to see if Clough was there as he was less likely to remember him from Suzette's. Charlie slipped into the front door and spoke to the waiter, who confirmed that the motorcycle belonged to a British officer with red hair, and he was sitting just there – he pointed to a table in the window – until a few minutes ago when he left by the back door. Apparently, he had run out of fuel and was asking where he could fill up his tank, they told him that Jean LeClerk had a small garage, but he closed in the afternoon and opened again from five until eight in the evening. Charlie thanked them and rushed out to impart this knowledge to us and said he must have seen us pull up at the other café and had made off. He had no fuel in the motorbike – then we all realised he was probably going to try to steal the Bentley to make good his escape and rushed back to where the Bentley was parked. It was still there safe and sound so perhaps we were wrong; he had intended all along to escape on foot and hide somewhere safe until the garage was open.

A British officer on foot would attract a lot more attention than if he were riding a military motorbike or driving a car, plus he would be able to cover a great deal more distance in a shorter time. Looking around the square I thought I caught a flash of red hair at right side of the church; I shouted and pointed him out. I could see clearly that it was Clough, he set off running through the graveyard to the right of the church; Charlie went through the lychgate to the left to cut him off. Jamie positioned himself in front of the main door to the church as we expected that when Clough reached the back wall of the churchyard, he was unlikely to scale it and jump into the river that we had passed over as we drove into town but would double back and try to escape through the church itself. He was right because when Clough saw he was cut off in both directions, he went through the vestry door and into the church with Charlie and I only a few paces behind him. He ran up the aisle towards the main door, out into the churchyard again to find Jamie waiting for him and he veered to his left to try to wriggle past Jamie, but I pulled him to the ground with one of my best front row forward rugby tackles, which knocked the wind clean out of him and he gave up without a fight. Some of the village people heard the goings-on at the church and came out of their houses to see what was going on. The elderly village gendarme came over to help and loaned Jamie a pair of handcuffs to secure the prisoner. When we told him the story of the deserter, he was most cooperative, he even went to LeClerk and brought five litres of petrol for the motorcycle. Charlie would ride with Clough in the back of the car, and I would ride the motorcycle back to St Omer behind them. We intended to hand Clough to the provost marshal in St Omer and then head back to La Coupole. While we waited for the fuel Jamie ordered four brandies for ourselves and one for the gendarme, and we drank to our success this afternoon.

Clough was a pathetic individual and all the bluster and aggression that was present last Friday had evaporated as he was just petrified of going into action in the big push that we all knew was coming. The pressure on him to lead his platoon over the top in the first wave of the attack just preyed on his mind and deep in his heart he knew he could not do it. Throughout his life so far, he had got by with a bullying exterior which he thought protected him from his cowardice but when I stood up to him openly in Suzette's and he was forced to run away to save face, it was the beginning of the end. When his comrades returned from Suzette's they made fun of him for all his false bravado and knew him for what he really was… a coward. This was when he had hatched a ridiculous plot to pretend that he was blinded by the gas attack and run away but with no real plan of how he was going to pull it off. It was doubly ironic that the people who he had abused so publicly were instrumental in bringing him to justice. He was foisted by his own petard as they say, because his bluff and aggressive attitude meant that the people around him thought he was a natural infantry officer. The gendarme toasted us, drank his brandy in one quick draught, shook our hands and then kissed us all on the cheeks before we set off back to St Omer. I was anxious to make it back before it got completely dark and the temperature began to drop, as I had no greatcoat or gloves to keep me warm. I told Jamie that I would go ahead fast to get back to the hospital and inform the provost of the prisoner we had captured. He agreed and I set off immediately, riding as fast as I dare in the twilight. I made surprisingly good time, but the lightness and manoeuvrability of the bike made it easy to cover the distance quickly.

Riding a motorcycle is a similar experience to flying a small aircraft as the rider is experiencing the elements at close quarters, so to speak. At the hospital I stopped at the main gate and ordered the guards to telephone the provost marshal to rendezvous with Captain Dalrymple at the main entrance of the hospital, as we had apprehended the deserter Herbert Clough in the village of Fruges quite by chance. I explained that Captain Dalrymple was driving Clough back to St Omer and would be at the hospital by six-thirty. I sat on the motorcycle and waited and after about twenty minutes the provost major arrived with a prison van and was looking for Jamie. I introduced myself and said that they were still on the way and explained how, quite by chance, we happened to see the motorbike and then Clough in the village of Fruges about eighteen miles to the south-west of St Omer where he had run out of petrol and arrested him. He was pleased and we chatted until Jamie's Bentley came down the driveway and stopped alongside the pair of us. Jamie jumped out, saluted the major, formally handed over the prisoner who was bundled into the prison van by the two military policemen and I handed over the motorcycle. The major smiled and said if we wanted a transfer from the Flying Corp to the provost, he would have us as we had solved two cases in one day.

Major Moss was rostered to fly as my wingman for the first patrol of the day on Wednesday and Captain Rydings from the Wing HQ for the second and third sorties of the day. I met with both, briefed on the flight plan and the objective of the missions today. Rydings had been a flight commander before, now serving as the intelligence officer in Wing headquarters but was an experienced combat pilot. Major Moss said that they would continue with this arrangement until Terence was well enough to return to flying duties or a replacement was drafted in. I was delighted to have experienced pilots flying on my wing but did not like the sound of a replacement drafted in for Terence who I would have to train again. Today's sorties were to consolidate what we had already discovered about enemy troop encampments and to try to estimate the numbers of troops, the equipment they had brought with them and to locate the ammunition, fuel, and supply dumps where possible. The grid reference that I had provided from Monday was to be our starting point and I would fly low at around 1,000ft to get a closer view. We all agreed that at this altitude we were more vulnerable to attack from above and would have to keep a very sharp lookout above and behind. We knew it was a riskier strategy should we be attacked but decided that we would break and climb rapidly immediately we sighted the enemy, relying on the superior performance of the SE5 to get us out of trouble.

At 07:50 we were strapped in, ready to go, took off dead on time, climbed away to an operational height of 3,000ft, made the passage to Poperinge and Ypres, crossed the enemy front line and set course for Langemark where the first camp was located. The cloud cover was sketchy, there was enough wind to keep the cloud formations moving quickly in an easterly direction, we were able to hide ourselves at the cloud base and slowly descend to 1,000ft for the first pass over the enemy without detection. We passed low over the camp, and I estimated that judging by the number of tents, the camp had a capacity for 10,000 soldiers but the lack of any organised defence with only sporadic rifle fire suggested that it was largely empty. I signalled Major Moss to change heading for the camps on the outskirts of Roeselare and we kept at the lower altitude but increased our speed and dashed towards the next location. This time we could see from half a mile out that there was a much activity around these encampments with vehicles moving supplies and marching columns of men everywhere. Again, I estimated from the numbers of tents that the capacity was 10,000 or so and could see from the large numbers of soldiers disembarking at the railway station that it would soon be at capacity. Changing course towards the south-west we lost the patchy cloud cover and were now flying in blue skies with maximum visibility and were at greatest risk from attack, but I wanted to pass over the area where I had seen the tanks which was between Moorslede and Kortrijk.

Despite the clear skies, the tanks had completely disappeared, and I guessed that they were now perfectly camouflaged beneath the canopy of trees in the forest in this area. Major Moss signalled to me that there were enemy aircraft to the east of us at 3,000ft, I acknowledged with a thumbs up and we immediately went into our plan to gain altitude as fast as we could. The enemy flight of four aircraft were in formation and had not yet seen us, continuing in a north-easterly direction at patrol speed. I had a choice to make; I could break off and head for home as our patrol was completed or even though we were outnumbered by four to two, we could take them on and try to destroy at least a couple of them. I only gave it a moment's thought, immediately banked into the climb to get behind them and could see that Major Moss was right behind me. We climbed fast and in about six minutes we were at least 500ft above them, creeping up on their tail. They were not keeping a good all-round watch and I was amazed that we had not been spotted by now. We gradually crept closer and closer until I thought I was in a good enough position to pick off the leading aircraft of the rear two of the formation. I leaned out of the right-hand side of the cockpit and pointed at aircraft number four, Major Moss responded immediately that he understood, and we started our attack. We dived on top of the targets and sprayed them with machine-gun fire in two short bursts and I think that I must have been lucky enough to hit the pilot with my second burst because the aircraft immediately went out of control and fell away plunging to the ground. Major Moss's firing was so accurate that pieces of wreckage were immediately flying off his target and then smoke appeared along his underside, and we knew he was done for. Moss followed him down until he was sure that he was finished and then raced back up to join me.

The first section immediately broke formation, fled for their lives and I immediately went after the flight commander. Although my aircraft was faster and more manoeuvrable, the German pilot showed great skills in throwing his aircraft across the sky to evade my bullets. I chased him and managed to fire off three bursts without any result and made the stupid mistake of becoming so eager to destroy my prey that I lost sight of the fourth German aircraft. He gave me a rude awakening when I heard the first of his shots peppering my fuselage and I immediately had to take evasive action, banked hard right, and pulled the throttles back to gain more power to climb out of danger, rolling away from my attacker as fast as I could. He was not going to let me go that easily and stuck to my tail but all the time I kept the bank on, he was unable to bring his shots to bear. All this time I was wondering where Major Moss had got to until I heard quick bursts of rapid machine-gun fire behind me and passing from right to left, and he appeared on my left shoulder waving and pointing downwards. I looked down and could see the fourth German crashing to the ground in flames. The German flight commander had used this time to make his escape, had dived to the ground and was flying straight and low heading for home at high speed. We had no chance of catching him so turned to return to La Coupole with three more kills added to the B flight tally.

Major Moss was ecstatic in the debriefing room that he had been able to shoot down two and had not enjoyed himself so much for a long time. He was full of praise for my leadership abilities and my aggression as a combat pilot and said it was no wonder that my tally was going up so quickly. I passed on the intel gained flying over the encampments that there were at least 10,000 reinforcements already in place about ten miles behind the front line, and another camp with the same capacity ready for occupation. I surmised that the key was fast resupply and transportation of large numbers of troops by rail right into the area and that the destruction of the railheads was a vital target to hinder their re-supply operation. Major Moss agreed with my observation, the report was made, he thanked me for giving him the opportunity to fly with him again and was looking forward to Friday morning already. The further two patrols later in the day with Captain Rydings were useful as we pressed into German-held territory deeper, following the railway lines to see where troops were billeted but we had no contact with the enemy air force. However, Jamie and Charlie downed one apiece on their patrols making another five-a-day scoresheet for B flight.

Thursday was a bad day for 354 Squadron as A flight lost their flight commander, shot down in an ambush by four German aircraft over Menen during the last patrol of the day. His wingman managed to escape and said he saw Captain Williamson's aircraft on fire, crashing into a farmer's field. He managed to escape by the skin of his teeth and was pursued for ten miles before he gave them the slip. The whole squadron was grief-stricken with the loss of a pilot and the mood was sombre and sorrowful for the next couple of days amongst all ground and aircrew alike. I had spent the day resting, catching up with writing letters and generally recharging my batteries for Friday's patrols. However, around four in the afternoon I was summoned to Major Moss who told me that I was being promoted to acting captain in the field and would be taking over the command of A flight with effect from Monday next. Captain Rydings would continue to fly as Two section leader until Terence returned from hospital and took on that role in place of me. He said I could adjust my rank badges over the weekend and would be known as

Captain Morgan from 00:01 Saturday next. He went on to say that flying with me again had reinforced his view of what a good combat pilot I had become, and that A flight needed a good shake-up to get rid of the common perception that they were an unlucky flight as this was their second casualty in so many weeks. "They have not shot down any enemy aircraft and their morale is low, he explained. "I think you will be good for them because I am sure they are good pilots that just need the right kind of leadership to lift them from the black mood cast over them by the loss of their flight commander."

I was amazed because four months ago I was just promoted to lieutenant, and this had all happened so quickly. I thanked Major Moss for his confidence in me and saluted and left his office. I walked back to the B flight hut with my mind in a whirl, went into the crew room and sat in an armchair, in silence with my thoughts. After a few moments Jamie dropped into the chair next to me and said, 'How does it feel to be Captain Morgan?' I was taken aback that he knew already. He lowered his voice and said that he knew because Major Moss consulted the remaining three flight commanders, and my name was the unanimous approval to fill this slot. "I think you are ready and will be good as a flight commander," he added, "but we will keep it quiet until Saturday when we can celebrate together."

Friday's sorties were uneventful, but we achieved most of our objectives and although we penetrated over fifteen miles into German territory, we had no contact with the enemy. We passed over the suspected site of the tank formation north-east of Menen on each patrol to try to discern any movement but either these tanks had moved to another location, and we had been unlucky and missed them in transit, or they were hunkered down and well hidden in this dense woodland. My intuition was that they were well hidden and that I had been lucky previously to have spotted the last movements of these tanks into cover but whether that would be enough to order a bombing attack on this piece of woodland I was not so sure. We did, however, observe troop trains disembarking large numbers of troops at various stations to the west of Roeselare which was further evidence of the build-up of fresh troops by the enemy in this area within easy marching distance of the Ypres Salient in preparation for a renewed offensive by the Allies. I wondered if squadrons further down the line were seeing similar evidence of renewed troop movements by the enemy as we were. Rydings and I flew three sorties on Friday and were both tired when we finally debriefed in the crew room that evening.

Relaxing with a mug of tea afterwards, the crew room was full of gossip about the news that the Royal Flying Corps was being disbanded and a new force, separate from the army, was to be created on the 1st of April, 1918 to be known as the Royal Air Force. Aircrew would automatically come under the command of the RAF but could choose whether they transferred their commission from the army to the new force or not. Those who chose to remain in the army would continue to wear their present uniform and rank but those who commissioned into the RAF would adopt new ranks at an equivalent level and would wear the new light-blue uniform and rank badges. There was much heated discussion about the pros and cons but in the end, it was a personal choice for each individual officer. Non-commissioned ranks had no choice but to switch to the new air force and this would take effect at the end of the month. There were still some officers who believed that the RAF would be like many of its wartime officers, just hostilities only, and that the War Ministry and Admiralty would kill off the fledgling service as soon as the war ended. I could see, however, what Lord Trenchard was trying to do in trying to establish air power as a vital component militarily of our defensive capability and prising control of the budget and strategy for air power out of the hands of generals who still saw the battlefield in terms of the Crimea or South Africa. I decided that I would transfer to the Royal Air Force and would convey my intention via the adjutant's office in the morning. The details of the new uniform were not so drastic as we could continue to wear the jodhpurs and riding boots of the present uniform, but the tunic was a cavalry hacking jacket in light-blue worsted with a light blue shirt and black tie. All aircrew would receive new design RAF flying wings or brevets to be worn on the left breast in place of the RFC badges. On Saturday morning I sent a telegram to my tailors in London requesting a new RAF officer's tunic with RAF pilot's wings and medal ribbons plus dress hat and forage cap. I felt confident that they would be able to supply the finished articles within a couple of weeks but was sure that there would be a transition period of change if they were not received on time.

I found Spragg in his kitchen space and asked him to take my uniform jacket and change the rank badges on each sleeve from lieutenant to captain but to keep it quiet as it was not promulgated until the next morning. He said that he would have my jacket ready for tomorrow lunchtime because he had to wait until 08:00 for the stores to open to get the new rank badge. When I went into my room, I found some letters and a signal message on my nightstand next to my bed addressed to me and was confirmation of the award of the Distinguished Flying Cross for my first five kills. I could wear the ribbon immediately but would not receive the actual medal for a few weeks when it would be presented by the wing commander. I rushed back across to Spragg, showed him the signal, and asked if he could get the DFC ribbon from the stores also and sew that up next to the Military Medal. He said that he would and that the whole lot should cost about 17s 6d. I was happy to pay him what he asked, and I am sure that he made a little profit from that too.

Back in my room I sorted my letters and saw I had a letter from Mum and Dad, one from Wesley and two from Ruby so I knew that I had a pleasant evening ahead, catching up with all the news from home. Mum and Dad's letter was full of news about the family and life at home and filled me in on what was happening at the chapel, the allotment and in the village more generally, containing truly little of any substance but provided that light and happy connection that reassured me that life was still going on as usual at home. Wesley wrote with the news that he had been confirmed as detective sergeant, seconded permanently to the security service and had been moved back to Cardiff where he was working with a special unit that was hunting deserters, fifth columnists and spies in the industrial zone of South Wales.

I savoured the two letters from Ruby until last and finally lay back on my bed to read them slowly.

The first letter was full of lovely chatter about our friends from the rugby club, life at home in the Station House and some salacious gossip about Freda Watkins and Dai Rees, of course. The second letter was more serious in tone because she wanted to tell me that she had missed the two menstruation cycles since I was last home which might mean that she could be ten weeks or more pregnant. She was not sure, but her next cycle was due towards the end of March and if she missed that too, it would be likely because she was pregnant. I was stunned but not really surprised and then concerned that I was not able to be there with her, although Ruby was at great pains to reassure me that she was alright and not to worry. She was happy if she were pregnant as we are already engaged to be married and having made that lifetime commitment, she knew our baby would have a loving family upbringing. I stopped reading at that point and sat back to collect my thoughts; I was happy with the thought of becoming a father but worried that Ruby was coping with this alone. The further complications of my feelings for Monique–Yvette weighed heavily on me too and I knew that I had to sort this out sooner rather than later. I then resumed reading the last page of her letter when she had news about Gwyn and Mair Davis, which must be very new because my parents did not mention anything about Gwyn. News had been received in the village that Mair's husband had been lost at sea when the battle cruiser he was serving on was torpedoed by a Japanese submarine in the South China Sea and went down with all hands. Mair was now a widow and had inherited the house and moved back to the village, and it was rumoured that after a suitable period of mourning she and Gwyn would get married and he would move back with her. I thought there was no wonder Mum had not mentioned this, because it would be seen as scandalous by many of the chapel congregation and certainly beyond what she and Dad would approve of.

I got out the pad and started to reply to Ruby, expressing my joy that we might have a little baby on the way and my sadness at not being able to be there to share the burden with her. I declared my love for her and hoped that I would get some leave in the early summer to get home to be with her. I told her that I had been promoted to captain and would become flight commander of A flight from Monday next. This was good news because a substantial increase in pay comes with the appointment, which would boost our savings positively. My savings had grown by over £60 since returning to the front and with the additional boost in pay would continue to rise even quicker. I told her that I had received another medal but did not go into details of what for, as I knew she would be worried that I was in too much danger. I also told her the whole story of Terence's wound and of Herbert Clough, the deserter, stressing that Terence was not badly hurt and how we had managed to capture Clough after he had faked being blind to be evacuated to hospital where he had escaped and run away. I told her about the coincidence of spotting the runaway in a small village where we had gone to visit Terence in convalescence. I was careful to leave out some of the details that might alarm Ruby, particularly about the dogfights and about being in Suzette's place. I wrote a short note to Wesley congratulating him on his advancement in the police and asking whether he had an address for Gwyn as I wished to write to him as well. These letters would go with the postbag tomorrow morning and should be in Wales within two days.

Saturday morning was dull and raining so we stayed in the crew room drinking tea, chatting, and generally messing about until Spragg arrived with my uniform jacket, which he had also cleaned and pressed for the occasion. I went into my room, slipped it on and looked at myself in the mirror.

I thought it looked fine and when I walked back out into the crew room, there was immediate uproar as Charlie noticed that I was now a captain and had the DFC as well as the Military Medal. He was whooping and throwing screwed-up balls of scrap paper at me and shouting at the top of his voice when the door opened and the St Omer provost major was hovering in the doorway, not knowing whether to come further in or not. Jamie recognised him straight away and jumped up to greet him as Charlie subsided back into his chair. Major Rydall was smiling and said he had always heard that fliers were a bit eccentric, but what was the celebration for? Jamie got him seated, Spragg produced some tea and biscuits and then withdrew to his cubbyhole where he could eavesdrop on everything that was said in the crew room.

'We were just celebrating some good news,' Jamie explained. "Derfal has just been promoted captain and appointed flight commander A flight and awarded the Distinguished Flying Cross, so we are extremely happy this morning and may be exceedingly drunk this evening." The major congratulated me and said he had come to speak with me as it happened and wondered whether there was somewhere private where we could talk. I said I was happy to talk in front of my two comrades and that he could go ahead and say what he wanted to say. He had come to tell us that Herbert Clough was to be tried by summary court martial in St Omer in ten days, and he had requested that I stand as prisoner's friend. I was amazed and somewhat taken aback that he should request me to defend him, as I played such a large part in apprehending him in the first place. Major Rydall said that he understood my reluctance and that he had tried to persuade Clough to choose one of his brother officers from his battalion but that '… Clough was determined it must be you because he says you are the only person who has ever stood up to him and told him the truth and that you are the model of an officer he wished to become. He also believes that you will take on the duty seriously and defend him to the best of your ability.'

I was not sure about Clough's motives in requesting me – was he just playing some elaborate game to get back at me by making me go through the court martial process? He was, of course, right that I would take the role as seriously as anything else I would do and not shirk my responsibility in any way. I was somewhat daunted at the prospect of fighting to save someone's life in a military courtroom where if found guilty the only sentence would be the death sentence. I would much rather take on a squadron of enemy fighters alone than voluntarily take on this job. Then I thought what a poor, frightened individual Clough was when we arrested him with all the bravado and aggression knocked out of him and wondered whether this meek soul deserved to die just because he could not face up to the danger of the front. His whole life appeared to be a façade that had ironically led him to the thing he feared most. If he had lived life more honestly, he could have made some worthwhile contribution to the war effort without exposing himself to such personal dangers. He was a foolish man, but I thought that a man should not be shot by firing squad for being a fool. In that moment, I decided that I would take on the defence of Clough and agreed to become his friend at the court martial.

SEVENTEEN

Defending Herbert Clough

Before he left, Major Rydall said he would arrange a pass for me to enter the military prison in Arras to speak with the defendant as often as I wished to prepare for the defence, and the prosecution documents would be provided for me by Monday morning. The court martial was expected to be held on Tuesday the following week in St Omer Barracks and was only expected to last for one or two days. I was inwardly horrified to think that a trial at which a man's life would be at stake deserved greater scrutiny than just one or two days but did not express this out loud in front of the provost major. I asked him to arrange the pass for the prison immediately. I intended to visit the prisoner today as there was little time to prepare any kind of defence before the court martial was scheduled to begin, so it was imperative that I took some instructions from Clough straightaway. He said if I travelled via St Omer provost office after twelve o'clock the pass would be ready for me to collect.

I arranged to borrow a motorcycle from the transport section and set off for the military prison via the provost office in St Omer as arranged. I signalled the prison governor that I was to be Clough's friend at his court martial and wished to see him at the prison at three o'clock; they replied that Major Rydall had already informed them, and the prisoner would be available to be interviewed at my request. The ride from St Omer to Arras was very pleasant although it was a blustery early spring day, but somewhat spoiled by the anticipation of the task I was about to take on, which I knew was going to be exceedingly difficult. I was not optimistic about my chances of getting an acquittal. I thought I might be able to build enough mitigation to commute the death sentence to imprisonment but in all honesty, I could not see a court made up of infantry officers would have much sympathy for a known braggart and a bully who deserted his post as a platoon commander in the front line during the build-up to a new attack. However, I had said yes to the request from Major Rydall, and I would carry it through.

The military prison in Arras was a forbidding place, surrounded by high grey walls topped with miles of barbed wire and visitors had to go through three lines of security before being admitted to the prison itself which was divided into French, British and Canadian sections. The soldier warders in the British section were pleasant, respectful, and somewhat sympathetic towards an officer selected to defend an officer deserter who they despised and felt I had been given a very unpleasant task to do. I was led into a dull and almost bare room where there were two chairs and a small table screwed to the floor in the centre. The sergeant who showed me to the room asked if I wanted him to stay, I said that I was confident that Lieutenant Clough would pose no problem to me, and he withdrew saying he would just be outside the door if he was needed. I waited a few further minutes when the door from the secure side of the prison opened, Clough was brought in by two guards, placed in the chair and they left the room. I was amazed at the decline in Clough's appearance and demeanour in such a short period since I had last seen him. He was dishevelled, he looked unkempt and could do with a shave and a haircut. He would need to receive some grooming and smartening up before appearing before the court martial. I noticed bruises on the side of his face and the beginnings of a black eye, and I suspected the bully had had a taste of his own medicine from fellow prisoners or warders but when I asked him about his injuries, he shrugged his shoulders and said nothing. He began to stammer out his thanks that I had taken on his defence, but I cut him off short and told him that he might not be so thankful when he was marched out in front of the firing squad.

This version of Herbert Clough was far removed from the blustering individual who had bullied his way through life so far and was now reduced to his lowest ebb, as the victim of his own behaviour. I spent the next hour explaining to him the court martial procedure as far as I understood it, although my experience was only based on the court martial of Captain Vaughan over a year ago. He kept stressing that he was not guilty and was at great pains to explain that his affirmation of innocence was of no importance in a military court where the whole purpose of the court is to ascertain guilt or innocence based on the evidence presented.

"They will not care whether you say you are innocent unless we choose for you to give evidence on your own behalf," I explained, "but I will only do that if we find incontrovertible evidence to dispute the facts as presented by the prosecutor. I will not receive the prosecution documents until Monday, I will study them, and we will discuss their version of events on Tuesday next to see if there are any discrepancies but from what I already know about this case, I think this will be clutching at straws. My advice would be that we do not contest the prosecution's version of events unless there are major flaws in what they present, we accept the inevitable guilty verdict and that I work hard with you to build strong mitigating circumstances that will enable the judge advocate to recommend leniency of sentence." Clough did not like this approach at all, and his old character began to re-emerge from the shambling mess in front of me as he berated me, banging the table, for being afraid to take on the military authority and prove him innocent before the court martial. He shouted in my face that he only chose me because he thought I was courageous and not afraid to stand up against injustice, but I knew that this was not true as Rydall had told me that he had approached his company commander and two lieutenants from his unit, and no one was interested in speaking up for him. I thought that he was gambling that I was the only officer who he vaguely knew who might take him on.

I stood up and started to pack away my papers to indicate that the interview was over, and he subsided and sat down again and put his head in his hands. I explained that I could only continue to act as prisoner's friend if he cooperated with my strategy and if he did not agree then he should seek someone to replace me, but to be quick about it because time was running out fast. I told him that I thought he was guilty as charged based on the evidence I had seen already and I was prepared to accept there may be issues with the prosecution evidence, but we had not seen it yet. I knew that he was an objectionable individual who was happy to use his position to bully and harass others and this was the reason that his brother officers from his battalion did not want anything to do with him and he was on his own.

"However guilty you may be," I told him, "I am prepared to argue mitigation before the court martial that this braggartly personality is not your real persona and is probably a tragic consequence of something in your previous life, family or school that has made you adopt this behaviour as a defence mechanism to protect your vulnerable inner-self. If you will agree to this strategy, I may be able to save your life unless you can produce independent witnesses who will testify under oath with verifiable evidence that you didn't run away, didn't pretend to be blinded in a gas attack that took place six miles away from your known position and then run away again from the hospital in St Omar on a stolen motorcycle when you feared discovery."

He blinked at me with tears running down his face just like a little boy at school. I thought of Jamie's nickname of 'housemaster' and wondered whether it was appropriate. I told him to think over what I had said to him and if he decided to sack me to do it soon, otherwise I would be back on Tuesday to go over the prosecution case in detail. The hardest thing for him to do was to be honest with himself and recognise that something in his past life had made him like this and be prepared to talk about it with me. I told him that I had a full programme of flying patrols during the following week but would be available on Tuesday and Thursday to spend time with him to build the case for his defence and would not be rostered for flying until after the court martial was over. I knocked on the door, Clough was taken away back to the cells, I collected my papers together and the sergeant escorted me back to the entrance. On the way he nodded toward the DFC and said, 'How many have you shot down?' I was a little embarrassed when I said six who I recognised had been brave German pilots and here I was trying to save the life of a brazen coward. I was glad to get back out into the fresh air and to shake off the damp and rather fetid prison smell that pervaded the place, but forty minutes ride back to La Coupole on the motorcycle soon cleared my head.

Jamie and Charlie were waiting for me so we could set off for St Omer to celebrate my promotion and decoration, but I was reluctant to get into a heavy drinking session tonight as I had much thinking to do about Clough's defence, on Sunday I needed to meet my new flight members ready for taking command in the air for Monday morning's sorties and we also had promised to visit Terence at Fruges Priory on Sunday afternoon. In the end they persuaded me by suggesting that we invited the A flight boys to join us at Suzette's and that we would leave by seven. Jamie and I sat for the next hour talking through everything that had happened with Clough this afternoon at the prison and he declared that he thought I was mad to take this on, but also respected my housemasterly decision to try to do my best for Clough. I explained that unless there was a miracle, I could not get an acquittal, but I might be able to help him possibly escape the firing squad.

At six-thirty, I went to bathe and dress for our trip to Suzette's and when I heard the noise erupting in the crew room, I knew we were nearly ready to go.

My three new flight members were there chatting noisily to Charlie and John Rydings and we were to travel in two cars. I chose to ride in the A flight car so I could chat with them privately on the way there without interruption from my B flight friends. The car belonged to Alexander Brown who was the B section leader, Giles Lacey and Larry Fortescue were the two wingmen. They were all lieutenants and had been with the squadron the same length of time as me I hardly knew them; I did not know much about them as individuals or as pilots. I realised that there would be an intense period of getting used to each other over the next week or so. We did not have the luxury of much time to do this as we could be fighting for our lives against a determined enemy in the sky on Monday morning. Anyway Alex, Giles and Larry seemed good companions as we rode towards St Omer and I was encouraged that they would be good to work with.

We piled into Suzette's in high spirits and because there were eight of us, we had been allocated the big table in the middle of the room and we sat down and ordered champagne to start the party. Jamie made some mock-serious speeches about my qualities, full of jokes and asides and ribald catcalls from the others, then finally they all drank a toast to my promotion. Once we had all sat down, he started again in similar vein about how desperately bad the German system of training must be that their pilots were certainly throwing themselves under my guns allowing me to become an ace in double-quick time. The high command had noticed this and realised that it was hardly fair, and the rules of chivalry demanded that we offered to send some of our best instructors from Training Brigade to advise them on new training methods to even things up. Again, there was uproar and by now officers from other tables were joining in too when finally, Jamie stood up and lifted me on to my chair and they all drank to my health. Formalities over, we all looked at the menus and chose our meals for tonight. I was ravenous after my busy afternoon and evening on what should have been a rest day after a hectic flying week and chose a fish soup followed by coq au vin, which should fill me up as I could sense already that this was going to be a long night.

Giles Lacey turned out to be a bit of a raconteur and regaled us with funny stories about his time as a cavalry officer before switching to the RFC. He said he had never liked horses and horses didn't like him and took every opportunity to throw him out of the saddle but unfortunately for him he had been born into a titled family who were one of the leading breeders of horses in England. His father was the Duke of Buckingham, and he was Lord

Eckington, a title reserved for the second son of the Duke and was destined for the cavalry as were all the Eckingtons before him. He had always had much more affinity with machines, fast cars and planes were his thing, so he transferred to the RFC when he could. He did not use his title at all, except I was to find out later that his batman always called him 'milord' and never by name. Alex Brown was quite lively too but lacked the good humoured and self-effacing manner that enabled Giles to send up himself and his aristocratic background without malice. He was the son of a solicitor from a small country town in middle England and was quite self-conscious about his background. I thought that he felt that Giles was in a way denying his birth right through his whimsical behaviour. I was to learn that Alex was a good pilot and conscientious officer but lacked any flair for leadership on the ground or in the air. He could be trusted to follow orders implicitly without question but did not have much initiative to make decisions on his own. Larry Fortescue was the newest to join the flight and this was his first operational tour since training school, but I could see he was a straightforward young man who was confident and sure about his own ability and I could see considerable potential for him to become a leader in combat. He was also a grammar schoolboy like me and although his father as a family doctor had been able to afford to keep him in school long enough to earn his Higher School Certificate, he had deferred a place at medical school to enter the RFC and intended to train as a doctor after the war was over.

The party got more raucous after the food was eaten and the bottles of red wine were opened, but I decided to give the wine a miss and to drink brandy instead which had much less effect on me. Suzette's girls started to arrive and thronged around the tables in their usual fashion. I recognised some of the faces from our previous visits but did not see Yvette or Clara and I breathed an inward sigh of relief. I was happy with a brandy, good chatter, and a bit of flirting with the girls and was keeping my eye on the clock so that I could persuade at least one car to return to base around midnight. I was enjoying the company of my new flight members who were content to enjoy the banter and chatter in getting to know each other better whilst Jamie and Charlie were more intent on chasing the girls and negotiating a trip upstairs. The A flight team were happy to leave just after midnight, so I rode back to base with them, and I was glad to have made the first bridge between my old flight and the new.

I would move my things into the flight commander's room in the A flight hut in the morning and meet for a briefing with the boys at 10:00 when I would formally introduce myself and brief for the sorties we were to fly on Monday. Spragg packed my kit in the morning and took it over to A flight where my new batman was Lance Corporal Albert Caldwell, a trained steward who shared his time between the officers' mess and looking after the A flight commander. Caldwell was a man of about fifty who had one of those hangdog expressions that did not express much emotion, but he seemed to know his business well enough and had most of my kit unpacked and put away before I arrived in the A flight hut. He also had collected the parcel from the military tailors that had arrived for me, which was on the bed. He had not opened it and asked me if he should deal with it, I gave my permission, he unwrapped the packaging and my new RAF uniform and dress cap etc. was inside. I slipped the jacket on, it fitted perfectly and looked very smart. From the 1st of April I was to cease to be a captain RFC but would be a flight lieutenant RAF and would wear the new uniform of the fledgling independent air force. Caldwell introduced me to Airman Hall who looked after the three lieutenants; he was a younger man who seemed quick-witted and capable.

I briefed the flight on the way that I expected them to operate as a unit working together for each other, and that I wanted us to develop our flight formation flying as well as pair synchronisation when on patrol. As far as possible, pairs would fight together to protect each other and maximise our chances of destroying the enemy and my watchwords were to be thorough preparation, watchful and alert in the air and strike the enemy first. I told them that our sorties on Monday were all offensive targets and would be first at 08:00 to mount a surprise attack on the German fighter airfield at Stader, ten miles east of Ypres, where the plan was to destroy as many aircraft on the ground as possible, and the second at midday would be a strafing run through the enemy reserve encampment at Roeselare to cause fear and confusion. Finally, at 16:00 we would escort a small force of bombers to drop incendiaries on the woods near Moorslede, where the enemy tanks were suspected to be hidden. I explained that the reason that the airfield was being attacked first was to try to minimise the number of aircraft available to the Germans for combat patrolling and to minimise the likely aerial defence of the other two targets. We would fly the sorties in flight formation and would make our attack runs in pairs, which meant when two were committed to the attack the other pair was watching for potential challenge in the sky.

I explained that I would use all three sorties to observe the flying characteristic of each of them to indicate whether the flight was organised in the best formation in terms of playing to our individual strengths. I would fly with Lacey as my wingman and Brown was to lead the second pair with Fortescue as his wingman. The detailed briefings would take place at 06:00 in the morning and take-off for sortie one was at 08:00. I finally stressed that the RFC was not a flying club but an armed force whose sole purpose was to destroy the enemy and that I expected A flight to take every opportunity to destroy enemy aircraft wherever possible, in the air and on the ground.

"So far 354 Squadron has destroyed twenty-six enemy aircraft since the beginning of 1918,' I stressed, 'but A flight has yet to record its first kill. B flight has twelve, C flight five and D flight nine and it is my intention to instil a more aggressive spirit into the flight and take the fight to the enemy.' I suspected that the previous flight commander was too cautious in the air and had placed the other careful pilot, Alex Brown, in charge of the second section, which had the effect of frustrating the natural aggressiveness of Lacey and Fortescue, but I kept these thoughts to myself. I vowed to test Lacey and Fortescue's abilities in the air over the coming weeks.

After lunch, I met with Jamie and Charlie, and we set off to make the journey to see Terence at Fruges Priory hospital. Both seemed still to be a little hungover and I was glad that I had left Suzette's a little earlier than they had. Jamie asked me to drive and soon both he and Charlie were snoring aloud in the back of the car. I smiled to myself as I thought of the roasting they were in line for if they appeared before the Mother Superior in a semi-drunken state and hoped that I would sober up enough to pass muster. It was another mild March afternoon, so the ride was comfortable enough and I certainly enjoyed driving the big and powerful Bentley through the French lanes but the pilot in me still preferred the excitement of the motorcycle best. The square in front of the hospital was already quite full of people waiting to be admitted to the weekly visiting hour, so we sat in the car until the door opened, a nun stood on the steps and rang a hand bell to indicate that visitors' hour had begun. We followed the crowd in and enquired at the desk where we would find Terence and were given his room number on the second floor.

Terence was sat in the window of his room in a comfortable armchair looking out over the gardens, but he jumped up excitedly when he saw us. The sudden movements must have been painful, but he bore the pain stoically such was his excitement to see his friends again. We had such a lot to tell him and in double-quick time we gave him the story of my promotion, the award of the DFC, appointment as A flight commander and being appointed prisoner's friend for Herbert Clough. He sank back in his chair in disbelief that so much had happened whilst he was stuck in here, and it was only seven days. Terence wanted to know who was to be his new section leader when he returned to the squadron, but Jamie reassured him that that post had already been filled. He looked a bit confused and asked who it was, but Jamie cut him off and said that the new section leader was a lieutenant named Terence, and he still looked a bit confused because he had the same name as him. Jamie slapped him playfully on his good shoulder and said that it was him, and a replacement was being sought to make up his slot.

Whilst we were there the doctor came in to speak with us and Terence together. He explained that the patient was doing well, and his shoulder was knitting back together well and his bullet injuries to his upper arm were healing quickly. Within a few days all need for medical treatment would cease and he could be discharged from hospital but would not be fit to resume flying duties for a further two weeks subject to approval from the military doctors at St Omer. He went on to say that convalescent beds were at a premium, he would like to discharge Terence within the next seven days, and he could be given leave for two weeks, but the patient was adamant that he did not want to take two weeks' leave but wished to return to the squadron at the earliest moment possible. Jamie replied that Terence was vital to our plans to develop squadron efficiency in preparation for the support of the next big offensive and he would speak with the squadron commander and arrange for Terence to return to the squadron on light duties pending returning to flying duty when fully fit.

Terence's face and the doctor's lit up in agreement and the doctor said that the discharge would be Friday next at 09:00 and would we arrange for transport to collect him and take him back to La Coupole. The doctor left us to talk excitedly about his return to the squadron and going to Suzette's place to celebrate. Finally, he asked me why I had agreed to defend Herbert Clough and listened carefully as I explained my reasons as clearly as I could. He thought for a few seconds and then said he was glad that I had agreed to do this because during his childhood, as he was small and quite weedy, he was the butt of the attention of bullies at school who he had now come to realise were as much victims as he was. He asked me directly what chance I thought there was of an acquittal and I said that there was probably none. The bell for evening prayer was rung after an hour, our short visit was over, and we departed wishing Terence a good rest and looked forward to seeing him again in five days when he would be collected from the hospital.

Whilst I was in Fruges, the provost marshal had sent over the prosecution papers for the Clough court martial plus details of the make-up of the court and of the rules governing the conduct of the trial. Colonel F. J. Robertson from the judge advocate's office had been appointed as judge for this trial, Lt Col David Lloyd-Williams MC KC 2nd Battalion South Wales Borderers was appointed chairman of the court and four other officers, Major George Murdoch, Scottish Light Infantry; Major Carrington, the Lincolnshire Rifles; Captain Sexton, 2nd Battalion, Devon and Dorsetshire Regiment and Lieutenant Middleton, South Yorkshire Grenadier Territorials. The prosecutor was named as Major Sir Andrew Harding QC who was an experienced prosecution barrister, currently serving in the Territorial Army.

I spent several hours reading through the prosecution documents and could see that there was little in the actual chronology of the events that were known that could be disputed, but the prosecution intended to show that every stage of Clough's actions had been premeditated and inevitably led to his desertion. They intended to show from the list of witnesses they were going to call that they would highlight Clough's character as a bully and a braggart, and they had lined up several private soldiers and junior officers from his regiment to testify to this under oath. All of this was documented fully and would appear exceedingly difficult to challenge unless I could get a chance to speak to witnesses individually before they came to the witness box. They were on much less solid ground on why he behaved like this and they intended just to dismiss Clough as a craven coward who lacked any kind of moral fibre and was not worthy of our concern in any way. It was obvious that they believed this would be an easy case to win and were pressing for the maximum sentence of death to be brought down upon the head of Herbert Clough. There was no recognition of any kind of mitigation for why this officer had better than average reports from the OCTU and from his regiment.

That evening my head was spinning with the Clough case as I struggled to make sense of the events that had led to this peculiar situation. I simply could not understand why an infantry officer with nine months' service on the front should suddenly run away from his regiment and behave in this cowardly way. I did not think it was enough to just state that Clough was motivated by cowardice unless there was proof that this was so. The broad path of my defence was beginning to form in my mind, but I wondered whether Clough would be brave enough to comply with my thinking and go through with it in front of the court martial. My head was still spinning when I climbed into bed for, I knew I needed to get seven hours in before the briefing at 06:00.

Our first sortie was against the fighter airfield at Staden about ten miles north of Ypres. We studied the reconnaissance photographs of the airfield taken on Sunday morning where we could see that the squadrons of aircraft were lined in rows as if on parade and not dispersed around the airfield to make it more difficult to attack. My plan was to fly directly to Ypres and then turn north-west in the direction of Oostende but about halfway to Oostende over the area of Zarren to come round onto a south-easterly heading to bring us on to the airfield from a westerly direction, which I reckoned would be the least expected direction of attack. The recon photos had been taken on a Sunday morning and I guessed that there might more activity on the airfield on a Monday morning, but we would have to see. As we approached the airfield, we would select our targets and attack. If there was more than one line of aircraft on display, we would attack in section pairs to maximise destruction as we flew at right angles to the line giving two-second bursts at our chosen targets as we passed down the line. We would only have time for a few minutes over the target, one pass would be all we could manage so we must be as accurate as we could without shooting and aim at specific aircraft rather than just scatter rounds all over the airfield. Immediately we had finished our pass, we would climb for altitude as quickly as possible to be ready to challenge any enemy aircraft who chased after us. Everyone assented that they understood the brief and we were strapped in and ready to go by 07:50 and airborne within ten minutes.

The weather was in our favour because the cloud base over the target was expected to be about 1,000ft, which enabled us to approach without being seen. Over Ypres we deliberately drew attention to ourselves by using our flashlights as if we were sending course direction messages, and turned for the coast to convince the watchers in the German trenches to report a patrol heading for the coastal strip between Nieuport and Oostende, but they were unable to see that when we hid in the base of the clouds we had changed direction to line up on Staden airfield. At 3,000ft we tested our guns, then swung onto our approach to the German airfield and began our dive to break through the cloud base about 500 yards before the airfield perimeter. I could immediately see that there were three lines of aircraft lined up in front of their respective hangars and that they were just preparing the aircraft for the day's sorties, as I could clearly see mechanics, riggers and armourers swarming around. I knew that we did not have the time or ammunition to attack all three lines just sitting like ducks at the fairground. We had to conserve enough ammunition to be able to defend ourselves if attacked on our return flight to base.

I signalled Alex Brown to take the second line and I banked slightly, taking Giles with me to fire at the first line. I brought us down to a hundred feet and we were so close that we could see the faces of the German soldiers on the ground, looking up in horror as they saw two hostile aircraft approaching with their guns blazing. We flew in echelon along the line of stationary aircraft aiming for the cockpit and engine compartments and with my first burst I could see hits on the first and second aircraft in the line and the third burst into flames. Giles tore the wing off the next and set the fifth on fire. The sixth aircraft collapsed on its undercarriage and the seventh exploded under Giles' guns, and my last burst went through the next two aircraft. I saw pieces of the rudder and fuselage flying into the air and I pulled up to let Giles give the remaining three aircraft a full two-second burst and then he pulled up behind me and we looked over to see how the second section were doing. They seemed to have inflicted quite a lot of damage too but would have to wait for the debrief to know what we were claiming.

I was happy that the flight had performed well enough, we climbed for the clouds again and headed straight back to base without encountering any contacts with the enemy. The debrief showed that we had attacked twenty-four Storch fighters on the ground and the tally was that I had destroyed two and damaged three. Giles destroyed three and damaged one. The second section were not as successful, but Alex destroyed one and damaged one and Larry destroyed two and damaged three. Our total tally was that we had destroyed eight enemy aircraft on the ground and severely damaged eight others, which I felt was a great victory brought about by surprise and careful planning. I was impressed by the performance of both wingmen, who showed themselves to be good combat pilots and a little disappointed in the over-cautious approach of Alex Brown. I sent them for a half-an-hour rest before briefing for our second sortie, the raid on the reserve encampments near Roeselare.

The second sortie might prove to be more difficult to pull off than the first because our first strike would have awakened their defences to the potential for more attacks of a similar kind. I expected that the ground defences would be much more alert and that they would have put fighter aircraft in the sky to meet the challenge before we struck further targets. Again, we flew a similar track as earlier this morning as far as Ypres, but the weather report had indicated that the cloud base was now much higher, so the option of flying hidden amongst the clouds was a less attractive option. I had chosen to go in fast and direct at 2,000ft towards the railhead at Roeselare, which served the reserve encampments and to sweep low over the platforms and directly over the tented areas with the objective of creating maximum chaos and confusion. It was unlikely that we would be fortunate enough to arrive over the railhead as trains were arriving or departing or disembarking troops, but if they were we would concentrate on trying to cause maximum damage to the locomotive and rolling stock as possible. As we lined up for our run over the station, I could see that a train had just disembarked several thousand soldiers, who were marching away from the railhead towards the tented camps, so I signalled Alex to strafe the marching columns whilst Giles and I tackled the train before it got away.

We banked right to allow the second section to fly through and on to their target while we banked hard right to align ourselves on the departing train. I was glad that I had chosen to come in low because I could see the railhead was now ringed with anti-aircraft guns, but they were high angle and could not be brought to bear on low-flying targets very easily although sporadic machine-gun and rifle fire did start to come from the ground which could bring us down if the round hit me or Giles or some vital control wire which could cause us to lose control. We focussed directly on the locomotive that was piling on coal and wood to build up a greater head of steam for the highest speed possible for a faster getaway. The carriages were now empty trucks, with a machine-gun flatbed truck at the rear of the train and one in front of the locomotive to afford some protection. I indicated to Giles that we should attack singly rather than as a pair and would dive on to the engine from both sides at the same time, causing the German gunners to split their fire. He gave me a thumbs up that he understood the plan and broke away to circle round to take up his position on the opposite side of the train. We attacked from a position slightly behind the locomotive so that the machine gunner's vision was obscured by the engine's cab and tender. When we both opened fire, I could see that we were inflicting damage within the cab to the control panel; at least one of the crew had been hit and the external steam pipes running from the boiler were extruding super-heated steam into the cabin and I was sure that I saw a second crewman leap to safety from my side of the locomotive. The train was no longer under control, and we hoped that it would be only a matter of time before it derailed itself on a curve or bend because there was no one left to apply the brakes.

Satisfied that Giles was still applying maximum effort to the destruction of the locomotive, I allowed my aircraft to slip sideways to give me a shot at the machine gunners on the flatbed car hitched to the front of the locomotive. A one-second burst was enough to silence them and those who survived were seen to be jumping clear of the train. I could see that there were a set of points coming up that were to switch the train out of the railhead and back on to the mainline to Brussels and it was necessary that for the train to safely negotiate the switch, the points must be opened, and the speed reduced drastically. From the air we could not tell whether the points had been shifted or not but taking no chances, Giles strafed the adjacent signal box, blew out the front windows and peppered the inside with machine-gun rounds just to make sure. The locomotive came on still running at above sixty mph with no sign of slowing for the points, and I could see a railway man anxiously waving a red flag at the footplate hoping that someone in the cab would apply the brakes before it was too late. The flatbed truck hit the points first and we could tell that they were open because the truck almost managed to clear the points on the tracks, but its speed was far too high to enter the bend into the mainline and it began to derail. Because of the high speed it twisted and fell back across the rails and the locomotive ploughed into it, still going at a great lick. The locomotive pirouetted into the air and fell back spilling hot coals and steam everywhere as the rolling stock behind slammed into such a sudden stop, they started to switch and bend into unusual shapes as they came off the tracks. The force of the momentum of the derailment of the train carried the wreckage over all the mainline tracks, cutting the German frontline off from its supply chain maybe for at least a week or so whilst the wreckage was cleared away and the trackside switchgear restored.

This was a good job done. I waved Giles to rejoin me and we headed after Alex and Larry who I could see had completed a run across the camp and were climbing away and heading for Ypres. I could see that they had set some tents on fire and shot up others but had missed some choice targets that did not seem to have been touched. There was a large vehicle compound close to the tents that they had ignored that was full of fuel bowsers and lorries, and a communications centre for wireless and telegraphic communications was also still standing. I wondered why Alex had chosen not to attack these higher value targets that were not particularly well defended and posed little increased threat to him and his wingman. With these ideas in my head, I led Giles after them, rejoined in flight formation and decided not to return directly over Ypres and back to base but to head south towards to Menen and approach La Coupole from the south. I felt this might throw the Germans off-track who would expect us to take the direct route and I certainly seemed to be right, because we did not have any enemy contact on our return. As we approached our base, I immediately saw why the enemy were not up looking for us because they had launched a retaliatory raid against our base, and I could see that it was at least a squadron in strength.

La Coupole was a large base and well defended by a ring of anti-aircraft batteries, operated by a company of Royal Artillery and they were putting up a strong barrage to try to prevent enemy aircraft penetrating our outer defences. Each hangar was further protected by machine-gun emplacements to engage attackers who got through the outer screen, and these were staffed by RFC ground staff as part of the airfield defence plan. Luckily, over half of the aircraft of all three squadrons were in the air at any one time, drastically reducing the numbers of aircraft parked out on the open airfield. I signalled the flight to follow me, and we climbed rapidly to the east again so that we could dive out of the sun on to the German attackers. At 5,000ft we could look down at the air battle over La Coupole below us and see that there were about twelve Storch fighters being engaged by three SE5s, which must have managed to get airborne and take them on. I gave the hand signals for the flight to follow me into the dive out of the sun, choose their targets carefully and to attack singly, and when everyone had acknowledged that they understood I banked straight into the dive. I felt we had an advantage coming from altitude out of the strong morning sun; we could take out at least four of the attackers and drive the others away from the airfield.

As I hurtled down towards the swarm of Storch aircraft I identified one with the squadron commander pennant on its tail and decided that I would try to take him out if I could. They did not seem to be aware that we were plunging down on top of them, but were totally focused on the threat of the aircraft that were coming at them from the ground and I could see that two more were on the runway taking off as we dived down. The Germans were flying quite close together but seemed to have broken from their formations and were stooging around singly making them easier targets to pick off one by one. I knew that we had to impose maximum penalty on the enemy in our first pass and should take out four aircraft, which would level the odds for the more prolonged fight. I lined up a good deflection shot on the squadron commander, but also kept my eyes on a second Storch a little ahead but several hundred feet below him for my second target. My prey still did not know I was behind him as I fired my first burst, which I knew would inject a strong taste of reality into his cockpit. He immediately broke right but unfortunately for him straight into my second burst, which caught him full-on, as I had gambled that he would break to the right and my thumb was ready to press the instant he made his move. Immediately, a vapour trail appeared from under his wing that indicated he was losing fuel and then small flames began appearing along the top of his wing. He dived away in quick time heading for the ground because the deadly combination of fire and leaking fuel meant he could not survive long in the air. I guessed he would try to land on our airfield and become a prisoner of war. I did not follow him down because he was done for. I hoped he was able to land safely before he exploded in mid-air, and I kept on to my second target.

He was now aware that I was above him and diving fast. I had just shot down his squadron commander; he tried to pull up fast so that I would overshoot, and he could try to gain more height, then attack me from above. It was probably a tactic I might have tried if I had been in his position, but he was a bit too slow in pulling the nose of his aircraft up, which meant he was vulnerable for a few seconds longer than he would have liked and he realised that he had telegraphed his intentions clearly to me. I gave him a full two-second burst and hit his aircraft many times from the propeller to the tailplane. It just seemed to stop flying in mid-air as the engine stopped and the aircraft fell away, out of control. I followed him down this time because I could see that my fuel was getting critical, I was getting short of ammunition, and I wanted to confirm that he was destroyed. I turned on approach and I saw an SE5 going in ahead of me with smoke trailing from his underside, above me I could see a Storch crossing over the airfield with an SE5 in 354 colours hard on his heels and I could hear the machine guns firing even from this distance.

The aircraft ahead of me landed and taxied from the live runway. I came in fast, taxied over the 354-flight line and I could see that the other aircraft that had just landed was Alex Brown, who was stomping away in the direction of the crew room. I was fuming with him as our comrades were still fighting for their lives above us – but that would have to wait as I needed my aircraft rearmed and fuelled as quickly as possible, so I could get back into the sky and rejoin the fight. The crew chief said three minutes for refuelling and a further five for rearming the machine guns, so I sat in the cockpit strapped and ready to go while they got my aircraft serviceable again. Quickly enough the thumbs up came, my prop was swung, the engine roared back into life, I taxied over to the runway and took off again. As I climbed away from the airfield, I noted with some satisfaction a black Storch fighter being wheeled undercover in the 354 hangar and I was pleased that my first target had survived.

I climbed as fast as I could and vectored on to the lead SE5, which I could see had Major Moss's pennant on the tail. He waved as I came on to his wing but searching the sky, I could see that the odds had changed dramatically as there were now only five Storch aircraft to eight SE5s, and the Germans were trying to withdraw to the east, disengage and run for home. Major Moss gave me the hand signal that I should assume command and broke away heading for the ground. I guessed he was running out of fuel. I marshalled the remaining SE5s, and we chased the Germans until it was obvious that we could not catch them before they reached the German lines. I recalled our aircraft and ordered Giles and Larry, who were still airborne from the second sortie, to land immediately whilst the remaining aircraft flew a defensive patrol over the airfield until we were sure that no further threat was posed from the air.

When I landed, I went straight to debriefing where I was able to claim two aircraft shot down and half a train shared with Giles Lacey. Alex Brown described shooting up the tented encampment but said he did not see any other targets of any value, even when I pointed out the vehicle compound and communications centre clearly marked on the map. Giles claimed a half share of destroying the train with me and one Storch shot down over La Coupole; Larry Fortescue claimed one Storch destroyed in the defence of the airfield. He said he saw the vehicle compound and communications building and wondered why we did not attack them instead of shooting up empty tents. I was delighted because A flight had broken its duck, claimed four aircraft and a train destroyed on our first outing together. The damage to La Coupole was minimal because the anti-aircraft barrage had kept most of the German aircraft at bay, but we had lost one SE5 on the ground, two fuel bowsers and the control hut had been strafed but not put out of action. Two airmen had been wounded and Airman Spragg had been killed by a stray bullet from the Storch attacker. I called Lieutenant Brown into my room, we sat down at my desk, and I told him that I was disappointed in his performance today, that I felt that he did not have the aggressive spirit to be a section leader yet. He was the only member of the flight not to engage the enemy fully and expended less than a third of his ammunition whereas Giles, Larry and I were completely out of ammunition when we landed. He only destroyed some empty tents while vital enemy transport and communication resources were left untouched.

"I saw you stomp off to the crew room when you landed with minor damage to your aircraft," I told him, "When you should have taken one of the spare aircraft and rejoined the fight to defend this airfield. I think that you will benefit from some time flying as wingman to a more aggressive combat pilot so from today I am going to ask Lieutenant Lacey to take over as section leader and you can fly as his wingman. Lieutenant Fortescue can switch to take Lacey's place and fly as my wingman in the meantime."

After he had left me, I felt that I detected some relief in Alex when I relieved him of the responsibility of leading the section and I mused over this as I waited for Giles to come in to see me. When the knock came, I was just drifting into a doze after a hard day in the air, but I was immediately wide awake when Giles came into the room. I congratulated him on his performance in helping destroy the train, for shooting down an enemy fighter over the airfield and he expressed his regret at having to destroy such a wonderful machine. I told him I thought that he used his initiative, had good battlefield sense, and could see the tactical picture clearly when in the air. As a result, I was going to rotate the flight personnel and he was going to take over the second section, Alex Brown would fly as his wingman and Larry Fortescue as mine with immediate effect. I needed to see Larry before we briefed for the final sortie of the day when Caldwell knocked and brought me a signal flimsy from Wing HQ telling me that the bombing raid planned for today had been scratched due to bad weather over the target. Relieved, I sent for Larry and told him he was now my new wingman and he left me with a big smile on his face, as he knew he would now get into the real action.

I was glad that I could rest, as I needed to prepare myself for a day with Clough at Arras prison tomorrow working on our response to the prosecution case. Before I could do this, I wandered over to the squadron hangar to see my prize, and there it was in the middle of the floor with a gaggle of sightseers clustered around it. In its black livery and squadron markings, it looked a sinister and lethal machine, but I satisfied myself with the fact that it could not turn or climb as fast as the SE5 and the burnt and broken fabric on the wing was evidence of that. I left the sightseers to gawk, went into the squadron office to see Major Moss and found even more sightseers in there. Finally, I pushed my way through the scrum around the door and into the office where could see a German officer sat in the chair opposite Major Moss, drinking tea. I came to attention to acknowledge my squadron commander and he came round his desk and slapped me on the back on a good day's work done. He then introduced me to Major Joachim Von Richter who commanded the raid against us today, was shot down and had to crash land on our airfield. I smiled and said that I already knew who he was because I was the one who shot him down. The German major stood and saluted me and in reasonable English congratulated me on my excellent flying and chivalrous conduct in not machine-gunning him when he was helpless in his dive for the ground. I gave him a little bow, then turned to my major and explained the changes I had made to the flight roles. He agreed and reminded me that I would be on prisoner's friend duty all day on Tuesday at Arras military prison.

EIGHTEEN

Clough's Defence

I spent most of Monday evening reading through the prosecution version of events with the simple chronology of when things had happened but could not find anything much that could be challenged as false in court. It was the evidence that the prosecutor sought to offer as to why Clough had behaved as he did that was far more troubling. Much of this evidence was hearsay, not corroborated and, in my opinion, was introduced purely to blacken Clough's character and influence the board against the defendant. I was not sure whether I should challenge this or use this evidence to build my case for mitigation. I was glad I still had the use of the motorbike until the trial was over and set off early immediately after breakfast for the prison. On arrival I went through the same security checks as before and was greeted by the same sergeant, who jokingly asked me if I had shot down anymore and I replied, 'Two German fighters and a train since I last saw you.' I remarked that in the RFC we did not sit on our arses waiting for the next push but took the fight directly to the enemy in his own back yard. He blushed, he could see that he had offended me and led me in silence to the same interview room as before.

Within two minutes, Clough was brought in by two guards and I was appalled by the state of him. He had received further bruising, presumably from beatings administered by staff or other inmates; his clothing was stained with blood and dirty and he was unkempt. I was furious and I ordered the guards to take the prisoner back to his cell. When he had been removed from the room, I summoned the sergeant and ordered him to take me directly to the commandant's office. He tried to protest and say that it was not possible but when I told him that he was obstructing an officer of the court in the pursuance of his duty and that I would call the provost marshal to arrest him and put him in custody, he realised that I meant business. He led me through a much plusher and more comfortable area at the front of the prison to the adjutant's office and opened the door for me. The commandant's office led from the adjutant's room. I could see that his desk was empty, and the secretary nodded towards the door to indicate he was in with the commandant. I smiled and strode purposely towards the door. I thought I heard her say something about, "you can't go in there'" as I opened the door and stepped into the commandant's office. Two startled faces looked up at me and immediately the younger officer jumped up and tried to shoo me back out of the room. I side-stepped and saluted the commandant as smartly as I could and introduced myself with my rank, unit, and appointment as prisoner's friend to Lieutenant Herbert Clough, stating, "I wish to speak to you urgently about the treatment being meted out to a serving British officer in your prison."

The weedy-looking adjutant tried to interrupt me again. I turned on him and told him to leave us as the discussion I was about to have with his commanding officer was confidential and governed by the rules for the administration of court martials. The old colonel behind the desk waved him away, invited me to sit in the chair vacated by his adjutant and said he could see that something had upset me. I explained to him that this was my second visit to the defendant and on both occasions, he had been severely beaten and was in a poor state. His uniform was dirty and soiled with blood and he was unkempt as if he has been denied hot water to shave and wash. I reminded him that although Lt Clough was accused of desertion, it was up to the court martial to decide whether he was guilty or innocent, not prison staff or inmates. Clough was a British officer and as such should be treated with the respect due to a holder of that rank. I told him that I was acting as an officer of the court, somewhat reluctantly, in this matter and I expected to be able to meet with Lt Clough in uniform, clean and presentable in the way that he was when he was brought here from St Omer.

"I have been prevented from consulting with Clough this morning because of the state that he was presented to me, in no fit state to be interviewed,"I said. '" make no accusations because I have no evidence that the injuries were administered by prison staff under your command or by prisoners under your control, but it was clear that in either case it should have been stopped after the first occasion."

I told him that I believed that he was ultimately responsible for keeping Lt Clough safe and well so that he was fit to appear before the court martial in seven days. "Unless something is done today to drastically change this situation," I told him, "I will lodge a complaint for a mistrial before the judge advocate that I was prevented from preparing a defence by your failures and those of your staff to uphold your duty of care towards the accused." The old colonel started to snort and bluster and challenge my authority to talk to him like this, threatening to break me and destroy my career in the army if I continued. I told him that he had better be quick as within seven days I would an officer in the Royal Air Force outside of army jurisdiction and that I had no army career as I was a territorial, hostilities-only officer who would resume my civilian career as soon as the war was over. I finished by saying, "This is not about you or your staff taking the law into their own hands but a serious duty to ensure the trial of this officer is conducted without fear or prejudice, for the life of Herbert Clough is at stake. I wish to interview Clough at 13:00 today which gives you adequate time to attend to his personal hygiene needs and clean him up, clean and press his uniform and present him to me in a soldierly manner." I stood, saluted, about turned, and marched out of the office, and out into the fresh air. I retrieved the bike and rode to a small village just outside of Arras and found a café where I could sit and go over the notes again whilst I let my anger subside.

When I returned at 12:45, I sensed that there was a change of attitude towards me from the prison staff who were now overly formal and at pains to ensure that I was accommodated in every respect. I thought, perhaps, the colonel had taken my threat to press the court for a mistrial because of the interference in the preparing of Clough's defence by the prison staff seriously. I had no way of knowing whether a petition to the judge advocate on this basis would stand any chance of success, but I supposed neither did the colonel. I was shown into the same interview room but this time there was a jug of fresh water and some beakers on the table, and when Clough was shown into the room, he was in a presentable state. He had obviously been given hot water and soap to bathe and his hair had been cut: his uniform had been cleaned and pressed, he was wearing a clean shirt and tie and polished shoes.

The first thing I dealt with was to take a statement from him about the beatings he had been subject to and he confirmed that they were administered in his cell where he was held in isolation. The attackers were two of the prison warders, who had beaten and kicked him when he fell to the ground. There were two attacks; one when he first came into the prison and the second after our previous interview. I asked him for the names of the attackers, he did not know but was able to describe them in enough detail that I was certain I would be able to recognise them if I saw them. Then I realised that the two warders who brought him to and from his cell fitted the descriptions he had given. I double-checked that they were the only two involved in the attacks and he said they were, then I asked him if the two escorts were the culprits. I could see from his face that he was unsure what to say but after pausing for about ten seconds he nodded, and I made him amend his statement and sign and date it. Army prison guards were usually private soldiers who were too old or unfit for active service but had good conduct reports, so were promoted to lance corporal to carry out prison guard duties. I understood that as part of their job they may have to restrain violent prisoners sometimes, but they were only expected to use such force as was necessary to retain good order and discipline. In no circumstances, were they allowed to administer unprovoked beatings on a prisoner who was compliant and peaceful just because they did not like the offence he was charged with.

For the rest of the afternoon I went through the make-up of the court martial explaining that the three most important figures were the judge advocate, Colonel Robertson who was appointed to advise the court martial board members of the law; the chairman of the court martial board, Lt Colonel Lloyd-Williams from the South Wales Borderers and the prosecuting officer, Major Sir Andrew Harding QC who was a famous prosecuting barrister serving as a military prosecutor for the duration of the war.

"All of the officers who make up the court martial are infantry officers who have served at the Western Front," I told Clough, "but none are from your regiment. They have two functions to fulfil in the trial, their first job is to look at the evidence presented and decide whether you are guilty as charged. They are not interested in whether you are innocent for if they find the case is not proven against you, will be acquitted. The chairman of the court martial will lead their discussions about the quality of the evidence presented by the prosecutor and any evidence from the defence, as well as the cross-examination of witnesses, and then after receiving legal direction from the judge will consider whether you are guilty. If they find the charge proved they will find you guilty and the prosecutor will make a speech with a recommendation of the sentence that he wishes to be imposed, and the defence is then able to offer pleas of mitigation or call witnesses who will speak in your favour. The court martial board may receive further legal advice from the judge and then retire to consider the sentence to be imposed.

The chairman of the court martial will read out the recommended sentence before the court and the judge will impose the sentence." I was frank and honest with him that, in my opinion, the strong likelihood was that he would be found guilty, and the only sentence would be the death penalty. I pointed out to him that over 150 British soldiers had been executed by firing squad for desertion on the Western Front and it would need a miracle for a board of his peers from the infantry to have much difficulty in finding him guilty as charged.

I went through the chronology of events from the gas attack in an area of the front six miles from his unit location to absenting himself from the front line and making for the trenches behind the area of the gas attack; the squirting of toxic drops in his eyes to fake blindness and wandering around as if he could not see. Then his arrival at the hospital where he was diagnosed with possible temporary blindness attributed to the gas, his eyes were treated with cream and bandaged to keep out the light for at least fourteen days to see whether the effects would wear off. I explained that there was little doubt that he was blinded for a time, but this was a self-inflicted wound, he knew the effects would wear off and he could make good his escape. After that, meeting Terence who had kindly acted as his guide and then just after dawn, when everyone was still asleep, making off on the stolen motorbike and his subsequent capture in Fruges village that afternoon. Herbert did not dispute any of the events as they happened, but he did say that none of the events were planned, they just happened on the spur of the moment.

I accepted that, in his own mind, he thought that this was a true situation, but I failed to see how I could convince the court that an instant decision to desert from his post was any less serious than one that was planned, as the result was the same. I stressed, time and again, that we had little counterevidence to bring that would significantly challenge the version of events presented by the prosecutor. 'It is imperative that we are able to present in mitigation the reasons why you acted the way you did, that means that you must be prepared to be braver than you have ever been in your whole life and talk honestly about who you are and why you have lived a lie for so many years.' I showed him the evidence that the prosecution was going to enter into the court record. "On many occasions in your life you have acted in a bullying and cowardly way, from your school days with statements from your housemaster, your record at OCTU and documents relating to the serious injury of another trainee in which you were implicated but there was insufficient evidence to convict you, and a suspicion that you had threatened the witnesses; complaints made by several soldiers in your own regiment about your unfair conduct towards them as well as two lieutenants who have made statements about your bullying behaviour towards them. Finally, your own company commander has made a written statement in which he states that he does not wish to speak on your behalf. I told him that I cannot stop the prosecution entering these documents as evidence against you, but I might be able to prevent them calling the soldiers and officers to the stand, which will be very damming indeed unless you are prepared to be honest about your own story." He would have to accept that his past behaviour and the way he had treated people over the years may serve to multiply the condemnation in the eyes of the members of the board.

Herbert appeared to be in total collapse emotionally, he seemed to retreat into himself and became sullen and silent, sunk down into a world of his own misery. I told him that I would be flying on Wednesday but would return on Thursday to hear his side of the story. He had thirty-six hours or so to think this over and give me something with which I could fight for his life, for a guilty verdict but with a plea for mitigation might just avoid the death sentence. The army high command would be pressing for a death sentence as an example to others just before another big push, but it was the five officers on the board and the judge who needed to be convinced.

I knocked on the door, the same two escorts entered the room and before they removed Lt Clough, I asked them their names and they replied that they were Lance Corporals Darnley and Duff. I thanked them and the three of them left to return to his cell. The same sergeant escorted me from the interview room and again I said I wanted to go to see the prison adjutant before I left. I approached the office, knocked once, entered, saluted, and turned to face the young adjutant who had a look of fear and trepidation all over his face and was spluttering that the colonel was not there. I said that was fine as I only wished to speak to him, and I told him I had a signed statement from Lieutenant Clough alleging that Lance Corporals Darnley and Duff were the perpetrators of assaults on his person occasioning actual bodily harm, which I would lodge with the provost marshal in St Omer, Major Rydall.

"Darnley and Duff will be charged and held in custody pending trial by summary court martial for striking an officer. You will need to relieve the two of them from their duties immediately and hold them in custody until the military police arrive from St Omer to take them away. I shall arrange for a medical officer to examine Lt Clough today to compile a report of his injuries as part of the investigation." Before I left his office, I reminded him that if he failed to comply with my request or obstructed us in any way, I would have him arrested for hindering a court martial investigation. I rode straight to St Omer and managed to catch Major Rydall before he left for the day. He read Clough's statement, listened to my account of events, and agreed that Darnley and Duff were to be arrested and charged with wilfully striking an officer. He summoned the sergeant military policeman and ordered him to take a team and arrest Darnley and Duff and return them to St Omer for investigation. I asked him whether they used a medical officer to look at injuries after an assault, and he recommended Captain Salt RAMC who had served as a local coroner before joining up. As he shook my hand, he said that he would send Salt to Arras in the morning to examine Clough's injuries and send me a copy of the report, which would be important evidence against the two lance corporals.

It was after nine when I got back to A flight. I was dead tired, I needed to sleep as I was flying the first patrol at 08:00 and would need to be in briefing by 06:30. Caldwell produced a tray of tea and toasted cheese, which allayed my hunger, and I was asleep by just after ten. The morning sortie was to be a combat patrol by section one, which was Fortescue and I, and we were to patrol between Poperinge and the coast along the front line of the enemy trenches and to harass enemy movements and engage aircraft if we could. No target had been specified and we had been given a free hand to rove over this sector as we saw fit. This was not a sector that I knew well as we most frequently covered the sector further to the south, but it felt good to be set free in predatory fashion over enemy territory. I felt confident in my new wingman and knew that he was already an aggressive combat pilot, but this was the first time that we had flown together so I would keep him close to me today.

We planned to patrol from Poperinge, north-west towards Diksmuide and Oostende and back searching for suitable targets along the way. We knew that there was a large German air base just before Oostende near Oudenburg and were hoping we might encounter some aerial traffic around there. It was a clear morning with a forecast of a little light rain coming in from the Straits of Dover which might restrict visibility after 1,000ft but would pass south-east quite quickly when visibility would improve again. Towards Diksmuide we sighted a string of barges, probably from the docks at Nieuwport, being towed inland along the canal by a small steam tender. We could see the barges were heavily laden by the way they rode low in the water, but they were completely sheeted so we could not tell what the cargo was. We both dived fast and strafed the whole convoy going for the steam tender first and then the barges. I fired two bursts as I went over the first time and then circled for a second pass when I fired a longer burst. I could see that the steam vessel had taken hits and was losing its way rapidly, and a fire seemed to have been started in the second barge that prevented the crew from releasing the third barge from the tow. The fire was taking hold of the second barge; the flames were leaping up three or four feet and I was certain that this barge would founder, the third barge would probably be seriously damaged by the fire too, but the first barge was limping away behind the stricken steam tender.

We broke off the engagement and continued toward Oostende looking for aerial traffic from the Oudenburg airfield. We climbed to 5,000ft and could see the ancient Belgian city of Bruges in the distance. We spotted some slow-moving bombers heading down the coast towards Dunkerque but could not see their fighter escort. I searched the sky over and behind us but could not detect their presence until Fortescue pointed downwards and we could just make them out almost immediately below us, half in and half out of the incoming rain cloud. The poor visibility meant that they had not seen us yet; we were able to drop back and let them overhaul us until we were in the perfect position for our attack. Just as we committed ourselves to the dive, they must have caught a glimpse of us, and they broke formation and scattered in different directions. I did not want to hand the tactical advantage to them or be drawn by them away from the bombers lumbering along the coast so I pulled up into a steep ascent and piled on the power knowing that we could climb at a much faster rate than they could. I also turned towards the coast so that we could get amongst the bombers before the fighter escort realised what we were doing. At 5,000ft we had dived down on to the formation of six bombers, being cautious not to offer the rear gunners much of a shot as we came in fast and passed across their stern, firing all the time. Our shooting was accurate, and we hit the last two in the formation. They fell out of the sky, but we were not able to pursue the other four bombers – the hunters had now become the hunted as the enemy fighter escort roared towards us. I knew we could outrun them and turned westerly for a high-speed run for home. If we could keep out of the range of their guns for the next two minutes or so we would be safe enough, as they would not leave their bombers unescorted for too long. I guessed right for as soon as they realised, we were nearing our lines they broke off and returned to their charges rather than continue the pursuit.

I had gambled and it had paid off, although if the fighter escort had been more alert it could have been a different story. It was a good morning's work, and we would claim two barges and a steam tender damaged and one aircraft each for just under an hour in the air. In the debriefing I suggested that the returning four bombers could probably be jumped somewhere up the coast from Dunkerque returning to Oudenburg, and the 10:00 sortie led by Giles was tasked with destroying them. We were tasked with the 12:00 and 16:00 sorties but these proved uneventful and did not add further to our score, but Giles and Alex managed one bomber each when they ambushed the returning bomber group over Kokside when again they were left exposed without a fighter escort.

I was getting increasingly worried about Clough's defence and went to speak with Major Moss to request that I be stood down from the flying roster until the court martial was over. He agreed readily saying that as before, he and Captain Rydings would fly in my stead.

I was now to concentrate on preparing for Clough's defence if he was prepared to follow my advice and open himself up honestly to the court about why he deserted his post. I wanted to suggest to the court that Clough was afraid not of his own death, but of his lack of ability to lead his men effectively into battle which would lead to their deaths. All through his life from childhood to now he had lived with a massive lack of self-confidence, which he covered up by adopting a gung-ho and bullying attitude towards others, which was only a ruse to mask his own weakness. From his early childhood his father, school masters and friends expected him to exert strength and leadership in everything he did, when if they had only spent more time scratching under the surface of his personality, they would see that his weaknesses were exposed to view quite easily. He was gauche and awkward in company, seemed unable to make relationships with people and gravitated towards situations socially where he could dominate others through bluster and bullying. He was happy when he was able to browbeat others into submission and cruel in the perpetration of his bullying when he had a submissive victim in his grasp, but quick to run away when challenged and there were instances in his records at school and the OCTU when this was apparent.

I imagined that this arose because he was sent away to school from the age of six and had not enjoyed the warmth of a family life since. He had almost gone from the nursery to prep school, public school, OCTU and his regiment without the love, support, and guidance of a strong family life, which I thought may have contributed greatly to making him into the man he was today. I knew that this would be a difficult case to argue and that the default prejudice would be that he was just a coward and was beneath contempt. I would return to the prison again on Thursday and try to work with Clough again to delve deeper into the reasons for his behaviour. I knew that I detested the kind of man that Clough had become, which was why I stood up to him in Suzette's, but also, I detested a system that would seek to execute a man for his own weakness. Common humanity demanded that Clough deserved a fair hearing and even if the facts of the case were not disputed, the court should consider the mitigation carefully before handing down a sentence.

I am no psychologist but I would try to get the court to empathise with my notion that all soldiers before an action feel fear to a greater or lesser extent, but the division between running away and doing one's duty was a fine line and very often determined by a kind of herd instinct to do what all your comrades are doing and also, quite cynically, the lack of opportunity to run away once the battle actually starts. However, if you are a young infantry subaltern who has never been in action before and posted to the Western Front, where the life expectancy of a lieutenant was about six weeks, it is hardly surprising that the pressure on him was massive, especially as young officers could not rely on going with the herd or safety in numbers because they were to be the first over the top to lead their men into the onslaught.

My reception at the prison was cool but formal and it was if the warders had been ordered to treat me with kid gloves to avoid giving me any further cause for complaint, as they could see that I was an officer who took my responsibilities towards the prisoner seriously and would not allow others to obstruct that process. Most officers given the task of defending those accused of capital offences were reluctant to carry out the duty and were certainly not too worried if the prisoner was roughed up a bit in the prison. When Clough was brought in, he looked much better and was clean and tidy and presented smartly in uniform as he should be, which meant that part of the battle had been won. The two escorts were new to me, of course, and were at great pains to show that they were treating the prisoner as was expected. I dismissed them from the room and said that I would break for an hour when

Clough was due to receive his midday meal and resume after lunch. This gave me three hours before his meal to get him to talk about his childhood, school days and the incidents at the OCTU.

I began by asking him why he always ran away from things when he felt challenged by authority or someone was prepared to stand up to him. He was reluctant to speak and at first denied that this described his behaviour, but I continued probing and asked him about his relationship with his mother. He immediately softened his attitude and told me how she was soft, warm, loving, and protective of him as an infant and young boy, and although he had a nurse, his mother spent many hours each day in the nursery playing with him, reading, or walking in the garden. I remarked that this seemed a happy childhood and I could see from the changed expression on his face that the reality of his childish home life was somehow different from the idyllic picture he had just painted. I pressed on and asked if his father ever came to the nursery, and he went quiet and only nodded assent. I pushed further and said that he was lucky to have such attentive parents, his face went dark, and I could see a few tears on his cheek as he remembered the reality in his head.

Eventually, he told me the whole story of how his father disapproved of his wife spending too much time with him because he said this would make him too soft and girlish when he needed to stand on his own two feet and be a man. He told me that often he was aware of raised voices and could hear screams from his mother and then after each of these occasions his father would come to the nursery and beat him with a strap if he found him reading storybooks or playing with toys. Usually, he would not see his mother for two days or so until his father returned to his business but could see the bruises still visible on her face and arms. He told me that his father was away all through the week and sometimes for two weeks at a time, staying in a house he had purchased in London to be close to his factory and offices in the east of London.

His factory manufactured machine tools, which he exported all over the Empire and he expected his son to take over the business when he grew too old to run it. He said business was a tough environment with a great deal of cut and thrust competition and needed a strong and fearless character to run it. There was no place for milksops or weakness in business, which was why he was trying to bring him up and train him to take over his birth right and be able to pass it on to his son in the future. He always said that the punishments were for his own good and that he would thank him in the long run. He said that his mum and he were grateful when his father went back to London as we would have peace and she would continue to spend time with me in the nursery as much as she could. Sometimes, she would have to go back to London with him and was away for periods of up to a month when he was left alone and sad but when she returned home, they were together again every day. Sometime after his sixth birthday, his father returned home unexpectedly and was angry to find his wife in the nursery reading with her son, instead of working through the arithmetic primers he had given him for his birthday. He dismissed his wife and sent her downstairs and gave me an extra severe thrashing with the strap for disobeying his instructions. He reduced me to tears and he barked at me that my mother's attention had spawned a girly softy boy who could not take his punishment like a man. Three weeks after this incident, he sent me away to Boxwood Hall Preparatory School and this was the last time I saw my mother. My last memory of her was seeing her white face and red eyes stung by tears as the pony and trap took me away to the station. Two months or so after starting at Boxwood, he was called to the headmaster's office to be told that his mother had met with a tragic accident at home and had died.

A few days later my father collected me from the school and took me home to attend the funeral at the local church, where she was laid to rest in the family vault. Lots of people I did not know attended the funeral and they paid me no real attention as I wandered around listening to the gossip and discovered that my mother had been found by the servants at the bottom of the stairs. It was assumed that she had tripped and fallen to her death. Apparently, there was some concern that there were injuries on her body not consistent with falling down the stairs, but the coroner was unable to establish any evidence from the household that my mother had ever been beaten, and the case was closed as accidental death.' He returned to school and did not see his father again until he was ten, when he was a candidate to take the open entrance examinations for public school. Every holiday he was one of the small group of boys who spent their holidays at the school instead of going home.

He described how the regime at Boxwood School was a tough environment to spend one's formative years and although the teaching was clearly focused on cramming into them the right amount of knowledge to pass the public-school entrance exams, it offered little more. The masters did not see that their role was in any way pastoral and delegated much of that responsibility to the school proctors, who were mostly ex-NCOs from the army to maintain discipline. This illustrious band of men spent most of their time drinking in the local public houses and whilst they were away from the school most nights, allowed the senior pupils in each house to act as prefects and keep order and administer punishments. This led to a regime based on intimidation, bullying and cruelty. Older boys preyed on younger boys and anyone who was less robust or more sensitive in nature.

Clough's first year at the school was terrible. He told me he was beaten, kicked, humiliated, had his pocket money stolen and the more he cried, the more he was tormented. He complained to the proctor who just laughed and then repeated the same mantra so often espoused by his father, that he should stand up to them and be a man. He was too small and weak and could not see how he could do this effectively, so he decided to make himself as unobtrusive as he possibly could. This strategy worked partially, and for a time he received much less attention from the prefects but as soon as they noticed him again the cycle of bullying would start over. He said that living on your nerves was the worst thing, and he was dreading the long summer holidays at the school instead of going home and feared that some of the bullies would be staying at school too.

The summer holidays were not that bad. There was only one boy who thought he could boss everyone else around and because during the day there was little or no supervision, they could roam around the school grounds and into the village nearby without hindrance, so he largely avoided him. The only time he encountered him was a day when he was fishing peacefully on the bank of the small river running through the school grounds and was enjoying basking in the sunshine on this sleepy afternoon. Alistair Grey jumped on him, pinned him down with his knees, grabbed some of the bait and tried to force it into his mouth, which he thought was very funny. He had never fought back before because the bullies had always acted with plenty of back-up, ensuring that any attempt at resistance would result in swift retribution from the rest of the gang. Grey was alone and was relying on his superior size to dominate Clough, but Grey was not prepared for the unexpected. He managed to bring his knee up hard into the older boy's scrotum and rolled him off whilst Grey was grabbing at his testicles and crying. Clough jumped up and realised immediately he had the upper hand, so he kicked him hard again between his legs and rolled him into the river. He was shouting that he could not swim but Clough just turned his back and walked away. Eventually, he was pulled out of the river about 300 yards downstream by one of the school gardeners, but Clough knew he would keep his mouth shut because if he admitted that small Herbert had pushed him in the river his reputation was lost. Two days later when he was released from the infirmary, Clough had sought him out and found him sitting on a bench in front of the school still looking pale and shook up from his ordeal. Grey flinched when he saw Clough, who pulled his hair and punched him in the stomach and then told him that he was now in his gang and would do what he told him or else he would face another ducking in the river. He said he enjoyed the rest of the summer holiday terrorising the other boys with the support of Grey, and knew that when the new school year began, he would become one of the bullies and not be a victim.

At the age of ten, his father appeared on the scene again as he wanted to gain entrance into a public school for Herbert. He took him to visit several prominent schools and to sit the entrance examinations during the summer holidays. The rest of the time was spent working at the factory learning the business where he received some praise for the harsh way, he treated some of the workers, who were frightened of losing their jobs if they offended the boss's son. He failed the first two examinations, and this upset his father who surprisingly railed at the school more than at him. Fortunately, a place was offered for September at Grange Manor School at Sherborne, and he spent the next seven years at this minor public school.

By now his bullying mentality was well established as his self-preservation strategy and he terrorised many younger boys over his years at the school. There were two unfortunate incidents when his bullying went too far; one of his victims received serious physical injuries and in the other mental collapse which required removal from the school. On both occasions, although it was widely suspected that Clough was the culprit, the victims did not name him outright and he was not expelled, although detailed notes were attached to his file that attributed the blame to him in both cases. Every holiday he returned to London and went back to work at the factory, which in the run-up to the war was expanding in preparation for the increased demand for machine tools when the war finally came. Herbert had proved a quick learner and now his bullying techniques were well established, he took to terrorising the workers in the same way although he did not have the same influence over the skilled tradesmen, who just dismissed him as a schoolboy while being careful not to cross him, for he had already developed a reputation for being vindictive and holding a grudge.

After the lunch break, I got him to talk about the OCTU and particularly to tell me about the inquiry into the death of Officer Cadet Thomlinson during a training exercise in the Thetford Forest in 1916. Thomlinson was found hanging in the woods, about 300 yards from the OCTU tented camp. There was no evidence of foul play, and it was accepted that he had committed suicide. The court of enquiry received information from other officer cadets that Thomlinson had been subjected to a protracted and vicious campaign of intimidation at the hands of some of the other cadets, but they were unable to break the wall of silence and discover who was the culprit. Two names were frequently suggested; Clough was one of them, but no evidence was found to corroborate any of the whispers that the investigators had heard, and he walked free again. I explained to Clough that much of this evidence would be revealed by the prosecution, including the bullying at school, his incrimination in the serious injury to two students at public school and his involvement in the death of Thomlinson. He interrupted and said he was not accused in any of these circumstances.

"Just the fact that you were considered the prime suspect in all three cases is enough to blacken your character in the eyes of the court martial board," I told him. "I can try to refute the implication made by the prosecution lawyer but the idea that you are monster will have been firmly established in the minds of the court. Then the prosecutor will introduce as witness the soldiers who complained and the two lieutenants who suffered bullying from you, and finally your company commander will be on the witness stand and asked to explain why he was not willing to give you a recommendation or character reference. When this is combined with facts of your deception and running away, we could be sunk."

I told him that I did not want to retell the inglorious stories of his bullying. "I want to try to show the reasons why the experiences of your earlier life forced you to behave in this way and the cold upbringing, being the victim of bullying at school and the abuse from your father has led you surely to this point. I can tell your story for you and will try my best to offset the effect of the weight of evidence against you, but you have to work with me and believe in my strategy because without your permission, I have nothing to counter their arguments." He steadfastly refused to agree so I said that he should think it over and I would return on Friday at 13:00 to hear his answer.

NINETEEN

Clough; A Brazen Coward or Courageous Officer?

On Friday morning I was at the Fruges Priory Hospital with Jamie's car to collect Terence on his discharge from the hospital promptly at 09:00 as the doctor had instructed, and found Terence all packed up and ready, looking well and smart in uniform. Mother Superior graced us with her presence and wished Terence good luck and to stay safe but looked at me with some disdain and then remarked as she swept from the room that at least I had not been drinking this morning. Terence and I just erupted into laughter, thanked the nurses, and went out to the car. On the drive back I was telling Terence all about defending Herbert Clough and how difficult it was going to be to avoid a guilty verdict and the death sentence, as there was absolutely no one who was prepared to speak on his behalf although they are lining up from his own battalion to condemn him.

"To cap it all Clough himself is not willing to cooperate and offer any mitigation, even though I can see that he is not cowardly by nature but has been nurtured by the circumstances of his life to behave in the way he does." I was only glad that although my family was poor and we did not have any privileges of rank or fortune I was always loved, cared for and protected, which moulded my brothers and I into the men we were to become as adults. Clough had virtually no family life; a brutal father who it was rumoured murdered his mother, and he spent two-thirds of his life at school from the age of six. Terence was a good listener and he allowed me to get all this off my chest without interrupting. Jamie and Charlie were flying today but would be on the ground when we arrived back at La Coupole, and I would have to

281

leave him to spend the afternoon with Clough again. I was glad to see Terence back at the squadron and I looked forward to talking with him that evening.

Clough was brought in and immediately, I could tell that he had dragged himself out of the misery he felt the previous day and was more like his usual self. He looked more self-confident, more determined, and said he had thought through everything that I had said and appreciated the efforts I had made to prepare his defence, but he had made up his mind not to offer any mitigation or challenge anything in the prosecution case. I said that this was madness as it would bring a certain death sentence and he replied that he would rather die than expose his inner self to public scrutiny in the courtroom. I pleaded with him to change his mind, but the harder I tried the firmer was his resistance. I wondered whether he had asked for me to defend him as some elaborate means of getting revenge on me, as he was putting me through the most taxing period of my life so far. I felt totally helpless, which was a feeling unusual to me who had always been capable at most things, and I was tempted just to walk away and leave him at the mercy of the court, but I was a fighter, and it was not in my nature to duck a challenge.

My mind was working double-time in my head as I was configuring a strategy to defend Clough's actions by putting him into the witness box to give evidence about the assaults by Darnley and Duff at Arras prison. Once he was under oath, he would be required to answer my questions and face cross-examination from the prosecution and the chairman of the board. I would show that I could draw out the mitigation circumstances that had led him to these events. I was hoping to create enough sympathy for him that he might avoid the death penalty. I decided not to discuss this with Clough but if he refused, my hands would be tied, and my only options would be reactive to the prosecution line of questioning. I told Clough that I accepted his decision but cautioned him to reflect carefully on what he had said, and that I would come to see him again on Sunday to go over this again. I asked him if he had a best uniform and Sam Browne belt with his kit and he said that he did. I arranged to collect his kit from his battalion position and bring it with me on Sunday, as he would need to look his best for the court on the following Tuesday. I knew that he would be transferred from the prison to the citadel at St Omer barracks where the court martial was to be held on Monday. He would be held in a secure room in the officers' mess, and I had been allocated a room in the mess too so I could consult with him over the days of the trial. I could not see the court martial lasting for more than a couple of days unless

I could come up with some witnesses to speak in favour of Clough. After an hour, I left him and rode back to camp much troubled about what would transpire.

My mood was much lightened when I got back and met with Terence, accompanied by Jamie and Charlie who were already in party mood. Terence did not wish to overdo things so early on his release from hospital, so we decided to go to the village restaurant for a quieter evening and I invited my A flighters to join us too. Alex Brown declined as he said he was too tired, but Lacey and Fortescue agreed readily. I certainly needed some cheering up; a good meal in cheery company was what I wanted most at this moment and we set off together in two cars to the village. The patron was always pleased to see us and directed us through to the private dining room where his daughter was, as always, welcoming and showed us to a table laid for six. The menu was good as ever; we all ordered food and some bottles of wine to be going on with. We were all so glad to have Terence back with us and had missed him during his stay in the hospital but could detect that he had taken on a greater maturity because of his brush with death and I thought he would settle well into the role of section two leader in B flight. Soon the whole table was being regaled with Giles Lacey's funny stories and we were laughing our heads off. I forgot all about Herbert Clough. Jamie started a little bit of inter-flight rivalry by making fun of me as the barge killer, saying that he had heard that we were to be transferred to the navy as we were so good at sinking defenceless barges leaving B flight to rip through the enemy air force in the skies, but when we compared our recent scores, it was evident that A flight was learning fast how to kill the enemy. I was up to nine aircraft destroyed already, which was only two behind Jamie and I had a half a train and a barge to add to my tally for good measure. The evening was incredibly happy, and we all enjoyed several hours to escape from the pressure of regular flying to a more pleasant world in the company of our friends. We all knew that we might be the one missing from the table at the next happy meeting.

The next morning, I was going to go over to St Martin on the Ypres Salient front line where Herbert Clough's battalion was billeted, to collect his kit. Terence asked whether he could go along with me, and I readily agreed to having the company. I borrowed a small van from the transport section because I was sure that his kit could not be carried on the motorbike. I was not exactly sure where his company was placed in the line, but I knew that they were in the vicinity of the ruined St Martin Cathedral or thereabouts, a few miles beyond Poperinge. The weather was overcast with a strong threat of rain, which was another good reason for not using the motorcycle this morning. The van was small and dry and could go almost anywhere the motorbike could, and Terence and I enjoyed chatting as we drove until he dropped the bombshell that he would be prepared to speak on behalf of Herbert Clough at the court martial. I could not believe it and asked why he would do this. Terence told me that he had been a victim of bullying throughout his school days and when he was abused by Herbert Clough in Suzette's restaurant, he just collapsed inside himself, and it all came back to him.

"Your robust challenge to Clough and the support of my friends and comrades in the flight helped to show me that I was not the one who was weak, and that it was the bully who was the weak one. When I came across Clough again in the hospital in St Omer, he was a pitiful creature as he really could not see and was helpless. I think he had under-estimated the power of the drops and for how long he would be blinded. I did not know at that time that he had inflicted this wound on himself and readily gave him my help and saw not the blustering bully shouting in my face, but a poor distressed individual driven by fear, who when treated with kindness responded with gratitude and thanks." Terence said that he did not know what went through his mind during the night when his eyesight was beginning to come back, "… but I am certain that his decision to flee was made because he did not know how he could return to his unit and explain how he had become blinded when he was nowhere near the gas attack. In those few hours I saw the real character of Clough, the pain and hurt he had suffered in his life to make him behave as he did, and I am prepared to tell the court martial this." I was amazed and thanked him profusely for his bravery.

Passing the ruined fourteenth-century cathedral, Terence spotted the sign for Clough's battalion HQ, we pulled in and were given directions to the company command post where Clough had been based. We drove as close as we could get with the van and walked carefully down the communication trench to the large dugout that served as the company headquarters, ducking into the dark underground room which served both as a living space and the command centre for the company. I did not expect to receive a warm welcome, but I could feel the hostility of these officers towards us, and I wondered what we had done to deserve their anger. I saluted and asked for Major Bryanston, the company commander, but no one spoke, just looked across at a figure slumped at the table with a bottle of brandy and a glass in hand. He was wearing a shirt without a collar, trousers, and no badges of rank. I saluted the major and he looked up and asked in a drink-sodden voice what I wanted, offering no welcome or acknowledgement of who we were. I told him who I was and that I had come to collect the kit belonging to Lieutenant Clough. He just swore at me and called one of the lieutenants, who I recognised from Suzette's as one of Clough's companions on that night in the restaurant, and just said, "Sort them out". The major dismissed us with a wave of his hand and carried on drinking as we turned and followed the young officer out of the dugout.

Once in the daylight I could see that the lieutenant was embarrassed, and he called us to follow him along the trench until we came to a smaller dugout, which was a platoon base. He called out for Private Smith who came running, he introduced him to us as Clough's batman and told him to pack all Mr Clough's kit and 'bring it back here to this gentleman as quick as you can'. Smith disappeared into the dugout and we stood in the trench and waited. I asked the lieutenant why none of Clough's brother officers were willing to speak for him in court. He looked at me rather sheepishly and said that we were ordered not to.

'Why were you ordered not to speak in favour of a brother officer and by who?' He said he could not speak freely here as there were too many ears listening – if we were willing to meet him in St Omer this evening, he would tell me the full story in private, but he could tell me that Herbert Clough was not as black as he was being made out. We agreed to meet him at eight at the little café near to where Yvette lived rather than Suzette's, where there were too many military eyes and ears. Private Smith returned with Clough's kitbag, uniforms, and a trunk of personal possessions, which he said he would carry to our transport for us. When we loaded it into the back of the van, he turned to me and said, "Mr Clough is one of the best young officers I have ever served and please give him my best wishes. All the lads in his platoon wish him well and hope he gets off." I encouraged him to go further, and he said, "he was a bit hot-headed and could be sharp tongued at times, but that was not his real temperament which was kind and fair with his men, … and he helped me when my youngest was ill and needed medical treatment, he sent the money to pay the doctor to perform the operation. It was his hot head that got him into this fix in the first place because he wouldn't back down when he saw an injustice and he is paying the price now." I urged him to tell me more, but he clammed up and said that he had said too much already, but he could see that

I was a resourceful and clever officer and would be able to make something of the information. He saluted us and rushed off in great haste. I turned to Terence and we both knew that the business of Herbert Clough was not over yet.

That evening we met Lieutenant Welby in the café, and he brought with him another lieutenant who we had not met before called Cranley. We took a table on the forecourt where our conversation would not be overheard, and I began by telling them that Private Smith had independently confirmed our suspicions that something was not right with the version of events presented to us by the prosecution in this court martial. I ordered coffee and a bottle of brandy, and we settled down to listen to their story. Welby said that Herbert was a difficult person to get to know, he was blustering and held people at arm's length, and he could be particularly outspoken when he had been drinking.

"However," continued Welby, 'he was my platoon commander, he was good at his job and the men liked him and looked up to him, not least because he was always willing to stand up for them when they were in trouble even if it brought him into conflict with the company commander, Major Bryanston."

I wondered why this should be the case and cause conflict with his superior when he was performing as any good platoon commander should, so I pressed him to go further. Major Bryanston was a heavy drinker, we could probably confirm that from our small acquaintance with him today, and because he was often drunk, he delegated much of his duties to the company second-in-command Captain Faulkner, who was ambitious and hoped to replace Bryanston as company commander as soon as his health broke down completely through drink. He went on to explain that the major had served three years at the front and had been decorated for gallantry, but this latest appointment back to the front was too much for him. Faulkner plotted his downfall but there was one obstacle in his way, Herbert Clough, who joined the company in mid-1917 and quickly proved himself to be a competent and popular officer. When Captain Digby, the previous platoon commander, broke his leg Major Bryanston appointed Herbert as platoon commander instead of the candidate that Captain Faulkner had put forward. Faulkner was livid because he wanted one of his acolytes, Lt Betteridge, in this position because he knew that he could not browbeat Clough to do his bidding if he thought it was not right. Faulkner played dirty tricks on Clough and spread lies to show Herbert in a bad light, but it did not have much effect on Clough's running of his platoon. I asked Lieutenant Welby if he would be prepared to repeat what he had told us about this evening under oath in court and looked me in the eye, swallowed and said yes.

I now turned to Cranley and asked him what he was going to tell me. He started by backing up everything that Welby had said about Herbert as a platoon commander and said that he would swear that there was a conspiracy led by Faulkner including the major and two other officers, who I surmised were probably the two lieutenants who had made sworn statements against Herbert as part of the prosecution case. They had decided to ambush Herbert at night and squirt a toxic liquid into his eyes to make him blind for a short time and whilst he was unable to see, transport him secretly from their trenches and dump him behind the lines near where the gas attack had taken place. They knew that Herbert would be found, and it would be assumed that he had been injured in the gas attack and they knew he would be taken to a hospital many miles behind the front lines. Before they dumped the blinded Clough, they threatened him with death if he ever came back and this was a final warning. Their intention was to post him as absent and then build the false case that he had deserted his post when he was running for his life.

Their plan was cunning and very nearly worked for they banked on Clough getting his vision back within a day or two and using the opportunity to take off from the hospital, increasing the likelihood that if he were apprehended, the provost department would be certain to believe that he was a real deserter. It was a cleverly worked scheme, which removed Clough from being a thorn in Faulkner's side, destroyed Clough's character and would probably lead to his death by firing squad if he were apprehended and they were certain that little credence would be given to any story he told about what they had done. Cranley went on to tell us how Faulkner had manipulated Bryanston by controlling his access to the brandy bottle until he was so dependent on the alcohol that he would agree to anything Faulkner requested rather than go without his precious brandy supply.

I discussed how I would use the information that they had given me and reassured them that everything they had told me was in complete confidence, until I introduced their evidence into my defence of Herbert Clough. I would not divulge my list of witnesses until the end of the first day of the trial and because Bryanston, Faulkner, Betteridge, and Allen were being called as witnesses for the prosecution they would not be allowed in court to know who I was calling in my defence of Herbert in advance. Welby asked whether they would be allowed to stay in court to observe the proceedings after they had given their evidence and I answered that they would be returned to the waiting area in case they were called back for later questioning during the presentation of the defence case. I explained that I would not cross-examine the prosecution witnesses until after the court had heard their evidence. I pressed them on the support from the soldiers in the platoon for their commander and mentioned that I had already heard from Private Smith very favourable comments about the defendant and Cranley replied that he was certain that there would be no difficulty in finding members of the platoon to speak up in favour of their officer. I asked if there was a possibility of speaking to them on Sunday morning early and they agreed for us to be present at morning muster at 08:00 the next day. I thanked them both for their bravery in being prepared to testify and I could now see a glimmer of hope that I might have a defence to present next week.

Terence and I both wore motorcycle coats, helmets, and goggles, taking the motorbike back to the St Martin trenches so that we were less instantly recognisable than if we were openly in RFC uniform. We were able to ride the bike to within fifty yards of the platoon dugout and arrived just as Lt Cranley was calling the roll and issuing orders for the day. He invited me to address the men and I removed my helmet so that they could see my face, introduced myself and explained that I was defending their platoon commander at the court martial next week and that I needed all the help I could get if I was to have any chance of success. I told them that I would be remaining in the dugout for the rest of the morning should anyone wish to speak to me.

The platoon sergeant stepped forward, saluted, asked for permission to speak, and said that every member of the platoon was prepared to swear that Lt Clough was an excellent commander and treated them fairly, and were willing to sign sworn statements to that effect. He also called forward a lance corporal who said he was asked by Captain Faulkner to provide him with a small bottle of sulphuric acid mixed with vinegar which he said he was going to use to clean the rust and verdigris that was accumulating on some of his kit. He went on to say that one of his jobs was topping up lamp batteries and he had a supply of sulphuric acid for this purpose in his store.

I asked the sergeant and lance corporal and any other soldier with anything further to tell me to step into the dugout. Sergeant McArthy was first and said he could corroborate the lance corporal's story because he confided in him when the request was made whether he should comply with it, and he advised him to do so. Lance Corporal Green was a little reticent about speaking too openly but by careful coaxing he finally gave a full statement of what had transpired and was prepared to swear that Captain Faulkner had asked him to mix a solution of sulphuric acid and vinegar so he could get his batman to clean his kit for him. Green tried to persuade him that this solution was too strong for the job and could damage items made of leather and metal, but the captain insisted. He remembered warning Captain Faulkner that his batman should wear gloves and avoid any contact with his eyes when using the solution. Finally, I spoke again with Private Smith who repeated the sentiment he expressed the previous day and went even further to tell me that when he was serving dinner in the company dugout one evening, he overheard a conversation between Captain Faulkner and several others planning how they were going to ambush Lt Clough that night. I decided that I would call Lieutenants Welby and Cranley, Sergeant McArthy, Lance Corporal Green and Private Smith as witnesses for the defence. I would arrange for the two officers to be accommodated in the garrison officers' mess and for the other ranks in the garrison barracks and ensure that they were far away from the Citadel where the court martial was to be held. I did not want Faulkner and his supporters intimidating the witnesses before they had given their evidence.

Terence and I left by eleven to ride back to La Coupole, collect the small van with Herbert's trunk and uniforms and drive down to Arras to impart the news of the developments to him. Clough was looking good, the bruises were beginning to fade on his face, and I was glad that I had in my possession the medical report from Captain Salt who described the extensive injuries to Herbert's face and torso, administered by something like a rubber truncheon or a leather boot. He was certain from his analysis of the development of the bruises that Clough had been the subject of attacks on at least two occasions, at least three days apart.

Herbert was surprised when he was brought into the interview room to see Terence with me and looked at me with a puzzled expression, asking why he was here. I told him to sit down and relax and all would become clear in the next hour. I began by explaining that Terence was recovering from his recent wounds, he had returned to the squadron on light duties and had expressed a willingness to speak on his behalf as a character witness. Herbert looked aghast and said, "Why should he do this after I abused him so badly in the restaurant when I was drunk and then he shamed me in the hospital with his kindness?"

"I will let Terence explain it to you in his own words," I replied, "and you will see that he is sincere in what he says." I stepped out of the room and left Terence to explain his reasons more eloquently than I could. I arranged with the prison security section to store Lt Clough's trunk and best uniform overnight and to ensure that it travelled with him in the transport to St Omer in the morning. When I returned to the room, both Terence and Herbert appeared a little less tense but not completely relaxed, although I thought they were probably ready to discuss my defence strategy in more detail.

Herbert reaffirmed that he had not changed his mind and he would not allow me to divulge the details of his early life at home and school in mitigation and he would not challenge any of the events as described in the prosecution case. I snapped back at him to stop acting like a coward and before he could revolt against that accusation I said, "I have already discovered from speaking with your platoon in the last twenty-four hours that whatever kind of bully you might have been in the past, is not who you are now. Every single member of your platoon has signed sworn statements in your support, and I now have selected six witnesses to call on your behalf. I have managed to piece together what I think happened to you and I think I have the evidence to prove it. "I went through my version of the story, which I had managed to put together from the various information I had received, but I did not yet understand why they prosecuted this vendetta against him. "

Herbert explained that for months he had been worried about the mental and physical collapse of Major Bryanston who had proved himself a good soldier and an honourable man on many occasions in the past. He had always enjoyed brandy and many times would have a glass or two with his officers in the evening, until Faulkner joined the company as second-in-command and gradually, they began to see the major becoming more dependent on the bottle and his ability to command the company diminishing.

"Faulkner had effectively become de facto company commander," Herbert explained, "but when I challenged him about this and tried to insist that the major should be seen by a doctor he refused." Herbert had decided to seek an interview with the battalion commander and express his concerns for the health of Major Bryanston. He sent a request to battalion headquarters for the interview but somehow it was intercepted in transit. "Faulkner and his henchmen cornered me one night and threatened to break me if I tried to speak to battalion again. However, I persisted secretly although I had told them I would not, and kept quiet a little longer, but sent a second request to battalion, which was answered, and an appointment arranged with the colonel for the day after I ran away.'

"But that isn't true," I replied, "because you didn't run away, you were ambushed, and a mixture of sulphuric acid and vinegar was squirted into your eyes to make you blind for a day or two. Faulkner tied you up and transported to the area near where the gas attack had been earlier in that day and turned you out of the van to wander aimlessly around unable to see. I am sure that you believed that your life was in imminent danger from Faulkner and his associates, which accounts for the reason you ran away from the hospital. You did not take off your uniform and when you were apprehended you were still wearing it – I would like to hear from you what was in your mind at that moment." He said he did not know and that his mind was in turmoil, but he knew that he had to save Major Bryanston before his health was completely ruined and get a message to his platoon that he was safe.

Herbert was still quite frightened of the threats Faulkner had made and asked what might happen if we revealed this version of events before the court martial and they still found him guilty. I replied that he had nothing to lose because the outcomes would be the same, death by firing squad or death at the hand of Faulkner. "If you do not challenge the prosecution case," I stressed, "then death by firing squad is almost inevitable but if we put this alternative version of events before the court, backed up by the testimony of six witnesses, I believe that you will be acquitted, and Faulkner and his associates will be arrested to face a court martial of their own." Reluctantly, he agreed, and I briefed him that he must clear his mind of any thoughts that he was guilty and to conduct himself as a lieutenant who commands a platoon in an infantry company and show the qualities that earned him the support of his soldiers to the members of the court martial board.

"This will startle the prosecution who think that this is an easy win case and expect to see a broken man brought before the court on Tuesday," I explained. "I want you to show them that we have nothing to be ashamed of and are going to fight them at every stage." I told him that his trunk and uniforms were in the prison security office. They would travel with him to St Omer tomorrow and that he should take pains to dress in his best uniform for the opening of the case on Tuesday morning. I joked with him that he did not want to be upstaged by his prisoner's friend, who would be wearing his brand-new Royal Air Force flight lieutenant's uniform for the first time.

Before leaving I reassured him that we now had a chance of winning, which did not seem possible two days ago, and that I would visit him in St Omer Citadel tomorrow afternoon and stay with him until the case was concluded either way. Terence and I left around four in the afternoon, stopped for an early dinner on the way back to La Coupole and went over everything that had transpired over the last day and a half. Our mood was significantly more positive than it was before the weekend and I was extremely grateful to Terence for his support through these difficult few days.

Monday was the last day of March and I received a letter from Ruby confirming that she had missed her third menstruation and she was pregnant, and the baby would be due sometime in mid-September. She said she was delighted to know for certain and was so happy that I was the father of her baby and looked forward to a long and happy life together. Her parents were also pleased and not too concerned about the pregnancy because we were engaged to be married but felt we should try to get wed before the birth, if possible. I was enamoured with the possibility of being a father so much and felt that this now tied me much closer to Ruby and all my doubts would go away. I wrote back saying how excited I was with the news and would try to get some leave when the trial was over, and we could ask the Reverend Lewis to marry us in the chapel as soon as I got home.

The rest of the day I made detailed notes of how I would present my case and then packed to travel across to St Omer to meet with Herbert in his secure quarters in the Citadel officers' mess. Herbert was much more relaxed than the previous day, and he said that it was because it felt good to be out of a prison cell or trench dugout and to sleep in a proper bed again, but I thought he had reconciled himself to the defence I was proposing to make and had placed his fate into my hands. I reassured him that we now had a fair chance of a result provided our witnesses gave credible performances in the witness box, but I did not doubt any of them would let us down because they were speaking from the heart, not from a bed of lies. Herbert and I dined in his quarters on a passable meal from the mess kitchen, but we both agreed we would rather have been at Suzette's where the food was much better. I left him at nine to get an early night, as we needed to be at our best for the opening of the court martial in the morning.

My room was in the opposite wing of the building, which meant that I needed to go down the stairs, across the main reception and up the opposite staircase. As I passed through the reception, I passed a group of officers talking loudly, then I heard my name called and I turned to see a middle-aged and rather overweight major with grey hair and whiskers. He thrust his hand out and said," Sir Andrew Harding," and asked if we could have a private word. We stepped away from his companions into a small anteroom, which was empty, and we sat in two of the armchairs. He started by saying that we did not have much of a chance of winning because the evidence is clear, "Clough is a craven coward and a deserter and why would a bright young officer such as yourself wish to be associated with him?" He said that he was empowered to offer us a deal; " if we were to accept the prosecution case, they would remove the request for the death penalty, you will have done your job admirably and you will have saved the accused's life into the bargain."

I took an instant dislike to Sir Andrew, who was oily, patronising, and complacent that he would not have a fight on his hands in the courtroom. I thanked him for his offer and said that I could not make a reply until I had discussed it with Lieutenant Clough but would let him have an answer in the morning. He seemed pleased with that and said that we should share a snifter of brandy as a nightcap to celebrate a meeting of minds and a victory for good sense. I declined politely and said that I needed to get to my room as I still had some work today in preparation for tomorrow. I made my escape from the anteroom, and as I climbed the stairs, I turned these events over in my mind. I was certain that Sir Andrew was not taking this case seriously enough and had accepted the evidence presented to him without further investigation. He was sure that the damming evidence from Clough's school records and OCTU would prejudice the court against the defendant enough to guarantee a guilty verdict. I suspected that he would be a fearsome orator and relied on his ability to make eloquent speeches to the court to gloss over the scant evidence of Clough's guilt. I felt that he approached me with the attitude that he had already won, he was only going through the motions and that this meeting had been carefully engineered to intimidate me into accepting that it was impossible to for me to win. The question that was nagging at me was why, if he was so confident of winning, did he make the concession of imprisonment rather than the death penalty? By the time I reached the top of the second flight of stairs I realised that he was not confident at all, and that he knew he was going into battle ill-prepared with sketchy evidence and several anomalies that left many obvious questions unanswered.

I began to feel much more confident and more determined to win an acquittal for Herbert Clough. I made quick notes of the unanswered questions to remind me in the morning there was no documentary evidence that Major Bryanston had changed his opinion of Clough's performance after appointing him as platoon commander; there were no adverse comments added to his fitness report and no direct evidence of when and how Clough absented himself from his platoon positions. How had he travelled the six miles to the area of the gas attack and why would a deserter try to run away but stay within a few hundred yards of the front line, not run for the rear areas where he would be safe? Why had Clough, when he escaped from the hospital, not disguised himself but chosen to remain dressed in full uniform? Why did he remain in the vicinity of the front line and not attempt to reach Paris or the channel ports? What explanation was there for this unusual behaviour of a supposed deserter? There were more questions that were occurring to me as I was writing. I knew I must be careful not to overload my mind with too many but focus on four or five vital questions that would cast serious doubt on the case put forward by the prosecution.

TWENTY

Clough Court Martial

I took care to dress myself carefully in my new RAF uniform and to attach my medals to the ribbons as I wanted the court to see the contrast between Sir Andrew and me as the prisoner's friend. I knew that the members of the court martial would see me as a front-line officer and maybe would listen more carefully to what I had to say because of it. Herbert Clough looked smart and confident, although he confided in me that he was putting on this air of confidence as an act, inside his heart was pounding and he felt sick. However, he was pragmatic enough to know that he had to face this ordeal whatever the outcome and was determined to try his best to face it head on. The court was due to sit at 10:00 so with the military police escort we made our way to the courtroom at 09:30. The large anteroom in the mess had been cleared of its furniture and set up as the court martial with a large desk and chair for the judge at the back of the room and to his left, a large table with five chairs for the board. To the left were some desks and chairs for the prosecution and to the right a desk and two chairs for us. A chair was placed in the centre of the room for the witness box. Nearest the door were rows of seats as a kind of public gallery, where interested parties not involved in the case could observe proceedings but not take part. Witnesses for the prosecution and the defence were held in two separate anterooms away from the court to preserve their objectivity.

Herbert and I settled ourselves and I went over again our strategy for today and calmed him down as best as I could. Sir Andrew Harding arrived with his team, and I noticed that over his uniform he was wearing his legal gown, silk, and wig presumably to impress the court and was accompanied by a couple of assistants who carried his papers. I went over to him and wished him good morning and said that after consulting with the defendant we had decided not to accept his offer of a deal and would challenge his version of events vigorously. Harding's face was a picture of confusion as I suspected that he was not expecting to have to fight this case in detail and he would now have to think on his feet because he had no idea what kind of challenges, I would bring. The sergeant military policeman who had escorted us into the courtroom was now acting as the usher and at one minute to ten called us to order to receive the judge advocate. Colonel Robertson, an elderly but distinguished-looking man, entered and took his seat.

The first task was the swearing-in of the members of the court martial board and as the names were read out, the prosecution and the defence could object to one of the board members and they would be replaced by one of the stand-ins already waiting outside the court if required. There were no objections, the court martial board was sworn in by the court usher and then took their seats. I studied them carefully to see if I could tell anything about them from their appearance but, of course, I could not. They ranged in ages from early twenties to forties and I thought represented quite typically the range of officers one might find in an infantry front-line regiment. I did not know whether this would be a help or a hindrance to us. They were all serving at the front, maybe the younger ones might have sympathy for Herbert Clough or maybe not. I hoped that they would judge the evidence on its merits with open minds and not assume that he must be guilty because of some of the things in his past that did not show his character in the best light.

Colonel Robertson then went on to introduce Major Sir Andrew Harding QC, who was leading for the prosecution and then to introduce me for the defence. He then indicated that the prosecution may begin to present its case. Major Harding jumped up and said that he wished to present a legal argument before proceeding. The judge agreed and Harding began that he objected that the officer for the defence was no longer a member of the army and therefore had no authority to act on behalf of the defendant in these proceedings, as he was now a member of the Royal Air Force. The judge sighed, looked at Harding with scorn and replied firmly, "Are you trying to impugn the honour of this gallant and decorated officer that he is no longer worthy to stand in defence of the accused just because His Majesty the King has thought it fit to create a third service and to disband the Royal Flying Corps today?" Harding spluttered that he meant no slur on Captain Morgan's character but simply asked whether he has the authority to act in this court martial? The judge raised his voice to address the whole courtroom that he had noticed that both the prosecutor and defence were wearing fancy dress. This, in his opinion, was only appropriate for one of us and glared at Major Harding. He then turned to me and said, "Captain Morgan may I congratulate you on the occasion of your first day in the new service as flight lieutenant in the Royal Air Force," and he directed that from this point on I would be addressed by the court as flight lieutenant. He then called for a fifteen-minute adjournment so that Major Harding could dress himself in appropriate uniform attire before the case could begin. First point to us, I thought, and I could see that Harding was rattled and was resorting to tricks to discredit the defendant through attacking his defending officer, and I guessed that he was only doing this because he knew his case was thin.

Suitably attired, the case began in earnest with Harding's opening statement which was presented in a theatrical style more reminiscent of the Old Bailey in London but found less favour in these military proceedings. I could see from the judge's face that he did not approve of these long speeches and made a mental note of this for my utterances that were to come. I knew that I could not match Harding's eloquence and was amazed that he managed to elaborate such a long tale based on so little evidence. The key point he emphasised several times was that the facts of the case were undisputed and showed Lt Clough to be a craven coward who ran away because he was afraid of going into action at the head of his platoon. He said he would show that Clough was of such a low character that he pretended to be blinded by a gas attack so that he would be removed from the battlefield with the wounded. Once in hospital he threw off his disguise, made good his plan to desert and he would have got away with it if it were not for two RFC officers and their sergeant who apprehended Clough before he got far. He made a great play that he would also bring forth documentary evidence to show Clough's inglorious past and his cowardly nature from his schooldays and training at the OCTU up to the present day. He said he would be calling witnesses who had served with him in his company who would testify as to Clough's character and the facts of this case. He was sure that the evidence was compelling, and Clough would be found guilty as charged.

When he sat down after twenty minutes there was an audible sigh of relief around the courtroom and the judge asked if I wished to say anything. I was rather nervous but felt I should say a couple of things, I thanked the judge and stood and faced the court. "I have heard the opening statement from the prosecutor and felt that I needed to say just two things. First, I can reassure the prosecutor that the facts of this case are not undisputed as the prosecution asserts and I will bring forth witnesses who will challenge the prosecution version of events and secondly, that the documentary evidence from Lieutenant Clough's childhood and youth have had a massive bearing on who he has become today, and I will bring forward character witnesses to testify to that effect.'" It was now approaching noon and the judge adjourned the court until 13:15 for lunch, when the prosecution could begin to present its case.

Harding re-opened after lunch by calling Captain Faulkner to the witness box, where he took the oath and answered Harding's question in a clear and firm voice. I knew that he would have credibility with the court being the second-in-command of the company. He was asked about the performance of Lt Clough, and he described several occasions where his performance was below par and he had been reprimanded. He then went on to ask Faulkner about the day Clough absented himself from his platoon and to tell the court how he had become aware that he was absent from his post, which led on to further questions about what action he took. He said they searched the company positions and could not find him, then alerted the company commander, Major Bryanston, who gave orders that the military police and battalion headquarters should be informed that Clough had deserted his post. Harding said he had no further questions at this time and sat down. The judge asked if I wished to cross-examine the witness, and I replied that I had a few questions to ask the witness to clarify some of his statements for the benefit of the court.

I approached the witness chair, stood squarely in front of Faulkner, and said, "Good Morning, Captain, do you remember the only time we have met before, a week last Saturday when you tried to prevent me from speaking to the members of Lieutenant Clough's platoon? Why did you tell me that I was not welcome and to leave the company positions immediately? You knew that I was acting as an officer of this court and needed to speak to these men to establish whether they could help finding out the facts of the case and it should have been your duty to assist me in this task."

Captain Faulkner bristled and said, "I certainly did not say or do anything of the sort." I stepped a little closer to him and said, 'There are two witnesses who were present when you said these words and I will be calling them to swear under oath as to the words you used on that occasion."

I pressed on. "Can you tell the court what you were trying to prevent me from finding out?" Faulkner replied that nothing was withheld or hidden from me and that he was just looking after the welfare of the men who were terribly upset by the treatment, they had received at the hands of Lt Clough.

I took a step back and asked him to cast his mind back to what he had said in his evidence, that Lt Clough had been reprimanded on several occasions for poor performance. 'Did you mean by this that he had treated his men badly?"

Faulkner answered, "Yes, that was it exactly," and so I immediately followed up with a supplementary question, "Who delivered these reprimands?"

"It was Major Bryanston," Faulkner replied straightaway.

'Captain Faulkner, if what you say is true, can you account for the fact that Lieutenant Clough's service record contains no reference to these reprimands issued by his company commander and, indeed, the last entry written by Major Bryanston, his company commander, on the 18th of February, 1918 was very complimentary about his performance and suggested that he had potential to go much further in the regiment. He expresses satisfaction in his choice of Clough as platoon commander and that he was living up to his expectations well."

I turned to the judge and indicated that I was putting these extracts from Lt Herbert Clough's service record into evidence as exhibit D1. I turned to Captain Faulkner and pressed home my point. "I suggest to you that your account of Clough's poor performance is a complete fabrication and the official record written and signed by the company commander presents the more accurate picture." Faulkner retorted with fury that Major Bryanston was unfit for command because he was always drunk, and he did not know what he was doing most of the time.

"If what you have just asserted is true, did you report this to your battalion commander at any time?" He looked taken aback and said, "I didn't report it because of my loyalty to Major Bryanston, who had been a good commanding officer before he started drinking so heavily and I didn't want to destroy his career."

"Are you aware of any other officers who were concerned about Major Bryanston's health reporting this matter to the battalion headquarters behind your back?" He answered that he did not. So, I asked him," Would you be surprised to know that Lt Clough had written to the battalion HQ twice on this matter and had an appointment booked with the battalion commander to discuss his concerns on the morning he allegedly deserted his post?"

He said he would be surprised, and I asked him, "Would you concede that it would be a rather strange set of events where an officer who had an interview scheduled with his battalion commander the next morning would actually attempt to desert on that day, knowing he would be missed as soon as he failed to turn up for the appointment as planned?"

Faulkner replied, "I suppose so."

"What time did you discover Clough was missing?"

"I think it was when he was not present during morning stand to," he replied.

"Did any member of Clough's platoon express any concern about his absence and report it to you?" He said he could not recall if they did or not.

"I suggest to you that no one in Clough's platoon was worried about his absence because it was well known that he was going to battalion headquarters for a meeting with the battalion commander at 09:00. And it was so well known that I suggest that even you knew all about it and I put it to the court that this notion that you discovered him missing at 08:00 and conducted a search is another complete fabrication of the truth."

I asked Faulkner, "Can you describe to the court your relationship with the accused?" He replied that they were not particularly friendly, and their relationship was business-like as platoon commander to company second-in-command.

I delved further. "Captain Faulkner, what were your feelings when Major Bryanston chose to appoint Lieutenant Clough as platoon commander instead of Lieutenant Betteridge?"

He replied, "I was disappointed that the major had chosen Clough because I felt that Betteridge would have been a better choice, but it was not my choice to make so I accepted it and got on with working with Lieutenant Clough."

"Captain Faulkner, will you explain to the court what the specific qualities were you found in the performance of Lieutenant Betteridge that made him, in your opinion, a superior candidate for the vacant platoon commander post?"

Faulkner paused for a few seconds to collect his thoughts and then replied, "Betteridge was a bright and intelligent officer who had long been identified as having the potential for leadership."

"I see, Captain Faulkner, that does seem clear in your mind, but I am afraid that I still remain confused because I have read the service record of Lieutenant Betteridge for the period since he joined your battalion and his assessments are average, there are no references to his intelligence or any potential for leadership. Is this something else that you have made up?"

I turned to the judge and said that I would like to enter the record as evidence, exhibit D2, the excerpts from the service record of Lt Betteridge for the period April 1917 to the present date. I turned back to Captain Faulkner. "Is not the real reason you wished to prefer Lieutenant Betteridge in this matter that he is, in fact, the eldest son of your cousin, Anne Faulkner, wife of Albert Betteridge and therefore you are related? Can you confirm that Lieutenant Betteridge and you are second cousins and that is the reason you wanted to advance his career?"

Faulkner replied, "So what if he is my cousin? I put him forward because he was simply the best man for the job."

At this point, I introduced into evidence the birth certificate of one James Betteridge, born to parents Albert Betteridge and Amy Betteridge, née Faulkner, as exhibit D3 and then went on, "Yes, Captain Faulkner, I don't doubt that for your purposes your cousin was the best man for the job, in your opinion, because he was tied to you by blood and patronage in securing him a position. He had shown himself to be an average officer who was good at following orders and could be controlled by you more easily, whereas you feared Lieutenant Clough because he was an officer with a mind of his own."

I addressed the judge directly indicating that this witness was vital to the prosecution case as much of the evidence that he has presented was the basis upon which the charge was brought against the defendant. "We have discovered this morning, however, that there are many inconsistencies in this evidence as it was presented and his version of events is not backed up by the documentary evidence available to us in exhibits D1, D2 and D3. I request that this witness is not discharged but be held for further cross-examination as I suspect that as we hear from other witnesses, further inconsistences may emerge and that will need clarification from Captain Faulkner."

The judge agreed and spoke directly to Major Harding. "Your witness will remain in the waiting area because there is a strong likelihood that he will be recalled to the witness box as the trial continues." He then turned to Captain Faulkner and said, "Captain Faulkner, I need to remind you that you remain under oath and as such are not at liberty to discuss the events of this case with anyone other than Major Harding and you will remain in the witness waiting area whilst the court is in session until you are discharged. You may leave the witness box."

It was now three o'clock and Major Harding called his next witness, Lieutenant James Betteridge. There was a lull in proceedings before Betteridge appeared with the sergeant usher at the door and was led to the witness box, where he took the oath on the Bible and stated his name, rank, regiment, and service number. Major Harding began to take him gently through his testimony step by step and Betteridge told a story of joining the company at roughly the same time as Lt Clough but being allocated to serve within a different platoon. He did not have a great deal to do with Clough, being largely focused within the affairs of his own platoon but heard lots of stories about Clough's aggressive and bullying behaviour from the gossip circulating amongst the soldiers. I jumped up to object to the introduction of hearsay and the judged asked that the witness stick to specific instances of which he had personal experience. Harding had hinted that there was gossip circulating about Clough's behaviour and this would have raised a flag in the minds of the court martial even though no corroborating evidence was supplied. He moved his questions on to the events leading up to Clough's alleged desertion and asked Betteridge to describe any instances when Clough had come into conflict with members of the company. Betteridge recounted a story that Clough had disagreed with Captain Faulkner over the treatment of Major Bryanston's increased drinking. He indicated that he was sure that the captain, as second-in-command, was equally concerned about the levels of drinking but wished to protect the major's good reputation. He said that the captain had taken custody of the supplies of brandy and was rationing it out to the major to keep him functioning at a basic level and Captain Faulkner undertook most of the company commander duties himself so that the company appeared to be functioning normally to battalion headquarters.

Harding interposed at this point and said, "To your knowledge did Lieutenant Clough support this strategy?" Betteridge replied, "Clough didn't and argued strongly that it was wrong to conceal the facts from battalion because it gave a false impression of the company's readiness to go into action; it was against the rules of military discipline and finally did nothing for the health of the major. Captain Faulkner tried to persuade him that it was for the good of the company and for Major Bryanston and ordered him to take no action, but Clough disobeyed that order and said it was unlawful and wrote to the battalion commander's office. Fortunately, Captain Faulkner was able to intercept that letter and it was never received at battalion, and I witnessed the blazing row between Clough and the captain when he confronted

Clough with the letter, which I thought would end in violence. Clough felt passionately that the preservation of Major Bryanston's health by reducing his drinking and removing him from the frontline post was the best chance that he would be able to return to his wife and children after the war and this far outweighed any actions to hide the truth to preserve his reputation."

Harding then asked Betteridge if he had any cause to complain about Clough's behaviour and he replied that he made a formal complaint about Lt Clough using insulting language towards him. Harding led him on by asking what were the insulting words that he used, and Betteridge said that he had called him, "a spineless yes man who runs after Faulkner like a lap dog."

Harding pressed on. 'Was Lieutenant Clough expressing his opinion to you privately or were there any witnesses to this exchange?" Betteridge stumbled on by saying that he said these words openly in front of the men in his platoon and the whole thing was observed by Lt Allen.

Harding said he had no further questions and sat down. The judge asked me if I would prefer to cross-examine this witness in the morning or start now. It was three thirty-five and I knew that the judge would sit until four-thirty, so I thought I would cross-examine now. And I would be as quick as I could.

"Mr Betteridge, I have a small number of questions to ask you which I hope will clear up some of the things that don't add up in your testimony, so I hope that you will be able to assist the court in this." Betteridge was rather tall and gaunt and had the demeanour of an overgrown schoolboy as he stared at me with fear in his eyes.

I continued, "Mr Betteridge, can I ask you, are you a truthful man." he nodded his head and I reminded him that he needed to speak the words aloud and he said, "Yes I am."

"Good, I am glad to hear that because you are giving evidence under oath, and should it be found that you have lied under oath you could face serious charges of perjury for which the penalty would be a lengthy spell in military prison and the loss of reputation far worse than the loss of one's reputation for insobriety."

I paused to let these words sink in and then asked, "Mr Betteridge, is Captain John Faulkner your cousin?'

"Yes, he is my mother's first cousin," he replied.

Perhaps you could explain to the court, Mr Betteridge, the marvellous coincidence that when you joined the army from school you were miraculously posted to the very same regiment, battalion and company in which your cousin was already serving at second-in-command to a company commander?"

Betteridge smiled and replied, "Oh, it wasn't really a coincidence because Cousin John promised my mother he would get me a place in his company so he could look after me."

"So, your cousin John is willing to break the rules to get something that he wants? Just answer yes or no." Betteridge fumbled and said he did not know but I rounded on him and said, "You have just told us that he manipulated army rules to get you into his company under his wing."

"But that was to protect me."

"Ah yes, Captain Faulkner is strong on protecting others when it suits him. This sounds rather like when you told the court that he did not report Major Bryanston's drinking to higher authority when he should have done, to protect the major's reputation."

I switched tactics and said to Betteridge, who now looked as if he was going to cry, "Tell me about the gossip you heard about Clough's bad behaviour."

"I heard lots of stories of Clough shouting at soldiers and charging them for trivial offences as well as insulting his brother officers."

"Yes, I understand but did you hear this gossip from the victims treated so badly by Lieutenant Clough or was it just tittle tattle put about to discredit Lieutenant Clough's reputation after he had been appointed platoon commander instead of you?"

"I... I... I... don't know," he stammered.

"OK, Mr Betteridge, but can you name anyone in the company who was a victim at the hands of Lieutenant Clough?"

He seemed confused and turned to Harding in a silent plea for help, but I did not let up and went in for the kill. "Were any of the complaints made by the members of Mr Clough's platoon itself?"

Betteridge relaxed and said, "Yes, most of them."

"And you can testify that you have seen these complaints in writing and know that this to be a true and accurate statement?"

He immediately said, "Yes, of course."

"Are you sure about this?'" He looked at me quizzically. I turned to the court and said that I was putting into the record the signed statements by every member of Mr Clough's platoon, who had voluntarily made statements testifying to their support for their platoon commander. There were thirty-three signed statements under the heading of exhibit D4.

"So, I will ask you again Mr Betteridge, did you see written complaints from members of Mr Clough's platoon about his poor behaviour? I ask you to think carefully for a minute before you answer."

He looked pale and in a small voice said, "No."

"Mr Betteridge I must remind you that in answer to my very first question you told us you were an honest man but that was clearly not true and why should we believe anything you have told us when you have deliberately lied to this court to suggest there were complaints made against Mr Clough when there were not?"

He flushed red and in a cracked voice said, "I have not lied, everything is true because Captain Faulkner told me it was so."

"And I suppose Captain Faulkner told you what to say in court today?"

Harding immediately jumped up to object to my leading the witness to incriminate another officer, the judge agreed and asked me to rephrase my question.

"Mr Betteridge, would you be surprised to know that your company disciplinary records contain no instances of complaints being made against Lieutenant Clough at any time, just as there is no record of him receiving any reprimands at any time and I put it to you that this is a complete fabrication like every other aspect of your story." I turned to the judge and said that I would be entering into the court records as exhibit D6 a copy of the company disciplinary record from the period April 1917 to today's date to confirm what I had just stated.

"Finally, Mr Betteridge, let us turn to the alleged insult to your reputation and the complaint that you made. I have already shown that no complaint was made against Lieutenant Clough or recorded in the disciplinary record and there is no witness statement from Lieutenant Allen or any of the men of your platoon to testify that this actually happened."

"But he did say it to me," he barked back at me.

"I have no doubt he did but probably in private and I think I might have done the same in the circumstances.:

I turned to the judge and said no more questions were needed as this witness's testimony has been shown to be highly questionable.

The judge adjourned the court until 10:00 Wednesday morning.

Major Harding moved on to safer ground in the morning by calling witnesses who were credible and gave accounts of the events that they had witnessed personally. His first witness was Corporal Dale, RAMC who gave evidence of the time and place where he discovered Lt Clough wandering about eighty yards behind the front of the trenches where earlier in the day the Royal Warwick Regiment positions had suffered a gas attack. He stated that on examining Lt Clough it was obvious that his sight had been affected, probably by the gas and he was blind. His eyes seemed to have suffered damage consistent with gas injuries and the blindness could be temporary but sometimes was permanent. He was given first-aid attention and sent back to be transported to hospital in St Omer for a more detailed examination. Harding had no more questions, the judge asked me if I wished to cross-examine, and I jumped up and approached Corporal Dale.

'Corporal, I just want to check a number of points with you before we move on to other witnesses. "Can you tell us again what time it was when you discovered the defendant in a distressed state behind the Warwick's trenches?"

The corporal replied, "As far as I can be certain it was sometime after eleven o'clock that morning because we couldn't make our first sweep for wounded until the gas had sufficiently dissipated, which took about forty minutes because the winds were light."

"So, do you know what time the gas attack occurred?"

"The gas cloud was sighted at 08:40 but the majority of the Warwick regiment soldiers acted quickly and were able to put on their gas masks and they suffered relatively few injuries."

"How many other casualties had severe eye problems and temporary blindness like Lieutenant Clough?'

The corporal looked at me as if I were daft and said, "I have already indicated that the prompt action by the Warwicks prevented most injuries and those that did occur were mostly respiratory in nature where the soldier was slow in getting a gas mask on properly and got a whiff of the gas. Lieutenant Clough was the only casualty with symptoms of blindness."

"In your experience, is blindness a common result of exposure to mustard gas?"

The corporal replied, "I am not an expert in this form of injury particularly, but I have come across blindness before as a result of gas attacks and it is usually as a result of a long-unprotected exposure to the gas."

"Was Lieutenant Clough wearing a gas mask?"

"No, I thought it was strange because he was carrying a respirator, but it was still in its case."

"Corporal, could the temporary blindness be caused in ways other than by long exposure to gas?"

"Certainly, there are many substances that can cause temporary or permanent blindness if they get into the eyes, but they can usually be treated by bathing the eyes to reduce the irritation effectively."

"This will be my final question, Corporal Dale, in your opinion if someone had a solution of one-part sulphuric acid and three parts vinegars, squirted directly into the eyes what would be the result?"

The corporal replied, "This solution if directed into the eyes would be a dangerous mixture as it would be likely to burn the outer surface of the eye, however the vinegar would prevent the acid from penetrating beneath the surface and causing too much longer-term damage."

I thanked him for his evidence, and he was discharged.

Harding then called Major Humphrey Baldock, a consultant physician at the St Omer hospital who confirmed that Lt Clough was examined by him at the hospital at 15:00 in the afternoon on that day. His report showed that Clough's eyes were swollen, red and weeping continuously and that he appeared to have lost his sight. The major confirmed that the injuries were consistent with similar cases he had treated after gas attacks. He had bathed the eyes with saline solution and bandaged them to prevent too much light irritating his vision any further. Lt Clough was to be sent to a convalescent hospital for observation to see whether his sight returned partially or fully in the ensuing weeks. Lt Clough was kept in the observation ward overnight pending transport to the rear in the morning. Sometime in the night Lt Clough must have recovered some vision and absented himself from the hospital on a stolen motorcycle.

In cross-examination I asked the major whether he thought that a solution of sulphuric acid and vinegar would produce similar symptoms as a gas attack and he replied that, in his opinion, it would be impossible to tell the difference without laboratory examination of swabs from the patient.

Harding now called Lt Allen to the witness chair and again tried to rehearse the same story I had already discredited from Faulkner and Betteridge with little effect. Allen tried to convince the court that there was common gossip about Clough's bullying behaviour and harsh treatment of his men. He said that he had sworn out a complaint against Clough with the company commander for threatening behaviour, when Clough threatened to ambush him one dark night and give him a sound thrashing if he supported

Betteridge in his complaint against him. Allen also confirmed that he was a witness to the insulting language used by Clough against Betteridge.

In cross-examination, I referred Lt Allen to the previous evidence entered into the court record, which showed no complaints or reprimands issued against Lt Clough at any time. Further that his service record showed that his performance was rated good by the company commander. The suggestion that there were many complaints made by the men was countered fully by a lack of documentary proof, whereas all thirty-three of the men in Clough's platoon had signed sworn statements of support for their commander. The version of events put forward by the prosecution was an account dreamed up by Captain Faulkner and his two acolytes, Betteridge and Allen, and there was no independent evidence to corroborate what they said. I commended Lt Allen for his loyalty to his friends in that he was willing to lie on oath to save their skins. Harding immediately jumped up and objected to my last statement and ranted that Lt Allen was not on trial here and I should withdraw the impugning words. The judge agreed that Lt Allen was not on trial here, then said he was beginning to think that perhaps he should be… he then addressed me directly to withdraw my last words about Lt Allen.

Major Harding now sought to write into the evidence records excerpts from Clough's school reports, which showed he was a bully and had been suspected of being the perpetrator of several violent incidents in which boys were hurt. In none of the cases was Clough's guilt established, although some of his schoolmasters still believed he was a prime mover in both cases. Similarly, he referred to the unfortunate incidents at the OCTU but although Clough was a suspect amongst several others there was no conclusive evidence against him. The judge asked if I objected to these transcripts being entered in evidence and I replied that I had no objection to this information being made public, provided it was accepted on the basis that it was not true evidence but only circumstantial in every respect.

The judge adjourned for lunch and invited me to begin my defence immediately after the court resumed at 13:15.

TWENTY-ONE
Opening the Defence

I called my first witness for the defence, Lt Welby, who came to the witness chair and stated his name, rank, regiment, and service number before sitting down."Lieutenant Welby, can you tell the court how you come to know Lieutenant Clough?" was my opening question.

Welby replied, "Herbert Clough and I served together as second lieutenants in the platoon under the command of the previous platoon commander. We were both promoted to lieutenant at roughly the same time on seniority."

"Can you tell the court what kind of man Lieutenant Clough is?"

"He is a typical Yorkshireman although I don't think he actually comes from Yorkshire, that is he is brusque and plain speaking, sometimes people can take offence at this bluntness and this is a trait that comes out when he has had a lot to drink, but most times he keeps it under control. As a platoon commander and leader of men he has much to commend him. He will stand up for the men in his platoon in whatever circumstances and will punish them fairly if they are wrong and protect them if they are not. The men in the platoon like and respect him and know that when the next big attack comes that Mr Clough will lead them over the top."

"In your opinion, did Mr Clough have good relations with others in the company, outside of your platoon?"

"Mostly, although there were poor relations between him and Captain Faulkner that kept bubbling along and wouldn't go away."

"Can you tell the court what these disagreements were about?"

"I am not able to swear to all the details, but I can tell you what I know for certain. Firstly, the whole business of the appointment of Herbert Clough to replace Captain Bishop when he broke his leg was a massive cause for conflict between them. Captain Faulkner had his own candidate, Lieutenant Betteridge, to take over as our platoon commander but the company commander, Major Bryanston, chose Herbert for the appointment. Captain Faulkner was livid and chose to blame Lieutenant Clough for this and took every opportunity to blacken his name ever afterwards."

"In your experience did Lieutenant Clough do anything to cause this reaction from Captain Faulkner?"

"I am not aware that he did," was Welby's reaction.

"Were there any other disputes between them that might account for their poor relationship, as some witnesses for the prosecution have told us that Lieutenant Clough and Captain Faulkner disagreed over the increased drinking of Major Bryanston? Can you tell us what you know about this?"

Lt Welby said, "I know about this dispute because Herbert Clough discussed his feelings at length with me and Lieutenant Cranley on several occasions."

"Can you describe what he said to you?"

"We all knew that Major Bryanston was a fine officer with a long history of action on the Western Front, but we could see that he was tired, and it was our opinion that he would benefit from a break from the front line. The major had always enjoyed a drink and often entertained the company officers in the dugout to rounds of drinks during stand down. The major was a very sociable person and we liked and respected him."

I interrupted him and asked, "At this time, do you think that Major Bryanston's ability as company commander was affected by his drinking?"

Lt Welby replied, "I am not qualified to give a definitive answer to that question, but in my opinion, his social drinking added to his effectiveness."

"So why was Lieutenant Clough worried that Major Bryanston's drinking would damage his health?"

"After Lieutenant Clough was appointed platoon commander, Captain Faulkner was angry that his candidate was ignored, and his response was to appear to become closer to the major and they were often seen drinking brandy together in the company of Betteridge and Allen. These drinking sessions were loud and raucous and went on late into the night, and it was noticed that they usually only ended when the major passed out and had to be put to bed. Several weeks of this behaviour took its toll on the major who was less able to carry out his company duties as effectively as before. This was noticed by many officers in the company and Lieutenant Clough, as a platoon commander, spoke directly to Captain Faulkner publicly in an officers' meeting."

"Can you tell the court the substance of what was said?"

"Lieutenant Clough spoke up at the officers' meeting and said that he had noticed a decline in the health of the company commander which seemed to be affecting his ability to carry out his duties in his usual manner. He recounted that whenever he had spoken with the major, he appeared distracted and always seemed to have a glass of brandy in his hand and it was difficult to get an answer from him because he always refers us to Captain Faulkner. Other officers spoke up and said that they had noticed this too and they now realised that the second-in-command was now running the company in his place."

"What did Captain Faulkner say to this?"

"Captain Faulkner apologised to the assembled officers and asked our forgiveness that he had not spoken to us about this matter earlier, but he was motivated by care for the major's reputation in keeping it quiet. Major Bryanston had been drinking much more brandy than was usual for him and this had got to such an extent that he had to be put to bed each night drunk. He believed that if this became widely known, Major Bryanston would be removed from his post and his military career would be severely damaged or even ended. He told us that he had decided to enlist the help of two officers he could trust, to drink with the major and regulate his intake of brandy to try to reduce his dependency on the alcohol. This strategy did not work very well as the major always seemed to end up intoxicated, so he had taken charge of the supplies of alcohol in the company dugout and rationed the amount of brandy available in the hope of reducing his dependency on it and this was the reason that he had, temporarily, taken over most of the duties of the company commander until the major was feeling better."

"What was Lieutenant Clough's reaction to this statement?"

"Herbert Clough spoke to the meeting and questioned Captain Faulkner's strategy. He said there were two clear issues that we must consider – the health of our friend and commander and the military considerations. He said he appreciated that the captain was trying to protect the major's reputation and save his career by restricting his access to alcohol, and he should be congratulated for that but was he sure that this strategy would work? He went on to suggest that it would be better for Major Bryanston to seek medical help now to free him from his addiction and return him to his previous good health, even if that meant he was replaced as the company commander. Secondly, he said that the military considerations made it imperative that the battalion commander should know that one of his company commanders was unwell and unable to perform his duties effectively and it was our duty to make them aware of the current situation. He went on to say that the fighting efficiency of the battalion was affected by a potential decline in the readiness of our company and with the new offensive coming soon this was an intolerable situation for us to be in."

"How did Captain Faulkner react to Lieutenant Clough's words?"

"Faulkner was very conciliatory and said that Lieutenant Clough was right that we should inform the battalion, but not just yet. His plan was beginning to work and if the major's health began to improve then we would have done him a great service and retained our popular company commander, and the battalion would be none the wiser. He reassured the meeting that if his plan proved unsuccessful, he would inform battalion himself. He then issued a direct order that no one was to contact battalion headquarters about this matter except him.'

"Did Lieutenant Clough obey that order?"

Welby replied warily, "Herbert, Cranley and I discussed the outcome of the meeting together when we got back to the platoon dugout. None of us were convinced by the account given by Captain Faulkner and we suspected that the enforced drinking sessions with Faulkner, Betteridge and Allen were probably the main reason that the major was now more reliant on the alcohol than before. The suggestion about rationing the access to brandy by Captain Faulkner did not ring true as we had also seen with our own eyes Major Bryanston in a dishevelled state drinking at many times of the day. Herbert said that covering up the major's problem was against military discipline and that he was going to inform the battalion commander of what was going on."

"Did Lieutenant Clough write to the battalion commander?"

"Yes, he did, and he showed me the draft before he put it to the internal mail sack'".

"Do you know if Lieutenant Clough received a reply from battalion headquarters?'

Welby smiled."I know that he didn't receive a reply because the message was never received at battalion headquarters."

"Can you explain to the court how you know this to be so."

"The following day Lieutenant Clough was summoned to a meeting with Captain Faulkner, who had the letter written to the battalion commander in his hand which had been intercepted before it left the company headquarters. I don't know what was said but we all heard the raised voices and observed the angry expressions on their faces when Clough came out of the dugout."

"Did Clough tell you what transpired between him and Faulkner?"

"Not in full detail, except to say that he had been threatened by Faulkner never to disobey an order again. Clough told the captain that he would always disobey an order that he considered to be unlawful and went on that he was now more certain than ever that Faulkner with the help of Betteridge and Allen was deliberately forcing Major Bryanston to drink in excess and weakening his ability to function effectively. He believed Faulkner did intend to report the major's total collapse through drink to the battalion commander when the time was right to show him as the natural successor and be promoted to major. The only obstacle to his plan would be if someone reported this matter to battalion "before him, which was the reason for the threats he had made."

I had one final question. 'Lieutenant Welby, you have expressed considerable support for Lieutenant Clough through your testimony today, but can I ask you why you didn't speak up immediately in support of your platoon commander?"

"Yes, I can answer that question simply, I didn't speak out freely because Captain Faulkner ordered all members of the platoon to say nothing about the case to the defending officer."

I said thank you to Lt Welby and the judge asked Major Harding if he wished to cross-examine. Harding approached the witness chair and glared at Lt Welby, then said, "Mr Welby, are you a friend of Herbert Clough?'

Welby looked straight at the court martial board and said,"I am proud to say that I am."

Harding continued by insinuating that the defendant must be "extremely glad to have a friend like you who will spin a web of lies under oath for him."

I rose to object to this unwarranted slur of the character of both Welby and the defendant; the judge agreed, directed Harding to withdraw the last remark and then warned him that, in future, he must confine such remarks to his final address but in cross-examination he must ask specific questions only.

"OK, Mr Welby, I will withdraw that last remark and ask whether your friendship with Lieutenant Clough was strong enough for you to tell lies in court on his behalf?"

Welby retorted angrily, "I would not, and I can tell you that Lieutenant Clough would never expect a friend to perjure themselves on his behalf."

"Mr Welby, do you have any medical training?" asked Major Harding.

Welby replied that he did not. Harding continued, "To the best of your knowledge does Lieutenant Clough or Cranley have this specialist knowledge?"

Welby answered again that they did not. Harding now rounded on him and asked very aggressively, "Please tell us simply how three junior lieutenants were more capable of judging the company commander's condition than the company second-in-command, a superior and more experienced officer?"

Welby replied firmly, "But sir, we didn't. We believed what Captain Faulkner had told us, in his own words, was the problem drinking for Major Bryanston because we had seen the effects of it with our own eyes. The major was rambling, slurring his words, rarely dressed in uniform, always drinking brandy and it was plain for all to see. We did not disagree with the assessment of the problem but the strategy he said he was following to resolve it."

"Do I understand you to be saying Lieutenant Welby that you did not care to preserve Major Bryanston's good name?"

"That is not what I am saying at all, we liked and respected the major very much but felt that the only way to resolve his addiction to alcohol was a period of medical rehabilitation during which he would be returned to his former good health."

"Lieutenant Welby, did you assist Lieutenant Clough in his attempt to desert?"

Welby replied angrily, "I have sworn an oath on the Bible, and I will say for all to hear that I did not, nor do I believe that Lieutenant Clough attempted to desert."

I jumped up and objected that this was a new line of questioning and not a cross-examination of the evidence given by Lt Welby. If Major Harding wished to introduce evidence that Lt Welby was somehow involved in a conspiracy to assist Lt Clough in his alleged attempt to desert, why was it not introduced during the prosecution case when the allegation could be properly examined? The judge agreed, and again warned Major Harding to stick to the facts of the case and not try to entertain flights of fancy under the guise of cross-examination. Suitably chastened, Major Harding said he had no further questions for the witness. It was now four-fifteen, Welby had been giving evidence for three hours and Colonel Robertson decide to adjourn until the following morning.

I decided to begin Thursday with a testimony from Private Smith who came into the courtroom, saluted smartly to the judge, and stated his name, rank, serial number and regiment and then took his seat.

I approached him and said in a friendly manner, "Good morning Private Smith, can you please tell the court how you know the defendant, Lieutenant Herbert Clough?"

"Yes, sir, I am Mr Clough's batman, and he is my platoon commander as well."

"Do you like him?

"Yes, sir, he is a gentleman."

"Private Smith, can you explain more clearly what you mean by the phrase "he is a gentleman" and give us some specific examples?"

"Yes, sir, I can… Mr Clough was fair and honest with the men and although he could have a temper if someone let him down, his bad mood never lasted for long, and he was always quick to apologise if he got things wrong."

"Can you refer to any specific occasions which showed Mr Clough's character clearly?'"

Private Smith looked round, smiled directly at Lt Clough and I felt that in that smile the court could see the devotion of this ordinary soldier towards his officer and know that he was sincere in his respect for Herbert Clough.

"Shortly after Mr Clough became our platoon officer, I had a bit of trouble at home when my youngest took ill with tuberculosis and the only remedy was to send him away to a special sanatorium in the country, away from the smoke and smog in the city to clear his chest in the clean country air. This was fine, except that I could not afford to pay for the medical treatment or his board and lodging at the sanatorium. I needed to find £75 to secure the place for Tommy, but I did not know what to do. I went to the platoon Sergeant McArthy for advice, and he spoke with Mr Clough, who said he would make enquiries about charitable aid for soldiers in the front line for this kind of domestic emergency. After a few days he told me he had managed to secure a grant for my family and the money would be paid to the sanatorium for my son's treatment. I was so grateful for his assistance and thanked him for what he had done. He was very modest and said it was the least he could do for a man in his platoon but when my wife's next letter came, she said the money had been paid alright, by bank draft from the account of an H. Clough Esquire, who she thought must be the trustee of the charity, but I knew differently, didn't I."

"You mean that Lieutenant Clough paid for the medical treatment out of his own pocket but led you to believe that it was a charitable grant."

"Yes, sir, that is exactly how it was."

"Private Smith, why do you think Mr Clough tried to conceal from you that he had paid for the medical treatment himself?"

"I don't know sir... but I suppose he didn't want me to be beholden to him and when I thanked him, he did not want to make a big issue of it, and just hoped that his help might enable Tommy to regain his health."

"Private Smith, can you describe the nature of your duties in the company?"

Smith looked at me strangely but then answered,"I am an infantryman, but I perform other duties probably because I worked in service before the war where I was a footman and under-butler for many years. I volunteered to be a batman because of the extra pay; also acted as a steward serving food and drinks in the company headquarters."

"Does this mean that you spend a lot of time working in close quarters to your officers?"

"Yes, sir, it does, and I get to observe them far more closely than the average soldier."

"Does this impose any particular constraints on you, personally?"

"Well, sir... I do hear things being said that are not for common broadcast."

"I am sure this must be a great temptation not to tell others what you hear?" I asked.

"No, sir, it isn't like that at all... a good footman or butler can serve at table or in the anteroom and be totally unobtrusive, so that his employer and his guests do not know he is there. We are trained to hear but not to listen and never to divulge what we have heard to a third party, that would be more than our job's worth. If officers can't talk freely in their mess without fear that their stewards would pass on what they have heard the whole system would break down."

"Private Smith, can you tell the court whether during the course of your duties, you have overheard conversations amongst officers that might have an impact on the outcome of this court martial?"

"I have."

"Can you tell the court what you overheard the night before Lieutenant Clough's disappearance?"

Private Smith paused for a few seconds and then began. "There were eight or nine in the officers' dugout that night playing cards after supper and drinking. Major Bryanston was playing bridge in a four with Captain Faulkner, Mr Betteridge and Mr Allen and they were all drinking heavily. Another table of four was also playing bridge, I think, and I was busy keeping them supplied with their drinks. Eventually, the second four officers finished their game and went to bed, leaving the major's table alone. At about eleven-thirty I brought out their third bottle of brandy and they carried on drinking and playing cards, I cleared up and retired to the stewards' cubbyhole where I could hear everything that was being said at the card table. I do not think those around the table had any idea that the stewards in the cubbyhole could hear their conversations in full. Around eleven forty-five, I heard Captain Faulkner say that the old fool has dropped off at last and cursed that it had taken nearly three bottles to knock him out this time. I was then summoned and told to help the major to bed, which I did. When I returned the captain and his two lieutenants were still sat at the card table, but my ears pricked up when I heard the name, Lieutenant Clough."

"Understandably, when you heard the name of your platoon commander mentioned you listened more carefully, and can you now tell the court what they said about Lieutenant Clough?"

"Well, sir, they all said horrible things about Mr Clough, and it was obvious from the drift of their conversation that they didn't like him at all. Captain Faulkner disliked him the most and said that Clough was an obstacle to all their plans because he had a mind of his own and would not do as he was told. He had already disobeyed a direct order and had contacted battalion headquarters about Major Bryanston's drinking and now had an appointment with the colonel tomorrow morning at nine. The captain said that they must act tonight because if Clough speaks with the colonel they are lost."

"Private Smith, did Captain Faulkner say what the action was going to be?"

"No... he didn't, he asked them for suggestions and Betteridge said they should kill him. Captain Faulkner indicated that would be a stupid option because it would only serve to focus the attention of the provost department on the company, which they did not want. He went on to explain that they needed a plan with two objectives, to get rid of Clough and to focus attention on Clough and not us. "I intend that we should ambush him later tonight because he is the officer of the guard, restrain him until the morning and give him a good beating for good measure when he will be posted as absent. We can hide him in the back of the company van and drive him away from our positions for a suitable distance in the morning where we will set him free under the pain of death if he ever returns. We will encourage him to disappear and to desert. He will almost certainly be caught by the military police and be shot as a deserter, and we will have achieved our aim without any suspicion falling on us."

"Did you try to warn Lieutenant Clough of what you had heard?"

"I wanted to sir, but I was prevented from doing so."

"How were you prevented from warning your platoon commander?"

"I could not leave the dugout immediately but had to remain until they had finished and then I had to clear away, lock the drinks cupboard and prepare for the morning so it was another thirty minutes after the three officers had left the dugout that I finished my duty. I looked for Lieutenant Clough but could not find him anywhere in the company trenches and I feared that I was too late."

"Did you see Lieutenant Clough again the following morning?"

"No, sir, he hadn't slept in his bunk and was not present at stand to that morning but when I spoke to Lieutenant Welby, he said it was probably nothing to worry about because Mr Clough had to go to battalion headquarters for a meeting with the colonel this morning and had probably left early."

I turned to the judge and said that I had no further questions for the witness and the judge asked Major Harding if he wished to cross-examine. Harding sidled across to Private Smith and in an almost jocular manner asked him, "Was it your usual custom to eavesdrop on the private conversations of your officers?"

Smith looked confused and said, "No, sir."

"But Private Smith, you have just told this court that you could hear everything that was said between Captain Faulkner and Mr Betteridge and Mr Allen while you were in the steward's cubbyhole. Is this true?"

Smith looked a bit flustered but regained his composure and replied firmly, "I said that I could hear every word they said but I wasn't actually listening until they mentioned the name of my platoon commander in their conversation. I then paid close attention to what they were saying because they said they were planning to attack him and try to ruin his reputation with their plans, and I knew that this wasn't right."

'Private Smith, I put it to you that you have a reputation in your company as a gossip and it is well known that you frequently listen to the private conversations of your officers and then spread about "salacious tidbids about what you have heard in confidence, to the men in your platoon?"

"No, no I would never do that," Private Smith replied.

"But Smith, you are condemned out of your own mouth, and I will ask one final question. Why would Captain Faulkner discuss plans to injure a brother officer and secretly destroy his reputation anywhere within earshot of you, the most notorious gossip in the company?"

No more questions. The judge discharged Private Smith from the witness box. Major Harding had managed to distract attention from the revelation of a conspiracy against Clough by questioning the veracity of my witness quite effectively. I decided that I would call Lt Cranley as my next witness.

Cranley was tall, good looking and upright in his bearing and I knew that he would make a good impression on the court. I decided that I would restrict his evidence to specific parts of the case rather than try to rehearse the whole story again.

I began by asking, "What was your impression of Lieutenant Clough as your platoon commander?"

"Lieutenant Clough was a little hot-headed when he was first appointed and made one or two mistakes but soon realised that his job was to lead and care for the men of his platoon to ensure that they were an efficient fighting unit of the regiment, capable of fighting alone or in conjunction with the other platoons of the company. Our platoon is made up of riflemen whose main job as skirmishers is to harry the enemy on the battlefield. The rifleman's role is a dangerous one and Clough knew that he must train the men well and build trust and respect between the men and their officers so that the platoon functioned properly in action."

"So, Mr Cranley, he was a friend of yours?"

He replied, "I wouldn't go so far as to say we were friends because he was a difficult man to get to know but he was a very good platoon commander and we all respected and trusted him."

"Lieutenant Cranley, were you on duty during the night before Mr Clough was reported absent?"

"I was the second shift guard commander which patrolled the trenches between midnight and four in the morning"

"When was the last time you saw Lieutenant Clough?"

"I spoke with Lieutenant Clough during the handover from the first shift guard at midnight. Once Mr Clough and his guard were relieved, they disappeared rather quickly to get some sleep."

"Were there any incidents reported during your watch?"

"Not really, except that within literally a few seconds of Mr Clough disappearing along the empty trench towards his billet, three figures appeared out of the shadows and hurried after him."

"Did you see the faces of these shadowy figures?"

"I saw the face of Captain Faulkner but couldn't see the faces of the other two, but one I could swear was definitely Lieutenant Betteridge by his posture and build and the third was probably Allen, but I couldn't swear that it was. I was sure that these three were stalking Mr Clough and were intent on catching up with him, judging by the speed of their movement. Within a few minutes I thought I heard raised voices and despatched two of my sentries to investigate but they returned saying that all was quiet and that they had seen no one."

"Mr Cranley, were you ordered by Captain Faulkner not to speak up in favour of Lieutenant Clough?"

"Yes, we were."

I indicated that I had no more questions when Harding jumped up and said to the judge that he only had one question.

"Mr Cranley, you have stated that you saw three shadowy figures chase after Lieutenant Clough just after midnight and that they were, in your words, stalking Mr Clough. Did you actually see them catch Clough?"

"No."

Harding said he had no further questions and Lt Cranley was dismissed.

The court was now adjourned for lunch and I decided that I would conclude my case that afternoon by calling Lance Corporal Green, Sergeant McArthy, Private Thornley and Captain Salt RAMC, and I would save Terence Bradby for when or if I needed to plead mitigation. I also had a surprise witness up my sleeve, but I was not sure that I would use his testimony or not at this stage.

Lance Corporal Green testified clearly and succinctly and in answer to my questions corroborated what all the other witnesses from Clough's company had stated about his character and behaviour. I then moved on to question him about the solution that Captain Falkner had asked him to make up.

"Lance Corporal, were you approached by anyone to prepare a solution of sulphuric acid and vinegar for their personal use?"

"Yes, sir, I was approached by Captain Faulkner who asked me to make up a solution of one-part sulphuric acid to four parts vinegar for him."

"Was this a usual sort of request?"

"No, sir, it was highly unusual as sulphuric acid is a dangerous substance and strictly controlled under regimental routine orders."

"Why did Captain Faulkner come to you with this request?"

"He'd come to me because one of my duties was to check and top up the batteries that powered the lighting in our trenches and he knew that I was responsible for the supplies of sulphuric acid stocks held within the company resources."

"Did Captain Faulkner tell you what he wanted this solution for?"

"Yes, he told me that this solution was excellent for cleaning the verdigris and rust from his belts and buckles, which are being discoloured by the damp atmosphere in the trenches. I told him that it would probably do the trick but that even at this consistency the sulphuric acid was very harmful to exposed skin, eyes and should not be ingested and I recommended that a solution of one to eight would be much safer and just as effective as a cleaning agent.'

"Did the captain accept your advice?'

"No, sir, he did not, but said that he had used this solution very effectively before without any problems at all. I did not like it but because it was such a small amount, I made the solution for him and gave it to him next day, warning him that his batman should wear gloves at all times when using the fluid for cleaning."

"Did you pass on the warning to Captain Faulkner's batman yourself?"

"I spoke to Private Thornley when I passed him in the trench the following day and casually remarked that he should be careful when using the cleaning solution. It was strange because Private Thornley did not seem to know what I was talking about."

I turned to the judge and said I had no further questions. Major Harding stood up and faced Lance Corporal Green, thanked him for his honest evidence and then said that he only had one question. "Are you in possession of any knowledge, that you can testify to under oath in this court, that Captain Faulkner did not use this solution to clean his kit as he told you?"

Lance Corporal Green said that he was not and was discharged from the witness box.

I called Sergeant McArthy next, and began by asking him to state his name, rank, service number and current position. He spoke clearly with a

Liverpool Irish accent, and it was immediately clear to all in the court that he was a man who knew his business well and was confident in what he had to say.

"Sergeant McArthy, how long have you known the defendant?"

"About eleven months since he joined my platoon as a second lieutenant."

"Did you have cause to work closely with him in the course of your daily duties?"

"Of course, I am the platoon sergeant and one of my most important functions is to assist the platoon commander in training young officers when they come to the front line for the first time."

"Why do you have to do this?"

"Simply to give them a chance of staying alive for longer. The turnover rate for junior officers was exceedingly high and their life expectancy after joining from OCTU about six weeks."

"You must be good at your job, Sergeant McArthy, as Lieutenants Clough, Welby and Cranley are all still with your platoon after a much longer period than six weeks?"

Sergeant McArthy replied, "I cannot take all the credit for that, sir. We have endured a stalemate on the Ypres Salient, which has meant that the company has not been involved in too much action other than patrolling, which has meant that our casualty rate has been much lower anyway. Secondly, after Captain Bishop broke his leg and Lieutenant Clough took over as platoon commander, he has proved to be a natural platoon leader and has encouraged and supported his two junior officers to develop as more competent officers."

"You have a high regard for Lieutenant Clough then?"

"He has his faults, sir, like all of us, but as a leader, he is first class. He can be fiery and hot-headed and a bit intemperate in his language but is quick to relent when he has been unfair. He has a natural empathy for the ordinary soldiers and will try to look after their interests when he can. This does not mean that he is a soft touch or that malingerers or defaulters can get away with things, but he seems to have a gift for understanding the genuine problems faced by the soldiers many miles away from home. The men in our platoon trust Lieutenant Clough implicitly and from that respect comes affection. Not one of the members of the platoon, including me, believe for one second that Lieutenant Clough deserted his post."

"Sergeant, can I ask you whether you can recall a conversation you had with Lance Corporal Green about supplying a solution of sulphuric acid and vinegar to Captain Faulkner several days before Lieutenant Clough's alleged desertion?"

He replied, "I can remember it clearly because Gerry Green was concerned about it for a number of reasons; it was dangerous stuff and a controlled substance, and if it became common knowledge that he had supplied it against regulations he may lose his stripe. I told him that he was in a difficult position because if he refused Captain Faulkner, who was the second-in-command of the company, he may face some repercussions in the future because the captain liked things his own way. I advised him to make the smallest quantity possible and give it to the captain as requested but warn him about the necessary safety precautions that go with it."

"Thank you, Sergeant, I have no more questions."

Major Harding looked at Sergeant McArthy and said, "I am surprised, Sergeant, that an experienced soldier like you could be fooled so easily by the cowardly behaviour of Lieutenant Clough. Of course, Clough courted the popularity with the men through a soft regime and buying their support with his own money as a ruse to cover up his own inadequacies. Wouldn't you agree?"

Sergeant McArthy bridled and then snapped back, "I would not agree! Mr Clough is as brave as a lion and has welded our platoon into an efficient fighting unit that would perform well in the next battle that was coming soon. He was not afraid to speak up for injustice and was prepared to face the unpopularity that this might bring from his superiors."

Major Harding had no further questions, so I called Private Thornley as my next witness.

"Private Thornley, can you describe your function in the company?"

"Yes, sir. I am a rifleman in HQ platoon and batman to Captain Faulkner."

"Do you look after Captain Faulkner's kit for him amongst other duties?"

"Yes, I do."

"Can you recall an occasion when Captain Faulkner gave you a small bottle containing sulphuric acid and vinegar in solution to clean his webbing and buckles and warning you to wear gloves when you used it?"

"No, sir. I don't remember anything like that."

"Do you remember a conversation with Lance Corporal Green about this solution?"

Thornley said, "Yes, I remember speaking with Gerry Green about this solution and I was as mystified then as I am now."

"Private Thornley, have you ever seen this bottle of acid and vinegar in Captain Faulkner's possession?"

"No."

'Thank you Private Thornley, I have no further questions.' Major Harding declined to cross-examine.

My next witness was Captain Salt RAMC, who was a small, stocky man with little hair and a smiling face. He approached the witness chair, swore the oath on the Bible and then introduced himself to the court. He said, "I am Captain Norman Salt RAMC stationed at the St Omer Military Hospital, but formerly consultant pathologist Charing Cross Hospital, London."

"Captain Salt, can you explain your role at the military hospital? "

"I am the resident pathologist at the hospital and am often consulted by the provost marshal's office when they have cases of unexplained death, but I also help out on the observation wards during busy times because of my background in general medicine."

'Were you on duty in the observation ward when Lieutenant Clough was brought in and diagnosed with temporary blindness attributed to the mustard gas attack in the Poperinge sector?"

"I was, but unfortunately I did not examine Clough as he was seen by Major Baldock.'

"Then how are you able to express a medical opinion in this case?"

"Major Rydall, the St Omer provost marshal, asked me to look at the notes and the results of the tests from the swabs taken of Clough's eyes at the time the following morning, after he had gone missing from the hospital."

"Can you share your findings with the court today?"

"On a more detailed examination of the results taken from the swabs I was able to say categorically that I could find no evidence that Lieutenant Clough had been exposed to the mustard gas during the attack on the lines at Poperinge, even though he was found close to the centre of where that attack occurred some hours earlier. The swabs told me that Clough's eyes had encountered sulphuric acid mixed with an organic substance, which I later identified as vinegar, whereas if he had come into contact with the gas, I would have expected to find traces of sulphur dichloride, chloramine and nitrogen mustard which were not found. Secondly, although mustard gas can cause temporary blindness its more common effects are damage to the lungs and respiratory system more generally. There was no evidence of any of these symptoms in Lieutenant Clough when he was examined by Major Baldock at St Omer hospital within three hours of arriving there, nor when he was examined by me when he was taken into custody some eighteen hours later, or when I examined him again at the Arras military prison three days later at the request of the defence."

"What further did you discover when you examined Lieutenant Clough that might be relevant to this trial?"

"I have drawn several conclusions from the evidence from the tests and my examinations of the patient. First, I am certain that Lieutenant Clough did not receive his injuries in the gas attack. Secondly, I am certain that the temporary blindness was caused by the ingestion of the solution of sulphuric acid and vinegar directly into the eyes. Thirdly, because I was able to gather evidence of the extent of dilation and damage to the surface of the eye from the observations of the patient's eyes at three hours, eighteen and seventy-two hours, I was able to plot the recovery of the eyes back to full vision and this threw up an interesting question. When and how was the solution ingested into the eyes and where did this occur? My plot of the recovery of the eyes suggested that the solution got into the eyes between twelve to fifteen hours before he was examined by Major Baldock, which indicates that the temporary blindness was caused some eight hours before the gas attack occurred, so Lieutenant Clough was almost certainly suffering temporary blindness a long time before the gas attack took place. Lastly, Major Baldock's report indicates that Lieutenant Clough displayed other injuries consistent with having been beaten and kicked by more than one assailant and that he had received these injuries at roughly the same time as the acid solution was put into his eyes. My conclusion would be that Lieutenant Clough suffered these physical injuries whilst struggling to avoid getting the substance into his eyes, and that he was beaten by at least three men so they could squirt the solution into Clough's eyes without getting it on themselves."

"Could Clough have got the solution into his eyes by accident?"

"I would think that this was almost impossible, given that the amount in each eye was almost the same and directed at the same spot on the surface of the eye. In my opinion the solution was squirted into his eyes by one man whilst his head was held securely by the other two. Accidental ingestion from splashing etc. would show evidence on the skin around the eyes of acid burns but none were present. Many people who have toxic substances splashed in their eyes tend to rub the affected area and trace evidence of the acid is often found on their fingers. Again, there was none in this case. I am certain that

Lieutenant Clough was attacked by at least three assailants between midnight and two in the morning when he was beaten, and the solution was squirted directly into his eyes. There are signs of rope marks on his wrists where he was tied up and I think he was dumped on the battlefield secretly sometime after the gas had cleared to confuse any enquiries that might subsequently be made.'

"Thank you, Dr Salt."

Major Harding approached Dr Salt. "Captain Salt, how long have you been practicing medicine?"

Salt replied, "Thirty years or so."

"Thirty years and you are only a captain? Why should we consider you as an expert witness in this case?"

Captain Salt replied firmly, "Major Harding, I am Professor of Pathological Medicine at the University of London and consultant pathologist at the Charing Cross Hospital and am on secondment to the Royal Army Medical Corp to provide pathology services to the Second Army HQ with a territorial commission. I have been consulted by the Metropolitan Police and other police forces in hundreds of cases of mysterious death or serious assault."

"Captain Salt, your evidence seems certain that Clough was not affected during the mustard gas attack and that the injuries to his eyes were caused by a solution of sulphuric acid and vinegar being ingested into both eyes."

"Yes, the scientific tests on the swabs taken from Lieutenant Clough's eyes show that this was the case without any doubt."

"I put it to you that it is a distinct possibility that this solution was administered to his eyes by Lieutenant Clough himself as part of the elaborate plan to escape from the front lines without detection."

Captain Salt looked perplexed but then answered, "Major Harding, I have already given my evidence based on unequivocal forensic evidence that this was not possible. Any person self-administering drops to their eyes would have difficulty directing the drops into the same spot in each eye and in most cases when this is done, some excess droplets leak from the side of the eye and run down the face. This mixture was strong enough to leave acid burn marks on the person's skin and no such marks were found on Lieutenant Clough's face or hands. Normal practice in hospital when administering drops to the eye would be for a nurse to hold the patient's head firmly whilst the doctor squirted the solution into the eye, thus avoiding spillage."

"Perhaps Lieutenant Clough took extra care to avoid spillage when he administered the solution to his eyes?"

"Major Harding, the solution that was ingested into both his eyes was highly acidic. It would burn the outer layer of the eye immediately and would cause severe pain almost immediately. The natural tendency for any person who gets a foreign substance in their eye is to immediately wipe it away with their hand and for the spillage to be evident on the face and hands, which have met the acid. I have already stated that no such evidence exists in the case of Lieutenant Clough, so I think that this is a highly unlikely scenario."

"Are you saying unlikely but not impossible?"

"I am not saying it is impossible, but the evidence overwhelmingly points to the solution being administered to Clough's eyes by a third party and that he was restrained whilst it was administered because of the lack of spillage evidence."

"Do you know who administered the solution?'"

"Major Harding, I am a scientist who deals in facts, and I have presented them here as plainly as I can but as to who the perpetrator was, that would have to be a personal opinion, and would not be relevant in this trial"

"Captain Salt, if it is correct that the solution was administered by someone else, what would be their motive in doing so?"

"Again, I will repeat that, like your previous question about the perpetrator, motive is not within my remit because it can't be measured by scientific methods. I can tell you for certain that the accumulation of the evidence suggests that Mr Clough was restrained by more than one person, received a beating because of the supplementary injuries evident on his face and body, and the solution was administered sometime between midnight and two in the morning measured by the rate of dilation in the eye over a seventy-two-hour observation period. Mr Clough's wrists had been tied up with rope, the rope burns were clearly visible on his wrists, and I would estimate that his wrists were tied together for a period of between six to eight hours by the extent of the burns to the skin, which again is evidence of third-party involvement unless of course you are going to suggest that Mr Clough tied himself up."

This raised a ripple of laughter in the court, but Harding seemed unabashed and pressed on.

"Captain Salt, what was the motive for administering this solution to Clough's eyes?"

"Again, Major Harding, I do not have a crystal ball, but I can tell you that the intention was not to kill Lieutenant Clough as the quantity of acid

– although dangerous – was not sufficient to cause fatal injury nor was it strong enough to cause permanent blindness although, had he not received prompt medical attention, this result could have been different. However, if you wished to teach someone a lesson and effectively warn them away from a particular course of action in a very painful and uncomfortable way but without leaving too much permanent damage, this could be an ideal method. The fact that Lieutenant Clough was discovered wandering blindly in the area immediately behind the Warwickshire Regiment trenches six miles away from his own regiment positions also strongly suggests that there was third-party involvement, because with his impaired vision he could not have travelled this distance without being noticed on the way."

Major Harding said he had no further questions and sat down. The judge said that he would adjourn the court until 10:00 on Friday morning, when I may or may not present my final witness.

I received an unexpected visitor in my room in the mess on Wednesday evening and when I opened the door, I was amazed to see Major Bryanston standing there. He certainly looked better than the previous occasion we had met for he was shaved and smart in his best uniform, spoke clearly and his eyes were alert. I offered him a seat and asked if he would like a drink, which he refused. I could see that he was wearing the ribbon of the Military Cross as well as several campaign medals, so he was a soldier who had seen some service. He was clearly embarrassed to be talking to me and seemed to be searching for a way to start. I thought that I would make it easier for him and asked him straight out why he had changed his mind about Lt Clough and had not recorded his change of heart in Clough's service record. He said he had not changed his mind about Clough, because he had performed well and was shaping up to be a first-class infantry officer. He asked if he could trust me and said that he wished to be open and honest with me. All this was his fault and if he had been stronger, it would not have happened, but he was too weak and let it happen. I was confused and did not understand what he meant and asked him to explain more clearly.

He started at the beginning and said that in the past three years he had served at the front in various positions almost continuously, with little home leave. He said he had been a platoon commander, battalion adjutant and company commander twice and had always had a reputation of someone who coped with the hardship of being away from home and did not let it affect the performance of his duties too much. He said that he had three girls, seven, five and four, he was missing seeing them grow up and he had requested before his appointment to this company a posting away from the front line so he could see his family more often, but he was denied. He said that the only way he has coped with the pressure and the build-up to the next big push was by drinking more than was good for him. "At first, I enjoyed drinking socially with my officers but gradually the amount I drank each day increased until I could only shut out my fears and unhappiness when I was drunk. I was quickly becoming dependent on brandy to function at any time of day and knew it had to stop."

I asked him why he chose Lt Clough to take over the platoon after Captain Bishop's accident. He recounted how he had already planned to appoint Captain Bishop as the company second-in-command, 'Bishop had recommended Clough as his replacement, and I agreed. When Bishop broke his leg, in mysterious circumstances, he was sent back to England for specialist surgery, and I had no choice but to make Faulkner second-in-command in his place.' I asked why Bishop's accident was mysterious and he said, "he was knocked from the top of the parapet and fell fifteen feet to the trench below when he was on guard commander duty. He did not see who his assailant was as he was searching the enemy trench with his night glasses, and it was never established who the culprit was despite a full investigation. I asked if he had any suspicions about who might have knocked Captain Bishop off the parapet, and he said nothing was certain, but Lt Betteridge was seen in the vicinity just before it happened and was the one to discover Bishop lying in the bottom of the trench.

At first, Major Bryanston said he was pleased that he had Captain Faulkner as second-in-command because he stepped up and took over many of the more onerous duties of running the company, but gradually he began to see that he and his two acolytes were isolating him from the rest of the company. He hardly got to speak with anyone in person anymore, Faulkner took on more and more of the decision-making and he found himself rubber-stamping the decisions Faulkner had already made. Faulkner said he would help Bryanston reduce his drinking, but he realised that Faulkner was largely responsible for his drunken state as he always seemed to make sure that there was a bottle close to hand. The only person he felt he could trust was Lt Clough, who he knew would not be afraid to go against Faulkner and do what he asked him to do. I asked him to explain what he had asked Clough to do for him and he said that he had confided in Clough what he thought Faulkner was doing, supported by his two lieutenants, and asked for Clough to report this situation to the colonel at battalion headquarters. He said Clough was reluctant at first because of the damage it would do to his reputation, but the major reassured him that the damage to his reputation was nothing compared to the complete destruction of his health through excessive drinking. 'I begged him to find a way to tell the colonel what was going on and that my suspicion was that this was a deliberate plan to get command of the company himself.

Major Bryanston said that I seemed surprised to hear this revelation and he had expected that Lt Clough would have told me this himself. I told him how reluctant Clough had been to defend himself at all and how frightened he had been of the threats made against him by Faulkner, Betteridge, and Allen. I asked him if he would come to the witness box and speak on behalf of Clough in the morning. He said that he would, and I suggested that he kept clear of the prosecution team and Faulkner during this evening so his introduction as a witness for the defence would be a surprise. He agreed and we parted with a firm handshake. I now felt that the odds were now tipping in the favour of acquittal.

Thursday morning was tense in the courtroom, and I felt that those who crowded into the public gallery had an air of expectancy that something was going to happen today. As I made my way from my room to the court, I bumped into Major Rydall from the provost department, and he greeted me with a smile on his face and shook my hand. He said quietly, "I knew you were something special, Morgan, but I am so glad you agreed to take on Clough's defence because I think without you, he would have been facing the firing squad by now." As he left me, he said, "Good luck."

At one minute to ten the judge entered the court, took his seat and called the court martial to order for the fourth day. I immediately rose and said I wished to call my next witness, Major Bryanston. There was a ripple of murmurs around the room and then Major Harding was on his feet, perspiring and red in the face, shouting 'Objection!'

The judge faced Major Harding and said, "What are the grounds for your objection to this witness?"

Harding calmed a little, thinking that he was on firm ground and replied, "The defence team has given us no notice that they intended to call Major Bryanston, who should really be testifying for the prosecution.'"

Colonel Robertson addressed me directly. "Is this true, Flight Lieutenant Morgan?" I replied that it was true and then I explained that Major Bryanston had approached me the previous evening and requested that he be allowed to speak on behalf of Lt Clough. If he had ever been a prosecution witness, I didn't know, but he was determined to speak for Clough. The colonel thanked me and then said to Major Harding, 'In these circumstances I will allow Major Bryanston to take the stand and you will have every chance to cross-examine him on his evidence after the defence has completed his questioning.' He then remarked, 'You did not call Major Bryanston to give evidence when you presented the prosecution case but I for one want to hear what he has to say.' Flight Lieutenant Morgan, you may continue.'

Major Bryanston looked pale with a sallow look, especially around the eyes, and his uniform seemed to hang on him like a man who has recently lost weight, but his voice was firm. and I sensed that his resolve had not diminished from our meeting the previous evening. I opened my questioning by asking him why he had decided to testify as a character witness for Lt Clough.

"The past four days, I have not had the companionship of Captain Faulkner or Lieutenants Betteridge and Allen in the officers' dugout as they have been here in St Omer as witnesses for the prosecution. This has given me time to think things through and I am beginning to see things more clearly. Firstly, I have realised that every night I spend in their company I am always put to bed drunk and since their enforced absence, I have not been intoxicated once. I have discovered that I do not need to drink myself into oblivion and have not taken a drink for four days. The reduction of my alcoholic intake has enabled me to re-evaluate what has been going on and I have concluded that if Lieutenant Clough is convicted as charged this will be a grave miscarriage of justice."

"Captain Faulkner, Lieutenant Betteridge and Lieutenant Allen have all testified that they made complaints to you about Clough's behaviour and that you issued three reprimands to Lieutenant Clough as a result. Can you confirm that this is true?"

"I did not receive any specific complaints against Lieutenant Clough but rather on the contrary, I heard good reports about him from members of his platoon and I certainly do not remember issuing any reprimands against him. Faulkner and the two lieutenants were always speaking disparagingly about Lieutenant Clough, but it went no further than that. I cannot be more certain than that because of the befuddled state I was in at times through drinking. If such reprimands were administered, it would be recorded on Lieutenant Clough's service record and signed by me".

"Major Bryanston, you will be pleased to know that exhibit D1, excerpts from Lieutenant Clough's service record, backs up your version of events because no such reprimands were entered in his service record by you or anyone else. Do you know of any reason why Captain Faulkner should wish to blacken Lieutenant Clough's character?"

'I wish I could give you a definitive answer, but I do not really know for certain if there was indeed any one thing that Lieutenant Clough did to stimulate such a response. However, I can say with some certainty that Faulkner was extremely angry with me when his cousin, Betteridge, was not appointed platoon commander and vented a lot of his anger towards Lieutenant Clough, who was an entirely innocent party in the whole matter."

"Can you explain to the court why you selected Clough over Betteridge for platoon commander when the appointment became vacant?"

'Yes, the vacancy came up because I had decided to appoint Captain Bishop as my new second-in-command, and I asked him if he had any recommendation to make as to who should replace him as platoon commander. Bishop was certain that Clough would be the best man for the job. I also asked Captain Faulkner, who recommended Lieutenant Betteridge for the vacant position. I looked at the service records of both officers and Clough's assessments were always good whereas Betteridge was only average. Betteridge was a good steady officer, but his reporting officers had always felt that he lacked initiative and although good at obeying orders was lacking in leadership, so I decided to appoint Clough to the role."

"Thank you, Major Bryanston, for explaining that and again you will be pleased to note that excerpts from Lieutenant Betteridge's service record have also been entered into the record as Exhibit D2 by the defence which confirms your version of events. I am a little confused, however, because you told us a few minutes ago that you were appointing Captain Bishop as your second-in-command, but Captain Faulkner was the officer who received that appointment instead of Bishop. Can you explain this for the benefit of the court?'

"I can but the circumstances were somewhat mysterious and were never fully understood. Captain Bishop suffered an accident on the night the platoon commander appointment was discussed by me with Bishop and Faulkner, and he suffered serious injuries that required his repatriation for specialist medical treatment".

"Can you give us a little more detail about Captain Bishop's accident?"

"Bishop was guard commander on this night from midnight to four in the morning and during the night, he visited all the guard positions to check on any incidents for his report. It was his custom to climb on to the parapet and look through his night glasses to see what night-time activity was being undertaken by the enemy. It was presumed that whilst engaged in this reconnaissance he lost his balance and because he was holding his glasses in both hands, he fell fifteen feet or so into the trench below severely breaking his leg in two places and his right wrist."

"Were there any witnesses to the accident?"

"Sadly, there were not, although the platoon sergeant passed along the bottom of the trench and saw the captain standing on the ladder with his binoculars to his eyes just a few moments before he fell, and he saw Lieutenant Betteridge passing the other way along the trench just twenty yards before the captain's position. Betteridge was the one who reported the accident and called for help but swore that he did not see him fall. Captain Bishop was certain that somebody wobbled the base of the ladder, which caused him to lose his balance and fall but because he had the binoculars to his eyes, he could not see who it was. There was considerable suspicion that Betteridge could have wobbled the ladder and made him fall, but no evidence to disprove his version of events."

"Major Bryanston, are you suggesting that this was a deliberate attempt to remove Captain Bishop so that Captain Faulkner could take his place?"

"I strongly suspect that it is a likely explanation for the subsequent events that took place, but I am unable to prove it definitively to be so."

"So why did you appoint Captain Faulkner to be your second-in-command?"

"I had no choice because he was the next senior captain after Bishop, but I only made the appointment temporary pending the return to fitness of Captain Bishop."

"How did Captain Faulkner perform as your deputy".

"He immediately consolidated his position by setting himself up as a buffer between me and the company. He directed that everything went through him whilst at the same time forcing me to become increasingly dependent on alcohol, so that I became too weak to resist him. He used his two lieutenants to ensure that his orders were carried out and had quickly established himself as the de facto company commander."

"Did you try to break free from this tyranny?"

"I must admit that my power to resist was low and it was often just easier to go along with what he said when I was in an alcoholic stupor. One day Captain Faulkner had gone to battalion, and I was alone, and I sent my batman to ask Lieutenant Clough to come to see me urgently. Clough appeared within twenty minutes and confused as I was, I managed to convince him that this alcoholic addiction was not of my choosing. I described how Faulkner and his acolytes were systematically feeding more and more brandy into me to keep me in a weak and senseless position. I begged him to let the battalion commander know what was going on and save me from this tyranny. He was cautious at first and said that it would destroy my reputation, but I told him that I would rather be sober and dishonoured than be the puppet of this man."

"Did Lieutenant Clough carry out your instructions?"

"I am sure that he did, but I fear that his loyalty to me has led directly to him sitting in that chair as the accused.'

'Major Bryanston, I can confirm that Lieutenant Clough wrote to battalion headquarters on two occasions on your behalf, the first letter was intercepted by Faulkner who challenged him about it and issued direct orders that nobody should contact battalion without going through him but secondly he sent the letter by hand, direct to battalion, and was granted an interview with the lieutenant colonel at 09:00 on the morning of his alleged desertion."

I closed my defence and the judge advocate invited Major Harding to cross-examine but all he could say that he could see no reason to trust the word of an inveterate drunkard and would waive the right to cross-examine this witness.

The Judge addressed the court and said that we had heard all the evidence presented by the prosecution and the defence offered by Lt Clough to these charges and it was time for the court to retire to consider their verdict. You are not required to consider Clough's innocence but only whether the evidence presented by the prosecution proves to your satisfaction the guilt of the accused. He brought down his gavel and closed the court until tomorrow morning.

TWENTY-TWO

The Verdict

t was a long night waiting and both of us slept fitfully in anticipation of a result in the morning. The court martial board resumed their deliberations at 08:00 and we just had to wait. I was glad that I had managed to raise enough questions in the minds of the board that they had not come to a quick decision, but the longer it went on the more doubts began to set in about an unfavourable result and what would be my strategy in pleading mitigation. I kept wracking my brains as to what I had missed that had failed to convince them of Herbert's innocence but could not think of what it might be. At 11:30 the sergeant usher knocked on the door and told me that Colonel Robertson would like to see Major Harding and me in his room at 12:00. This was all he said, and I had no idea what had transpired that required this meeting.

Colonel Robertson welcomed us into his room, we took seats before his desk, and he told us that we did not yet have a result and that the board was split in their decision. "I could rule that we would accept a split decision but as this was a capital case both the president of the board, Lieutenant Colonel Lloyd-Williams, and I think this would be inappropriate in the circumstances and the board have asked if they can hear from Lieutenant Clough himself and ask him some direct questions that appear to be sticking points in their minds."

Whilst he was talking, I was doing the calculations in my mind and reckoned that this must be a three/two split which was why they were being cautious. I think if it had been four/one either way the judge would have accepted the decision, so I was beginning to think that this might work in our favour. I asked the judge how this would work, and he explained that if we agreed, Lieutenant Clough would take the witness box and give evidence on his own behalf under oath. There would be no questions from the prosecution or defence, but only from the members of the board who were seeking further clarifications. Major Harding said he would agree if he could cross-examine Clough as well, but I said I needed to consult with Lieutenant Clough before giving our assent. Colonel Robertson said he would expect an answer by 12:45 and if we agreed the court would reconvene at 13:15 prompt.

I went straight back to our room, explained to Herbert Clough what the board had requested and at first, he seemed reluctant to agree. I explained what I thought the split decision meant. "In the worst case it means that at least two members of the board do not think you are guilty but more likely I think that three think you are not guilty, but they know in a capital case that a four/one verdict is the very least the court will accept. There is to be no cross-examination, just a series of questions from the court martial board. The court will be in closed session with no public access allowed." Slowly he came round to accepting the proposition and I sent a message to the judge that Clough agreed.

The court reopened in closed session at 13:45. Herbert took his place in the witness chair and took the oath on the Bible. Colonel Robertson said that he fully recognised that it was the right of the accused to decide whether they wished to give evidence or not and he thanked him for agreeing to forgo that right and answer the board's question this afternoon. Lt Col Lloyd-Williams opened the questioning.

"Lieutenant Clough, we have heard evidence from the prosecution that suggests that because of your upbringing and early experiences at school and at the OCTU, you are a braggart, bully and a coward. In the defence case there was no attempt to deny this and an acceptance that it was largely true. You say that these early experiences had a formative impact on your character and that you are now a changed individual, different from the person you were then. Please can you explain, in some detail, how this change came about and why we should believe you?"

Clough remained calm and responded confidently. "Colonel, this is something that is difficult for me to talk about as I would rather forget the events of my past life and concentrate on my future. The only person to have given me love and affection in my early life was my mother and I do not know if you can imagine the shock and horror of discovering that your mother is being punished by her husband for showing motherly love and affection towards her little son. The beatings did not stop her from loving me though and I believe this was the reason she lost her life falling downstairs. There were some strong suspicions that my father pushed her down the stairs, but no action was ever taken against him.

'From the age of six to sixteen I lived permanently in school, not even being allowed home for the holidays, until my father took an interest in me again when he wanted to introduce me into his business. I was easy prey for the bullies at prep school and at public school, until the one day I fought back and defeated the horrible bully who tackled me alone and threw him into the river. I realised on that day that if you cannot beat them then you must join them to survive. I lived by this principle even when I joined the OCTU but here my experience transformed the way I thought about life and the way I should treat others.

"For the first time in years, I made a friend, Cadet Tomlinson, who came from a similar background to me, and we found that we had much in common. He was a stronger character than me because he had always resisted the bullying culture in school and stood up to the attention of the gang of bullies at the OCTU too, whereas I took the line of least resistance and became a hanger-on to the bully group. This bought me some immunity from their attentions pretty much. I witnessed some of the violence meted out towards Tomlinson and did not lift a finger to stop it. I realised that he was right when he said the bullies only ruled by fear and the tacit approval of those who knew what they were doing was wrong but would do nothing to stop it. I was ashamed that I had let my friend down, but the accumulated fear built up over the years prevented me from lifting a finger to help him when he ran away from the leader of the bullies' initiation ritual, which involved burning his arm with a red-hot knife blade. Just as the knife was going to be pressed against the inside of his left arm, Tomlinson pulled back, broke away and fled across the field and into Thetford Forest nearby. They all chased after him but returned within half an hour as they had not managed to find him. I waited for things to quieten down then I went to find him in the forest and after an hour or so searching frantically, calling out his name, I found him hanging from a low tree by his belt looped around his neck. I will never forget the red face and bulging eyes staring at me as I tried to lift him down. Every night, I would see that horrific sight in my mind's eye accusing me of betrayal before I could go to sleep and I vowed that I would never be party to such persecution and injustice ever again.

"When I passed out of the OCTU and came to the regiment I joined Captain Bishop's platoon where I found that there was no repressive culture, but only a regime built on mutual respect and support for the individual. I found that I was welcomed and even though I was newly commissioned and very inexperienced, the older and more experienced soldiers were happy to show me how things needed to be done because they knew they would have to rely on me on the battlefield by virtue of my rank. I was taught how to be a platoon officer who could be relied on by his men and maybe, for the first time in my life, I felt a sense of belonging and self-worth that had been lacking for so long. It was not all good though because sometimes I made mistakes and when I got things wrong, I reverted to my former character and shouted at people but gradually I have been learning to control my hot-headedness. I have learned that caring for the welfare of others is not a sign of weakness but a vital characteristic of an able leader.'

Major Carrington asked the next question. "Lieutenant Clough, why did you make an appointment with your battalion OC and then run away on the same day?"

'The answer is simple, Major, as I had every intention of meeting with the battalion commander the next morning but was prevented by Faulkner, Betteridge and Allen. These three officers were deliberately destroying the health of Major Bryanston through forcing him to drink to excess and would destroy his reputation too if they were not stopped. My loyalty to the major is entirely consistent with the principles I had been taught within his company, I had promised him that I would inform the CO of what was happening, and nothing would stop me from doing that."

Major Carrington persisted in the same vein. "Why then, if your intention was to inform battalion of what was going on did you run away in a completely different direction than battalion headquarters and then run away a second time from the hospital in St Omer?"

Clough bristled a little and I thought he was going to come out with one of his hot-tempered replies, but he subsided and answered clearly, " did not absent myself from the company positions at St Martin as I was waylaid by Faulkner and his two lieutenants who bundled me into an empty store dugout to the rear of the front trench just a few yards from my billet. They bound my hands behind my back and all three punched and kicked me to the ground where I was held down whilst Faulkner squirted some liquid into both of my eyes, which blurred my vision with an intense burning sensation. Faulkner threatened me by saying that he was giving me a chance to get away because if I tried to speak to the battalion commander or continue my duties in the company, he would kill me. The beating and the acid in my eyes were just a warning that he meant what he said. They stuffed a rag in my mouth and left me tied up in the corner of the dugout until the morning. Sometime just before dawn I was carried out and put into the back of the company stores van and left there until after stand to. Much later in the morning Betteridge and Allen drove me away from the St Martin trenches and after what I estimate to be twenty minutes, stopped the van, pushed me out, untied my hands and left me blinded and lost.

I ran away from St Omer hospital because I was sure that Faulkner would have reported me absent by then and the provost department would be searching for me. I also had the misfortune to be recognised by another wounded soldier, an RFC lieutenant, I had met before. I needed to get away and make my way to battalion headquarters to make my report to the CO as quickly as I could. I stole a motorcycle and made my way by the back roads towards the battalion positions but ran out of petrol in a small village where I was apprehended and handed over to the provost marshal in St Omer."

Lieutenant Middleton had just one question. "What did you have to gain from deserting your post?"

Clough replied, "Absolutely nothing, but I had everything to lose. My reputation, my position but most of all the respect of those who trusted me. I would rather die."

There were no further questions, he was discharged from the stand and the court martial board retired to reconsider the verdict based on what they had heard from Lt Clough. I could tell that Major Harding was still seething with anger, but I was satisfied that Herbert had conducted himself with a quiet dignity which did him great credit. We had only been back in our room half an hour before the usher summoned us back to the court in fifteen minutes because we had a verdict.

We took our seats and waited for the judge and the court martial board. The usher called the court to attention, they filed in, and Colonel Robertson said, 'President of the court martial board, have you come to a verdict?'

Lt Col Lloyd-Williams replied, "We have."

"Please read out the verdict," asked Colonel Robertson.

"We find the accused, Lieutenant Herbert Clough, not guilty of the charge of deserting his post in time of war with a recommendation that he be sanctioned for being absent without leave for the period of twelve hours when he absented himself from the St Omer Hospital."

The judge called the usher forward who swivelled the sword around on the table so that the hilt was facing the accused. He then spoke directly to Lieutenant Clough. "Mr Clough, the case brought against you for desertion has not been proven and you are hereby discharged without a stain on your character, and you may resume your duties. The matter of the absence without leave is something best left to your company commander to deal with, which I am sure that he will do with wisdom. The minute this court closes you are free to go."

Colonel Robertson continued, "I have one final thing to say, that I believe that the provost marshal should issue arrest warrants for Captain Faulkner, Lieutenant Betteridge and Lieutenant Allen, at the very least, on a charge of perjury but pending more serious charges to follow. This court martial is closed."

I shook Herbert by the hand, and he looked at me a little dazed, until I said to him that he was free to go and that he was buying dinner this evening to celebrate. The sergeant usher returned Herbert's sword to him, said he was glad the court had come to the right decision and we both thanked him before walking together out of the courtroom into the main anteroom where I ordered some tea for us and sat in the same armchair that I was sitting in when Harding had tried to browbeat me into a guilty plea six days ago. We sat quietly for just a few moments before our peace was disturbed by a torrent of well-wishers and the first to arrive was Major Bryanston, who made a gracious apology for being the unwitting cause of all his misfortune. He said he had offered to step down as company commander, but the battalion commander had turned down his request and wished him to continue to lead the company especially as the next big offensive was due very soon. The major said that he would continue if he could have Lieutenant Clough back; he would understand if Herbert preferred to serve in a different company, but he hoped that he would want to assist in rebuilding the company after the Faulkner regime. Herbert was glad to return and said he would report for duty whenever he was required to.

I intervened and suggested that Herbert should report on Monday morning because we had some serious celebrating to get through this evening. This was quickly agreed between them, but I could hear some vaguely familiar noises coming from the entrance hall of the mess and making their way along the corridor towards us. My suspicions were confirmed when Terence Bradby, Jamie Dalrymple, and my A flighters poured through the door whooping and cheering, followed a little less exuberantly by Welby and Cranley. Everyone gathered around Herbert, slapping him on the back and congratulating him, and the flyboys picked me up and carried me aloft around the anteroom in great high spirits just as Colonel Robertson came in. The boys lowered me to the ground rather sheepishly when they saw the red tabs on the colonel's collar, and I tried to apologise for their behaviour. The colonel smiled and said, 'If I were younger, I would probably have joined in as you deserve the accolade. Flight Lieutenant Morgan, you have acquitted yourself extremely well and achieved a verdict nobody thought possible five days ago. It was well done by determined and thorough application to your task, and I am sure that Clough will be forever grateful to you for saving him from the firing squad. I hope you consider remaining in the service after the war ends because there will be a great demand for young men to build a strong peacetime army.' The colonel took his leave, wishing us a good evening celebrating our victory.

Jamie and the others were insistent that we should repair to the town and start to celebrate with champagne and then a good dinner, followed by some dancing. Major Bryanston cried off saying that he needed to get back to the company but wished us all the best and hoped he could join us at some other time. The rest of us piled out of the front of the mess into Jamie's Bentley, and Giles Lacey had acquired a Hispano-Suiza from somewhere since I had last seen him. As we were loading up Major Harding came down the front steps looking for his own transport to pick him up and deliberately tried to blank us.

I could not resist it and strode over to him and in a loud voice so that all within earshot could hear clearly said, "Major Harding, sneaking away back into your own little corner. You were very quick to use the privilege of the courtroom to impugn the characters of brave front-line officers whilst you skulk safe in the rear area. You accused both Lieutenants Welby and Cranley of being accessories to the desertion by Lieutenant Clough, all of which was based on little or no evidence. Major, you are beneath contempt because if you had bothered to examine the scant evidence placed before you with some application you would have quickly seen where the guilt lay, and this case would not have been brought. I have seen how lazy you are – you believed that you would win this case so easily that you did not need to work too hard to test out the truth of the case you put forward. Are you prepared now to be a man and publically apologise to these three officers in front of their peers for the slur you made on their characters?'

He did not respond but hung his head low and tried to avoid making eye contact with any of us, muttering that he was a knight of the realm and a King's Council, and we could not talk to him like that. The boys just threw a few ribald remarks his way and then soon forgot about him as we set off into town for a night of celebration. Jamie headed for the main square and we went first to the St Omer Hotel on the south side of the square, where we were able to get cool beer and order some fresh baguette sandwiches to make up for our missed lunch, and to give some lining to our stomachs for the marathon drinking session that was to come that night. We sat on the terrace at the front of the hotel and drank our beers. Frequent toasts were made to Herbert and then to me, and the afternoon passed quickly in such pleasant company. The town was filling up with off-duty soldiers as the afternoon wore on and we enjoyed some friendly banter with groups of them as they passed by or stopped to order a beer in the hotel.

As the numbers increased, I could see the redcaps of the military policemen mingling amongst the crowd and a couple of times I spotted Major Rydall, the provost marshal, wandering and chatting good naturedly with many of the soldiers until he eventually stepped into the entrance to the St Omer Hotel. With the typical policeman's habit of looking around a bar to see who was in, he spotted me on the terrace and came through to speak with me. He was surprised to find I was with such lively company and to see Herbert Clough in our midst. We called out to him to join us for a drink, and he said that he could not drink on duty but then, after a pause, slipped the provost marshal armband from his sleeve and said, "I am off-duty now," and asked for a whisky. He sat down between Herbert and me and raised his glass to us both. He then turned to me and said that he wished to apologise for misleading me somewhat when he said that Herbert had asked for me as prisoner's friend.

"Everyone that I had asked had turned me down and the prosecutor's office was about to appoint one of their junior lawyers to defend him, which I knew would result in a straight road to the firing squad. I have a policeman's nose for when cases do not smell right and this one did not, but once the prosecutor decided to take it on my influence ceased. Then, I thought of a young man who I had the pleasure of solving a case with back last year and by sheer fluke he was known to Herbert Clough. I shall be forever thankful that I trusted my instinct and brought you two together for the good. Betteridge and Allen are already in custody and on their way to Arras military prison, Faulkner has not yet been apprehended but I am sure we will get him shortly." He lowered his voice and said to me, "the two prison guards who had assaulted Herbert had been demoted and sent back to their infantry regiments." He stood and finished his whisky and before he left, he told us that the town was going to be extra busy this evening because there were rumours circulating that the offensive would come next week, so he advised us to take ourselves into one of the officers only venues and stay off the streets if possible. He wished us well and slipping the armband up his sleeve, he stepped back on duty with a parting wave as he passed the front of the terrace.

A table was booked at Suzette's for seven-thirty, so we decided to park the cars in the alley to the side and have some drinks at the small cafés thereabouts before our table was ready for us. By now we had all switched from cold beer because it was making us bloated and requiring frequent trips to the lavatory, and we ordered bottles of cheap champagne to keep us going until dinner time. By the time seven-thirty arrived, I was ravenous, getting close to my capacity for alcohol and in need of a good dinner. I would change to brandy, which I could drink in small measure and slowly.

Suzette greeted us warmly and seemed a little confused when she saw Herbert and I together, remembering the night I had torn him off a strip and he had fled from the restaurant some weeks earlier. She, of course, had no knowledge of what had transpired since then and why we were in such a celebratory mood tonight. She was serving an excellent shin of beef with oysters this evening and I could not wait to get started. Jamie and Giles were trying to outdo each other with stories and keeping pace drink for drink with each other and Charlie Knowles. I noticed that Alex Brown, since he had become a wingman, seemed to have relaxed and was participating in a way that I would not have thought possible a few weeks ago. Larry Fortescue and Terence were getting along famously with the two young lieutenants. I thought that it was somewhat ironic that the two of us who should be celebrating the most were the quietest amongst them and drinking less than all the others. It was as if Herbert and I had finally begun to realise the enormity of what had happened today in the courtroom, and it was a sobering thought for both of us. I thought that had the verdict been guilty I would have found myself pleading for Herbert's life on Monday morning. I reflected on the insufferable Harding and for a moment regretted that I had spoken to him so stridently, but then dismissed the regret because he deserved to be told and I had enjoyed the experience very much. I thought more positively of the bravery of Major Bryanston, the kind and fair approach of Colonel Robertson and of course, the testimony of the men in Herbert's platoon who had all contributed to his acquittal.

Herbert leaned closer to me and said that he wanted to apologise to me for his behaviour in this room several weeks ago, that he was forever shamed that he had still not shaken off every trace of his bullying past. "I have discovered in Terence Bradby and you, two of the most fearless and upright officers I have ever encountered, and I salute you both, not just for defending me and getting me off this charge but for demonstrating the way that a real officer behaves. I will try my best to live up to your standards and hope I can count you as my friends." We shook hands on that, and I said we should join in the party before we became too maudlin. The table erupted in laughter at one of Giles Lacey's extravagant stories about falling off his horse during the annual GOC's parade and being dragged along by the stirrup on the march past, but still managing to salute the general as he was dragged by. You never knew whether Giles's stories were true or embellished a little, but they were truly funny and although Jamie tried to outdo him, he never managed to better Giles Lacey as a raconteur.

After the meal was cleared away, Suzette's hostesses began to enter the room and join the parties of officers at the various tables. I saw Marta, the slightly older brunette, make a beeline for Charlie Knowles and within minutes they were in deep conversation like the last time we were here. There was no sign of Yvette in the room, and I was glad, as I was still not sure that I could resist the temptation, but I could see her friend, Clara, circulating the room and heading for our table. She came over to me, said hello and I introduced her to Herbert Clough. We chatted lightly for a few minutes, and I enquired after Yvette. She replied quietly that Yvette had given up this kind of work to gain advancement at the hospital. Apparently, she was recognised by one of her clients from here who came to the hospital and she could not risk her double life becoming public knowledge. I noticed that Herbert seemed to be attracted to Clara, so I was happy to take a step back and let him monopolise her attention. I had been feeling guilty enough that I had not written to Ruby at all this week, being so preoccupied with the trial, but vowed that I would write and tell her all about the events in the morning. I had not received any letters from home this week either, but I expected to find them in my room at La Coupole when I got back. I was anxious to know how Ruby was getting on with the pregnancy and whether the Reverend Lewis had agreed to marry us in the chapel on my next leave.

I joined with Jamie and Giles and enjoyed the good fun and banter around them, and some flirting with the girls too, but by eleven o'clock I was ready to make my way back to the St Omer mess where I was staying tonight. I noticed that Herbert and Clara had disappeared so I made my farewells and said I would be back at La Coupole tomorrow morning. I left Suzette's and the side street was quiet and empty, but I could hear that the main street that led to the square and the officers' mess sounded extremely busy. I was amazed when I reached the corner to see the street thronged with thousands of khaki-clad revellers in far greater numbers than the small bars and cafés could cope with. Those who were inside the various establishments seemed to be enjoying themselves good naturedly, but I could hear raised voices and angry retorts from those trapped out in the street and unable to again entry anywhere. I could see that this was a very volatile situation, which could easily lead to widespread unrest if not handled correctly. I did not envy Major Rydall and his men who had to deal with this angry mob, and I was wondering if I could risk trying to cross the road and work my way through the back streets and alleys to the St Omer Citadel.

This was far more frightening than a dogfight as the odds were stacked too heavily against me, and I decided to make my way back towards Suzette's. I kept to the shadows and just as I got to within twenty yards of Suzette's door, a voice spoke to me out of the dark. "Where are you going Monsieur?" I did not know whether take to my heels and run for my life or investigate who my interrogator was. I took a step towards the mysterious voice and I could just make out a gendarme in uniform. He said, "It is not safe for an officer to be out alone tonight as the soldiers are very turbulent. Where are you going, Monsieur?" I told him that I was making for the officers' mess at the Citadel. He said that he could lead me to a place where I could cross the main street safely and show me the back way to the Citadel without going near the main square. I was grateful as he led me down some narrow alleys until we reached the same main street I had seen before, but some 300 yards away from the crowds. He pointed to a side street branching off from the other side of the road and told me to follow this for 500 yards and then turn right on to Rue du Militaire, which would take me to the gates of the Citadel. I thanked him for his kindness and slipped across the main street as quickly as I could. I followed his directions and less than ten minutes later I found the turning for Rue du Militaire. I made it to the mess within twenty-five minutes.

TWENTY-THREE

Return to Action

The following morning after breakfast I set off on the motorcycle for La Coupole. The streets of St Omer were now even more deserted than a usual Sunday morning. I looked forward to hearing from Jamie and the others how they fared when they came out of Suzette's place, but I suspected that I would have to wait until they surfaced later in the day, after they had slept off the alcohol, to get any sense out of them. All was quiet when I reached the A flight hut, and I was surprised at how good it felt to be back in my room. I took the chance to catch up with my letters from home and to write my replies. Ruby was enduring biliousness in the mornings and beginning to have cravings as well. The latest was for strawberries, which in April in Wales is almost impossible to satisfy. The Reverend Lewis was not happy that Ruby and I had sexual relations before our marriage but had been persuaded that as we were betrothed officially, he could marry us in the chapel. Ruby said that he needed three weeks' notice of the wedding as the banns had to be posted and read aloud in chapel on three consecutive Sundays, and she also expected that he would give us both a morality lecture before we tied the knot. Her mum had agreed to make the wedding dress and the bridesmaid dress for Freda, which was good because she was an expert seamstress and would be able to hide the signs of pregnancy. I also thought that it was good because it would keep the cost down. My mum had volunteered to make the wedding cake, provided we could manage to find all the ingredients necessary, and Mr Thomas had secured the use of the rugby club for the reception at no cost. I wrote back to her immediately with all the news about the trial and the verdict and expressing my excitement about the wedding plans. I would apply for two weeks' leave as a matter of urgency and hoped to get a date quite soon.

However, I could not tell her that there was going to be a new engagement with the enemy as the last big push to drive them back and break out from the positions we had been held in by the Germans for over a year.

After a light lunch, I wandered over to the squadron command hut to speak with Major Moss and confirm that I was now reporting back for duty. He was happy to see me back. "And just in time because patrolling activity is increasing during the next week as a pre-cursor to the opening up of the next big attack next Friday morning. We will start briefing tomorrow and all personnel will be restricted to camp until the battle is started to prevent the date and time being leaked to the enemy." I said that as it was two weeks since I had sat in the cockpit, I had decided to take my aircraft up for a short check flight later this afternoon just to refresh my memory and get back into the right frame of mind. He congratulated me on the win at the court martial and said that I must be proud of myself. I told him that I felt somewhat alarmed that unless someone can put together a robust defence, defendants are convicted on the thinnest of evidence. I was led to believe that the defence of Clough was a hopeless case, and the evidence was compelling, but a little more thorough investigation revealed a web of lies and a conspiracy against him. Finally, I got around to asking when it might be possible to get some leave, explaining about the sensitivity at home about my fiancée's pregnancy, and the need to get married in good time before the baby came. I explained that I needed three weeks' notice so the banns could be read, and I would like a few days at home with my new wife if possible. He did not turn me down at once but said it could be difficult with the new offensive, but he would try to work something out if he could.

Giles, Larry, and Alex were up when I got back to the hut. We sat in the crew room with a large pot of tea, and they recounted their adventures in getting home last night. Apparently, the mob swirled around the streets of St Omer getting involved in sporadic acts of violence, which were mostly brawls amongst themselves rather than the destruction of property or assaults on the police or local people. The rumours circulating about the next offensive had sparked fears amongst many infantrymen that this may be the last time that they could get to enjoy themselves in the bars and brothels of St Omer. Unfortunately, they came in such numbers that the town could not accommodate them and many of them were unable even to get a drink. When they left Suzette's, the gendarmerie advised them not to take the main roads but directed them through narrow back streets until they reached the outskirts of the town where the road was clear. I asked about Herbert and they said that he left with Clara and disappeared down the side alley arm in arm. In one of the side -roads they came upon a small group of soldiers blocking the road when they saw their cars approaching and for a few moments there was a stand-off, which could have turned ugly until Giles stood up in the seat of the Hispano, drew his pistol and waggled it about in the air pretending to be much drunker than he was. He said he would shoot if they did not clear the road and there were several retorts that he was so drunk that he could not hit a barn door with that pistol, when Giles fired one shot which passed so close to the head of the soldier speaking that they realised this crazy officer meant business and stepped aside. I asked Giles if he was that good a shot and he said no, but it was a lucky miss.

I told them that we were going to be busy during the coming week flying combat patrols in the run-up to the new offensive, which was scheduled for next Friday morning. We were confined to camp until after the offensive began except for our patrolling, of course. The squadron commander would begin briefing at 08:00 in the morning. I got changed into flying clothing and took my aircraft up for a twenty-minute check ride to ensure that I had not forgotten anything and found that I felt as comfortable as ever in the cockpit. I decided to have an early dinner and get an early night, as I expected that we would not be getting too much sleep during the coming few days.

All the squadron pilots were gathered in the briefing room to hear about our tasking for this week. Lt. Col. Harcourt, the Wing commander, said a few words to begin with about the forthcoming offensive which was intended to push out from the Ypres Salient and along the line north and south and push the Germans back decisively so that our advance would be able to overrun their retreat, and clear the way to Brussels and beyond. He explained that HQ Second Army was now convinced the destruction of the German resistance could be achieved because we had amassed the largest Allied army ever seen to make this possible. There were no divisions of British, French, Canadian and Empire troops and the big difference was the Americans with their men and material. He said 2 Wing had a big part to play and he would leave Major Moss to explain our part in greater detail.

We were called to attention and he left the room on his way to the next squadron pep talk. Major Moss told us to relax and get comfortable as this was going to be a lengthy briefing, and then launched into the specific role that had been selected for 354 Squadron. On the three days preceding the launch of the offensive, we were to fly high-level escort to the bombing raids pinpointed against all the railheads, signalling and switchgear on the main lines into Brussels and beyond. These targets would be raided twice on day one and once each of the other days and each sortie was expected to involve over three hours' flying, so the additional fuel tanks were being fitted again to give us the maximum range and duration.

"Our job is to prevent the enemy from attacking the bombers whilst engaged in their bombing operations, through aggressive patrolling to keep the enemy from breaking through our defensive screen and attacking our more vulnerable bomber aircraft. There will be a second line of escort much closer to the bombing formation should any Germans break through, but I am sure that you will stop most of them. You will operate from altitude so cold weather gear will be essential and your machine-gun magazines will be filled to maximum capacity, giving each of you a further fourteen seconds of fire power than on a normal patrol."

Major Moss then went through the two targets for the next day which were to revisit the railheads we had attacked several times before, but we did not need to concern ourselves too much with the details as we were flying the high-altitude escort. We would take off and make the fastest ascent to nearly 10,000ft that we could, which would probably take us nearly twenty-five minutes, but by the time we had reached our ceiling we would be in position over the intended target, watching for the enemy scouts and fighters below. Our job was to sweep the skies over the targets free of enemy fighters as far as we could, to allow the bombers a free path in and out of the target zone. The rest of the day was frenetic with much activity in checking our aircraft were ready and serviceable for the flight and coordinating the sectors over the target that each flight would patrol. I reminded Larry, Giles, and Alex that we would be flying at altitude for over three hours and to wear additional warm clothing and carry a small flask of a warm drink, and that the additional weight of the extra fuel tanks and ammunition would make the aircraft more sluggish on take-off than usual so to compensate for it. I was certainly excited to be going back into action again and I could feel a tingling in the back of my neck in expectation. I wrote again to Ruby explaining that I had applied for leave and hoped to have some good news soon, then went to bed early again to be fresh for the morning.

Final briefing was at 06:30 and we were mounted and ready for take-off by 07:30 when the green flare went up for 354 Squadron to take to the air. The other squadrons which were on low-level close escort were already airborne and well on their way to rendezvous with the big bomber formations to the north-west of Hondschoote, towards the Channel coast. They had a forty-mile approach over enemy territory to their targets to the west of Brussels and this would require a high degree of coordination to get the bomber formation over the railway hubs all at the same time. It was hoped that the combination of high-explosive bombing from so many aircraft in a relatively compact area would cause maximum damage and severely restrict the German ability to reinforce their front lines when the main ground attack came early that Friday morning.

We also had a long flight of over forty-five miles to get to the bomber's target, but we were freed from the need to rendezvous with the large formation of slow-moving bombers and head straight to the target zone. We had planned to fly south-east towards Lille and then alter course easterly towards Tournai and Ath, approaching the targets from the opposite direction than the bombers. This should enable us to stay hidden in the high clouds until we were almost over the targets and ready to begin searching for our prey. We had planned to be in place and patrolling in box sections before the main bombing formation arrived – our timing seemed to be about right as there was no sign of the bombers when we arrived over the targets. We scanned the skies carefully looking for enemy fighters and particularly concentrated on the sectors to the north-east of us where we knew the German fighter airfields were situated. All was quiet, we could not see much movement at all, and I began to hope that our surprise was complete when I noticed some specks out of the corner of my left eye at seven o'clock, slightly lower than us but flying on a roughly similar course.

I was a little wary because I was sure they must have spotted us; they showed no sign that they had but continued flying straight and level. I signalled Larry to follow me and Giles and Alex to continue the patrol and we rolled out of formation to our right to circle back to locate above and behind our targets when I immediately saw as we began to retrace our flight path that we were being duped, as a formation of six German fighters had been tracking our formation and were about a mile behind us ready to strike once we committed ourselves to attack their decoys. I was tempted to continue head on and attack this approaching force but instantly weighed up our chances as not far off suicidal, so kept the bank on, came round the full 360 degrees to get back on course and raced on to warn Giles and Alex. Once we were back into flight formation, I knew we stood a better chance against the Germans who could not manoeuvre anywhere near as quickly as we could.

Given that we were outgunned in this contest I decided not to break and pick individual targets but to manoeuvre in flight formation and attack from their eastern flank in echelon, which I felt would concentrate our fire power and cause maximum damage, then once we forced them to break formation, we could select our targets and take them down individually. I felt sure that they expected us to break and for this to degenerate into a dogfight melee where their advantage in numbers would guarantee them victory. So, I repeated my movements of a few moments before, but this time banked to the right as a flight to swing us on track to attack them on their eastern flank as they passed in front of us. I could see that the German pilots were already spreading their formation further apart to enable them to break and chase after us individually once we broke and dived for safety.

They still did not believe that we were the hunters and not the hunted and paid the price for their complacency when the first burst of concentrated machine-gun fire ripped into them sideways on and they flew into a hail of lead. It was impossible to know who caused what damage, but one pilot must have been hit and lost control of his aircraft, which fell away towards the ground. There were no signs of damage, leaking fuel or smoke coming from the aircraft, but it was plummeting like a stone and then we saw part of a wing break off and knew he was doomed. Another aircraft closer to Giles' side was hit multiple times by him and Alex, set on fire and limped on as the pilot tried to keep airborne. We had evened the numbers and when they finally broke formation, we selected our targets, chased after them and I was fortunate as one of the aircraft at the rear of the German formation was slow to roll and chose to roll the wrong way into the arc of fire of my guns. I gave him two quick bursts, which seemed to have destroyed some of his control wires as he appeared to lose his rudder control. He was now almost powerless to avoid me and although he tried valiantly, his destruction was inevitable and when the smoke began to appear from the base of his engine, I knew I could leave him to his fate.

I saw Larry Fortescue streak past me, diving fast, right on the tail of a fourth fighter. I wondered where the decoy aircraft were now and whether they could be a danger to Larry. I became his wingman for a change, just to protect his back if these decoys were still stooging around. Larry made quick work of his target and that was the fourth German aircraft destroyed before the bombing had even started. Larry re-joined in his wingman position, and we circled round and climbed to restore ourselves to our operational altitude when we spotted the two-decoy aircraft making a quick escape and we opened our throttles wider to overhaul them as quickly as possible. They seemed desperately aware that we were behind them and tried frantically to shake us off, failing to notice Giles and Alex stalking them on their starboard side, swooping in, attacking together with full bursts that brought them both down.

A flight reformed and we attempted to resume the box pattern patrol, but on looking down we could see that the bombing raids were successful judging by the smoke and fire visible from this height and the bombers were already withdrawing towards the west. It was not long before we received a flashlight message to follow the bombers in their retreat from the targets. We were not able to intercept any more German fighters on the return leg and when we crossed our lines near Ypres, we were despatched to land, refuel, rearm, and then rest before the second sortie at 16:00. I was elated that the flight had performed so well; collectively we had destroyed six enemy aircraft. In the debrief we were able to piece together the sequence of the attacks and claims were lodged as two for Larry Fortescue, two for Giles Lacey and one each for Alex Brown and me. My total was now ten and if confirmed, I would receive a bar to my DFC.

Our second sortie for the day was to accompany a smaller force of bombers who were going to bomb a forested area near Staden, where it had been reported that German tanks were massing. Take-off was planned for 16:00 but the weather reports were forecasting that visibility was decreasing as the afternoon progressed which might cause the sortie to be scrubbed. Although our spirits were high and we ate a hearty lunch, we all tried to get a couple of hours' rest before final briefing at 15:00.

Low cloud was moving in from the coast and visibility was much reduced than earlier in the day, but the bomber group decided it was within limits and would go ahead with the raid. This time we would be at 3,000ft and would be flying close escort to the bombers as they overflew the densely wooded Staden Forest, where intelligence was certain that over one hundred German tanks were hidden ready for the counterattack when our offensive began. I remembered vaguely reporting seeing tanks in this location some time before, but we were unable to verify their position in subsequent reconnaissance missions. Staden Forest meant a much shorter flight from base than in the morning and the lower altitude made it less uncomfortably cold for us too. We linked up with the bomber group over Poperinge and each flight took post at a corner of the bomber formation, just slightly above their height and kept pace with them as they vectored in to drop their bombs on every part of the forest. The trees were too dense to be able to make out whether any tanks were located there and there was no anti-aircraft fire nearby, although there was plenty of small-arms fire coming up through the canopy which suggested something was hidden in the forest. We had no contact with any German fighters this time but returned to base without adding to our totals, dog-tired and ready for a rest.

TWENTY-FOUR

The Offensive and Breakout

We flew two more sorties on Wednesday and Thursday in support of the bombing campaign against the enemy communications in their rear zone. I managed to shoot down one more and Giles and Alex both got one more each. We already knew that the enemy held their reserves well back from the front and used the extensive railway network to move them around quickly to whichever part of the front line needed reinforcement the most at any given point in the battle. This gave them much greater flexibility to deploy their troops than we had but relied heavily on keeping the road and rail links open and serviceable. We, however, built up a massive force to make the initial offensive thrust with the intent of breaking the enemy resistance with our overwhelming power. General Haig had demonstrated with his subways strategy that if it was possible to get your first wave attack into the enemy trenches without coming directly under fire from their deadly machine guns, it was possible to take their trenches without a massive loss of life. However, our generals had been far too cautious and failed to capitalise on initial victories to make the bold and decisive moves necessary to push the enemy into a full retreat, but instead preferred to consolidate small gains and strengthen our positions.

There was much concern expressed at home and among the soldiers at the front about the appalling hardships endured during the winter of 1917 to 1918 in the muddy, wet quagmire of Flanders and the Passchendaele Valley. Nothing had moved along the Ypres Salient or Arras line for at least eight months; except for skirmishes and patrolling there had been little contact between the two sides. However, the Allies had built the biggest army ever put into the field in preparation for the spring offensive and had moved hundreds of thousands of men into position to make the breakthrough possible this time. It would have been almost impossible to keep this massive build-up a secret from the enemy, who knew full well that a new offensive was coming but were not exactly sure when, although the increased air activity would have given them strong enough indications that the attack was imminent.

There were many in the front lines who believed that the Germans were on their last legs and that one final thrust would see them run all the way back to the borders of Germany for a last-ditch stand on home territory. I was not so sure that I could agree with that assessment because having flown frequently over the enemy-occupied land many miles behind their front line I could see little evidence that their army was close to breaking point. The air battle conversely had been fought with a great intensity during the winter months and both the bombers and the fighter squadrons had constantly harried the means of communications and troop concentrations as well as driven the German air force from the skies over the battlefield. This was largely due to the superiority of our fighter aircraft but also because the new pilot training system introduced in 1916 had raised the quality of combat pilots immeasurably so that they were not just surviving longer but winning the battle in the air. The generals in the high command knew, undoubtedly, that the Royal Air Force was in total control of the airspace over the battlefield and believed that a counterattack, mounted by the German air force, was highly unlikely. The commanding generals knew that if they reverted to an over-the-top infantry assault through no-man's-land, they would hand the advantage back to the enemy who, with their superior machine-gun defences would inflict massive casualties on the first wave of attackers. Similarly, the subway tunnels had worked spectacularly well in 1917 but the enemy had learned the lessons of that defeat and re-sited their machine-gun nest to cover their close quarters and their flanks in case of second use of this tactic.

This time the siege companies had laid explosives in tunnels under the command-and-control posts but also three main ammunition and supply dumps at Langemark-Poelkapelle and Moorslede, timed to explode just as the offensive began. The artillery barrage was set to begin at 06:30 and last for twenty minutes exactly when the first wave assault would begin with an armoured tank attack, supported by the first wave of infantry projected by the bulk of the advancing tanks. Over 500 tanks were to be deployed on that first morning alone with 45,000 infantrymen in support. Their aim was to breach the German defences and pour through to surround and capture the enemy divisions whilst they were in disarray. Once this was achieved, the second infantry wave would advance, pass through the first wave, and support the tanks that would be now striking at the heart of German-occupied territory in Belgium. The British First Tank Regiment was to strike north-westerly and engage the German tanks believed to be in the Staden Forest area and the Second Tank Regiment was to link with the American tanks near Menen and to strike easterly towards Brussels. The objectives were to establish ourselves ten to twelve miles from our present positions on the first day. Day two had the most ambitious plan which expected the north-westerly strike force to capture Bruges and the easterly force to coordinate with the French from the southern sector coming from Valenciennes to threaten Brussels itself. Preventing the enemy from moving his reserves of men and materials freely was key to the success of the Allied plans so that our ground troops could gain the momentum and move quickly to occupy the space vacated by the enemy as they pulled back.

The role of the RAF and our American counterparts was vital to the success of the ground campaign, and we all knew that we would be remarkably busy during the first week of the offensive at least. Plans were being circulated by Wing headquarters for 354 Squadron to be detached to operate from the former German fighter field at Oudenburg once it was captured, which would increase our range of penetration into north-west Belgium and southern Holland. The day three and four objectives were to keep moving fast to capture Ghent, threaten Antwerp and to begin to circle Brussels.

On Friday morning we were strapped in ready to go, as when the artillery barrage began, we knew we had twenty minutes to get airborne and head for the sector of the line between Poperinge and Ypres/Passchendaele so that we were in position to support the tank attacks as they pushed forward. Even at 4,000ft the sight and the sounds of the barrage were amazing, and I must admit to feeling some sympathy both for our troops waiting anxiously to scale their parapets and follow the tanks towards the enemy, but also the Germans huddled down trying to keep safe as the thunderous storm of artillery shells rained down on them. I wondered how Clough, Welby, Cranley, and Major Bryanston were, crouched below the fortifications at St Martin waiting for the signal to go over the top. My thoughts turned also to my former comrades in the Monmouthshire Siege Company when the three great explosions wracked the earth below us like giant earthquakes as the ammunition and supply depots went up. As the smoke cleared, I could see waves of our tanks moving slowly forward across the broken and rugged landscape between the two front lines, the vast machines climbing over each obstacle with ease.

The Germans poured massive, small-arms and machine-gun fire at the tanks from behind their parapets but were not having any great effect in penetrating the steel hulls, whilst our infantrymen were keeping well covered behind the bulk of the tanks and our casualties seemed to be light. Some bolder defenders broke out of cover and tried to throw stick grenades or aim flame throwers at the tanks but were easily cut down. I led my flight down over the battlefield and flew low along the line of the enemy trenches, firing all the way and then concentrating fire on the command centre at the end of each section of trench. This would normally be a high-risk strategy as we were vulnerable from concentrated small-arms fire from below but because of the chaos and frenetic activity of the first wave attack, few enemy soldiers fired at the attacking aircraft. As we circled back for another run along the trench line, I noticed that one of our tanks was disabled and had lost a track, but four of the first rank of tanks were already climbing up and over the German parapets with British infantrymen following them in great numbers. The tanks had accomplished their first job and would begin to press forward whilst the infantry engaged in the hand-to-hand fighting necessary to secure the ground.

I waved the flight off as things were now too confused in the trenches below to risk another strafing run. I signalled Giles Lacey that we should gain altitude so that we could survey the battlefield and look for more suitable targets on the ground or in the air, and when we reached 3,000ft we had a panoramic view of the action from the sea to Lille and could see that the first hour was going well for us. Larry Fortescue, who had the keenest eyesight of all of us, was waving and pointing north-westerly towards the Staden Forest area that we had attacked a few days before. We could see many German tanks emerging from the trees, organising into squadrons, and moving off south-westerly to meet the British tank attack head-on. The German tanks had no infantry support and although I knew that there was little, we could do to stop the tank advance, we could search for the infantry support which must be waiting to rendezvous with the tanks before they engaged the advancing Allied tank formations and hampered their effectiveness. I also knew that it would take the German tanks over an hour to encounter our tanks, so it was vital that we get this intelligence reported to command as soon as possible.

I sent a flash-light message to Giles in Morse code to tell him to take over the lead of the flight whilst I landed to pass on this battle-field update. He acknowledged and I immediately set course for the nearest airfield, which was a bomber field near Bailleul. I knew roughly where it was but in the swirling smoke and low cloud, I was having difficulty finding the right approach, and the airfield was experiencing a lot of traffic as bombers were taking off and returning on a very lively morning. I waited my turn and then quickly landed to the side of the main track so as not to hinder the bombers' operations and taxied towards the control tower. I left my engine running but jumped down and approached the command hut where I related what we had seen over Staden Forest and the estimated number of German tanks now moving into counterattack. This intelligence had to reach the tank commanders urgently so they could be forewarned and prepare to engage and passed to the artillery who might be able to bring their guns to bear. The signals officer was summoned, and he got on to the wireless set to send the warning signals immediately. They thanked me, I climbed back into my aircraft and headed back to the runway queue to wait my turn to take off again.

A quick glance at my watch told me that it was only eight minutes since I had left my flight, but I had set in my mind the sector where I hoped to find them. I was being extra careful as I was flying alone without the protection of my wingman and did not want to be jumped by a roving German fighter. I headed in the general direction of Staden and climbed to 3,000ft to give me a better view of the events below. I was trying to estimate where the German tanks would have got to within the passage of time since we spotted them and where the most likely rendezvous points with their infantry support might be. I could see that our tanks had halted their advance and were settling themselves into defensive positions just below the line of the ridge, some four miles ahead of the infantry formations who were still engaged in securing the former German trenches and prisoners. I knew that the tanks would not advance alone without their infantry support, and I suspected that they would wait here until the infantry were ready to move forward again. I wondered whether my intelligence had been passed to them already, but this was idle speculation as I needed to find the rest of my flight quickly.

I could see some aerial activity up ahead and moved in that direction to investigate. As I got closer, I could see the tail markers of 354 Squadron on the aircraft engaged in the dogfight with four Storch fighters. There were three SE5s against four Germans, but they were holding their own and no one seemed to have suffered any serious damage. The Germans had not yet sighted me and I was able to manoeuvre to be able to dive on to the melee and take out at least one of the attackers with my first pass, or simply even up the odds if not. Yet again, I could see that the superior aerobatic qualities of the Bristol enabled my pilots to outturn the enemy with ease and they were just waiting for the opportunity to turn the tables on their attackers. I chose my moment carefully and lined up behind the rear-most Storch aircraft who was acting as a kind of protective wingman for the other three, and then dived straight on to him aiming for the cockpit and engine as I wished to kill the pilot and destroy his aircraft. My surprise was complete as he had no idea I was there; he was pre-occupied with watching the progress of his three comrades to look behind and above. I must have hit him because his aircraft lurched left immediately and then spun out of control, spiralling down to earth with a trail of smoke tailing out behind. I still had great forward momentum and was able to get in a passing shot at the third attacker. I saw bits of wreckage fly off his fuselage as he took evasive action. He appeared to be still in full control of his aircraft despite the damage I had inflicted, but he had dived to my left so quickly that I was unable to follow him but the Bristol he was stalking was now able to reverse roles with him and immediately took up the chase. I could now see that this was Larry Fortescue, who had been left exposed when I went off to pass the message, but he was intent on exacting revenge, and I could see his shots striking home. Whichever way the German pilot twisted and turned the SE5 was quicker and would not be shaken off. Larry's tenacity paid off and he was rewarded when the Storch just crumbled and exploded in mid-air, and I remember thinking that Larry would soon have a DFC too.

The other two Storch aircraft were having little luck in catching Giles or Alex, and seeing two of their comrades despatched so quickly, decided to break off and run for safety. Giles was tempted to chase them, but I recalled them and reformed the flight formation for two reasons; we only had enough fuel for another twenty minutes' flying, and I wanted to see if we could be of assistance to our tanks on the ground by accurately spotting the advancing German tanks before we headed for home. As we came over the last known positions of the German tanks, I was amazed to see that they too had stopped and were taking up defensive positions to await the arrival of their infantry before advancing again. I drew the positions on my map as clearly as I could, marking where I could see the German tank squadrons arraigned and placed it into my map case with a short, hand-written message. I ordered Giles to take the rest of the flight back to La Coupole to refuel whilst I intended to fly low along the British tank lines and drop my map case where they would find it. I estimated that I had just enough fuel to manage this task and make it back to the airfield, even if I had to glide in the last few miles. I flew low and about one hundred feet along the line of the front rank of tanks, roughly in the middle, I dropped the map case so that it landed close to the line of tanks then sent a flashlight message that the position of the advancing German tanks was marked on the map and wished them good hunting.

Before I broke off for my dash to refuel, I received an acknowledgement and thanks. I climbed to 500ft and took the risk of flying straight and level on the most direct course for La Coupole because evasive flying would use far more fuel than I had left in my tank. I throttled back to a more economic setting and made slow and steady progress back home. Every minute that passed, my fear of running out of fuel increased while my confidence that I would make it was disappearing. At last, I began to recognise the familiar landscape around the airfield and tried to gain a little more altitude for making the final approach. I was now two miles short of the runway but lined up well, when my engine began to splutter and cough and then with a couple of judders the engine stopped, and the propeller came to a standstill. I was confident that the aircraft could glide well enough to get me onto the ground safely, but I would not have enough altitude to go around for a second chance. It was now or never, and I hoped that the grass track was free of aircraft as I came in because I could not pull up. I tried to send a flash-light message in Morse code to tell them I was out of fuel, but I did not see an acknowledgement. I was now committed and was fighting to keep the aircraft airborne long enough to cross the threshold and place the wheels down on the grass. I became aware that I had just managed to clear the perimeter fence although it was a near thing, and now braced myself for the thump as the wheels hit the grass much harder than in a controlled powered landing. I felt the thump in my bottom travel up my spine, I pushed as hard as I could on the brakes and tried to keep as straight as possible until the aircraft came to a complete halt. I could see the crash carts rushing towards me as I climbed out and waved the medic off and shouted to the firemen to send the tractor to tow my aircraft back to the flight line for refuelling and rearming. I refused a ride back and enjoyed the walk back to the A flight line, composing my thoughts for the next patrol. I glanced at my watch again and was surprised to see that it was only 08:45; it seemed like a whole day had elapsed in the past two hours. I joined the boys in the crew room for a coffee and a rest and our next patrol was scheduled to take off at 09:30.

The intelligence briefing now was that we should shadow the second wave infantry advance as they moved through the positions now held by the first wave, and on to their rendezvous with the tanks holding about four miles into enemy territory. The generals did not wish to lose the momentum of the first attacks and wished to strike further before the enemy could regroup. As we swooped over the former German lines, we could see large columns of prisoners being marched to the rear and to internment in camps prepared to house them in advance and huge lines of British troops pouring forward in marching columns to meet with our tanks a few miles ahead. Our job was to patrol overhead and to keep German aircraft from coming too near. We could also see horse-drawn artillery being brought forward to provide additional support for the tanks' next thrust forward. By eleven o'clock the first elements of the infantry were connecting with the tanks and the artillery pieces were locating themselves into good firing positions, and I felt that the next tank strike was imminent. Unfortunately, we could not hang around to watch the outcome because we were to be relieved by B flight at 11:30 to return for refuelling and rest before our next patrol at 17:30.

Jamie leading B flight saw the whole tank battle unfold beneath him, where our armoured forces were able to move forward decisively with infantry and artillery support and succeeded in destroying twenty-six enemy tanks and capturing eighteen more in the British sector alone, for the loss of only six of our tanks. The swift movement of the British armoured attack caught the Germans unprepared and many of their losses occurred because they were hit whilst still stationary. The British tank regiment punched a hole through the German defensive line, pushing through Roeselare within four hours and further up the main road towards Y-junction where the road divides to Oostende on the coast or Bruges. The tank commander decided to send two of his squadrons of tanks supported by the West Yorks Volunteers, the Royal West Kents and Royal Green Jackets Regiment forward to capture Oostende and the Oudenburg airfield by nightfall and to hold until they were relieved, enabling the main force of tanks and infantry to strike forward toward Bruges. Again, Jamie did not see the whole picture because he was relieved at 13:30 by C Flight and then by D flight at 15:30.

At least when we were back over the battlefield at 17:30 we would be able to see how successful the bold tactics had been. The most dramatic aspect of the day for us was that the West Yorks Volunteers had captured the Oudenburg airfield almost completely intact, and we were to begin operations from there by tomorrow midday. Apparently, we heard that A Company led by a Major Bryanston had, although outnumbered nearly five to one, fought valiantly to capture the airfield in a serviceable condition. I thought ironically that this was a man condemned as a hopeless and pathetic alcoholic only a week ago in the St Omer court martial, now leading his men with great distinction amid the heat of the battle. The airfield was secured by the fierce actions of 120 men of A Company against over 600 German infantry troops, who were well dug into defensive positions but buckled under the sheer ferocity of the West Yorks attack. I was to hear a full account of the action from Welby the following day when I was one of the first to land at Oudenburg airfield, although our advance party of ground staff and engineers had moved in at daybreak. Welby took me through to the command tent they had set up by the side of the runway to meet Bryanston, who greeted me warmly. He gave me a full account of the action and the bravery and faultless leadership of Clough's platoon that had driven the wedge through the German defensive screen to secure the victory. He said sadly we lost Herbert Clough, killed by a bayonet thrust to the chest during fierce hand-to-hand fighting in front of the German command centre and Sergeant McArthy, who continued to lead the men into the command centre after Herbert went down but was shot in the last exchanges of fire before they surrendered. The lieutenant colonel was also killed leading B and C company up the Oostende Road to secure the port and Bryanston had been appointed acting Lt. Col .in command of the battalion. "I shall write a citation for Herbert for the award of the Victoria Cross and for Sergeant McArthy, the Military Medal," he told me, "But I would rather that they were both here to receive them. If Herbert had survived, I would have promoted him in the field to command A Company."

I was sad to hear this news, but I was now sure that Herbert had managed to secure that legacy he would be remembered for generations to come for the right reasons, and all his efforts had not been in vain. I was proud that I was able to have saved him from the firing squad. I found Welby and managed to get all the details out of him, but he could hardly contain his pride or his sadness for the terrible price the platoon had paid. Herbert volunteered to take on the task of capturing the German command centre, well knowing that it was an almost impossible task for thirty-five men against at least one hundred. He heaped praise on them and said they were Yorkshiremen and that he knew they were the best men for the difficult task of breaking the enemy resistance. They cheered him and would have followed him to almost certain death; they fought like lions, Cranley was wounded but would survive, but Privates Smith, Crane and Dobey were killed as well as Sergeant McArthy. "Six others were seriously wounded and, of course, Herbert was first to force his way through the door of the command centre and engage in hand-to-hand stuff," Welby told me. "He had lost his revolver by this time so was unarmed, but that did not stop him charging forward and pushing the Germans back. Even after being bayoneted in the chest, he kept urging us forward until his knees gave out and he slumped to the floor. Sergeant McArthy took up his lead and led the men on to capture the German commander before being shot and killed himself. I received the surrender of the German major, and the attack was over." Welby told me that he was now an acting captain and the new platoon commander, but that he would rather things were back as they were yesterday.

The 354 Squadron ground staff were already hard at work clearing away the damage and wreckage from yesterday's battle and getting the airfield ready for squadron operations to begin in the early afternoon today. The CO and his team flew in and started to get things organised, allocating the flights with suitable accommodation to operate from. Unlike La Coupole the pilots were not accommodated within the flight buildings, but all lived together in an officers' mess and the SNCOs in their own mess building too. The Germans had taken this airfield over directly from the Belgian Army. There were barracks for the airmen and a large central kitchen and mess hall to feed them. I thought that we were going to miss the temporary but cosy feel of our old home but felt that we would be more comfortable on this custom-built military base. I was surprised to see a sign, 'Royal Air Force Oudenburg, No. 354 Squadron' already being erected at the main gate as we had only been in possession of this airfield for less than twenty-four hours. As well as inheriting a well-equipped airbase with seventeen Storch fighters and a couple of Focke-Wulf two-seater bombers, we discovered that the kitchens and wine cellars were agreeably stocked too, and it certainly looked as if the Germans knew how to eat and drink well.

Amazingly by mid-afternoon all of the squadron aircraft had made the transition from La Coupole and patrolling was to begin again from 15:00. A flight was to fly the first patrol of the day and we were briefed to fly a reconnaissance sortie up the coast to Zeebrugge and reconnoitre the deep-water port, mapping out the enemy defences as far as we could. The infantry and tank force would attempt to capture the port and move to encircle

Bruges by linking up with the main force before the all-out assault on the city. We were given authority to attack any targets of choice that may present themselves along the way. I led the flight out over the North Sea and my intention was to fly offshore for about three miles, swing round to approach Zeebrugge from the north and try to get a good picture of the resistance they would put up to defend the deep-water harbour from capture.

As we approached the north-western side of the port, I could see a small flotilla of military auxiliary vessels massively overloaded with elements of the German Army attempting to make good their escape. I signalled the flight and we dived down on the first three ships and strafed them with prolonged bursts of machine-gun fire in two passes, which left them severely damaged and on fire. We broke off the attack, continued the reconnaissance and could see that although there were German troops well dug-in to defend the approaches to the port, the escape routes along the Bruges Road and in a northerly direction towards the Schelde estuary were thronged with long lines of marching troops, horses, and equipment. It certainly looked as if the German commander had decided to send additional troops to strengthen the defence of Bruges, and send some to the approaches to Antwerp, which he supposed would be the next objective after Bruges. He had left a much smaller force as a rear-guard to slow down our advance, but they would not be able to prevent us taking the port. I marked the German defensive positions in front of the port on my map, which would enable the task force commander to make his own assessment of the situation. Before returning to Oudenburg I decided that we ought to harry the Bruges reinforcements a little with a few passes of heavy machine-gun fire. By this time, the changes in the quality of light signalling the arrival of dusk were just beginning to occur, which made it more difficult for us to be seen in the sky. This reduction in visibility enabled us to swoop in low and pass over the rear columns before they had chance to disperse, and they were caught in the middle of the open road. We could see men falling as our machine-gun bullets struck home, but the noise of our engines and the firing warned the front columns to dive for cover at the side of the road and casualties were much less. I estimated the relief column was approximately two battalions in strength and I am sure that we inflicted casualties of around twenty per cent of the total with our attack. If the light was not fading so fast, I would have tried a second run.

I passed my map and drawings to the intelligence officer at debriefing, and he left quickly to convey them to the tank commander. I knew that I would not be flying again until midday tomorrow so wandered over to the mess to discover if there was a room allocated to me. In the entrance of the mess a Belgian civilian steward greeted me, took my name, and then led me upstairs to a corner suite with a bedroom, sitting room and private bathroom reserved for me. I was further amazed to find that my batman had unpacked my kit and all my uniforms were hanging in the wardrobe. I decided that I would take a hot bath, filled the tub, and lay in the hot water for nearly half an hour thinking about the demise of poor Herbert Clough. Around eight I went down to the dining room, managed to get some dinner before the kitchen closed and heard the buzz of excitement that the tank force commander had decided to make a night attack on the Zeebrugge defences so as not to slow up the impetus of his progress. The attack was scheduled for eight-thirty so after gulping down my food, I joined the others on the lawn behind the mess watching the flashes in the night sky over the port itself. This battle was raging less than four miles from our position; we could hear the tank shells hitting their targets and see smoke rising into the sky. I was feeling a little guilty that I had enjoyed a hot bath and some hot food whilst others were going into action, desperate for their lives. Before going to bed I met up with Jamie and Terence and we raised a glass of brandy in memory of Herbert Clough. At breakfast, the latest news was that the port was in our hands, resupply was underway by ship from Dunkirque already and the tanks had set off in the direction of Bruges with the infantry marching behind them, to link up with the British 2nd Tank Regiment and the Americans to completely encircle the city.

Our briefing this morning was to shift our patrolling to concentrate on the approaches to Antwerp and the control of the strategically significant Scheldt Estuary, which would truly be a great opportunity for the Allies to shorten our supply lines for the ultimate thrust into Germany. Our main task was to gather as much intelligence as we could about the location of the German defences for Antwerp and to mark positions on our maps, but also to attack targets of opportunity wherever they presented themselves. There was a strong feeling that the fluidity of the situation meant that the German commanders would be spreading their resources thinly to cover all eventualities and we needed to know where the weak points were.

The fall of Antwerp was strategically more important to the Allies than the recapture of the Belgian capital, which would only be symbolic, whereas control of Antwerp would mean that this massive deep-water port would become the gateway for the supply of all Allied forces and act as a kind of springboard for the final defeat of Germany. We were ordered to make exploratory sorties in the area between Maldegem and Vlaanderen, which was the area where the retreating German troops from Zeebrugge were reported to be massing and consolidating with reinforcements from Germany to form a defensive line from Vlaanderen to Ghent, to halt any future attack on Antwerp. There was not much aerial resistance any more as the German air bases in north-west Belgium had been captured or destroyed and their aircraft withdrawn to bases beyond the immediate reach of the advancing Allied troops. The speed and tenacity of this new offensive had seen the front leap forward thirty miles in the first four days, now stretching from Bruges in the west to the approaches of Ghent and almost encircling Brussels with the Fifth Army on our southern flank, pushing towards Maastricht.

A flight took off at 08:00 and flew cross-country, passing south-east of Bruges where we could see the battle for the city had already begun, over open farmland towards the town of Maldegem which lay on the main approach road to Antwerp. We could begin to see the German build-up of forces. The straggling lines of retreating forces were being deployed in forming a hastily set up defensive line, but they had little time to dig proper trenches, although we could see light field guns and machine-gun posts being set up and I signalled Giles that we would circle round and try to disrupt this activity as far as possible. As we swung round to line up for our first pass, I spotted a troop of horse artillery riding along the road to join up and strengthen this defensive position we could see being built, so I decided we would strafe the digging-in site first and continue to attack the horse artillery second. The aim would be to destroy the field guns if possible but if not to kill the horses and their riders, which would make operating these guns much more difficult.

We came in low and fast; large numbers of the soldiers broke and ran for cover, many of them fell caught in the path of our machine guns but some more experienced returned small-arms fire or kept their heads down where they were. We concentrated on hitting the field guns already in place and the machine-gun emplacements, and then swept on towards the troop of horse artillery who made the fatal mistake of breaking formation and heading into the open country on either side of the road, thus presenting a much better target for us as they tried to escape. Four or five horses were hit and stumbled and fell, which dramatically slowed down their escape and overturned some of the guns and limbers, smashing them beyond use. Other horses were so panicked that they bolted and threw riders off their backs, charging out of control in many different directions. I was pleased that we had caused such chaos in such a short visit but knew that in time they would prepare a defensive line of sorts to meet our advancing troops, probably later in the day. I marked their positions on my map and then as we crossed the Dutch border towards Vlaanderen we could see about eight barges, each crammed with men being towed across the estuary from Vlissingen by two naval tugs. They were moving very slowly and did not seem to have any fixed defences against air attack, so I decided we would have a go at this target as well. My priority was to force the tugs to cut the tows to be able to manoeuvre more freely to defend themselves, then strafe the drifting open barges to cause panic and as many casualties as we could. I had little hope that we could damage or sink one of the tugs but was sure that we could reduce the effectiveness of these reinforcements quite significantly by attacking the men. There was little or no cover for the soldiers crammed on the open decks and as we began to hit the first barges and inflict casualties, I was aware that many soldiers were jumping into the cold waters of the river laden with all their equipment, with little chance of swimming to safety.

Larry Fortescue was waving at me frantically. With his wonderfully sharp eyesight he had spotted two fast patrol boats putting out from the Dutch side, bristling with weapons, and judging by the height of the bow waves they were creating they would be within range within minutes. I did not like leaving a job only half done but knew we were no match for two German fast patrol boats, so I recalled the flight, we sped off towards the Belgian side and retraced our track towards Maldegem and on towards Ghent, drawing the German positions on my map as accurately as I could. We could already see our advancing forces and knew that they would be in contact with the enemy by the mid-afternoon if they continued at this pace. My report would show the positions of the hurriedly prepared German defensive line, which was not well dug-in and mainly consisted of infantrymen supported by light field guns and machine guns. We had not observed any tanks of heavy artillery anywhere along our flight path. The presence of fast patrol boats in the Scheldt estuary on the Dutch side may prove to be a hindrance to expanding resupply efforts through Antwerp if not eradicated.

We landed back at Oudenburg just before ten. I made my report, handed over the maps at debrief and was feeling ravenous, so the four of us were repaired to the mess to see if we could get a mid-morning snack before having a rest prior to our next sortie at 16:00. Whilst we were eating the delicious fresh bacon sandwiches that the corporal cook rustled up for us quickly, news came through that the garrison commander at Bruges had surrendered and the West Yorkshire Volunteers were detached to take over control of the city for the time being. The tanks and the main force of infantry had moved on quickly to catch up with the advance force already approaching the German defensive line between Ghent and the Dutch border. As I relaxed on my bed, I guessed where our sorties were going to be this afternoon, but my eyes closed very quickly, and I was dead asleep within a few seconds.

I managed two hours' deep sleep and woke refreshed and ready for the late afternoon sortie. I could see that some letters from home were on my desk in the sitting room, so I spent a happy half hour escaping into the world of the Welsh valleys as I heard about my family and the progress of Ruby and our little child growing within her. My brother Wesley had received a commendation for catching a ring of German sympathisers who were gathering information on the movement of military supplies from the docks Cardiff and Swansea and passing details of merchant ships, manifests and destinations to U-boats operating in the Irish Sea. The ring of spies had been operating in Swansea, Cardiff and Newport and he had controlled the team of undercover officers who had tracked them down and rounded them up successfully. Wesley was now a candidate for the inspector's examination, which he was going to take in early June this year. I was pleased for him and glad he had secured for himself a better future for after the war was over. I was still concerned about my other brother Gwyn, who was still intent on marrying Mair Davis and intended to keep working down the pit. Mum and Dad were alright but Mum had hinted that Dad was finding work underground very tiring now. Dad was fifty-eight and had been in the pit since he was fourteen years old, so it was hardly surprising that he was slowing down a bit by now.

Ruby was as excited as ever about the baby and was longing for the day that I would be home and that we could be married. All this talk of home made me think about what I would do after war was over and my temporary commission was terminated. I loved flying but I did not think there would be many opportunities in aviation for all the returning pilots to make a living. I ticked off my qualifications and experience in my head, but it did not push me towards any kind of occupation. I was glad that I had accumulated enough savings already to avoid being destitute at least, but I knew that my capital would not last long if I continued to live like a gentleman like Jamie and Giles, who had secure private incomes to rely on. Theirs was a different world and I would need to work for a living and secure a job where I could keep my wife and children in reasonable comfort. I knew I owed my parents a massive debt of gratitude for the education they went without to provide, which meant that I would never have to go down a coalmine to earn my bread. I determined that I was going to use my brains and take more qualifications, if necessary, to secure a career, not just a job.

By mid-afternoon we were being briefed to fly a sortie in support of the tank assault on the western side of Ghent, primarily to act as spotters for the lead tanks and to direct them onto the suitable targets. We were to communicate via Morse code with our flashlights so as to give the tank commanders up-to-date information and to keep the tank advance moving. The assault early in the day at Bruges would have been exceedingly difficult because it was a walled city and a breach would have had to have been made in the walls to enter, but Ghent was an open city and a breakthrough the outer defensive rim could lead to a dash for the centre by the tanks and hand-to-hand fighting by the infantry to clear the stretched defending forces. The West Kents and the Green Jackets with their accompanying tanks were striking at the German defensive line stretching up to the Dutch border and were expected to smash through this, then swing round to straddle the main road to Antwerp and to hold this position to deter a counterattack from the Antwerp garrison until Ghent was captured.

By 16:30 we were approaching the rear-most units of our attacking tank force. I was searching for which of the lead tanks would be carrying the battlefield commander, who we could identify by the First Tank Regiment guidon being flown from an aerial at the rear of the tank and with a black and white striped flag displayed beneath it. This was the reason we had approached from the rear of the formation, so as we could pick out the identifying flags more easily. I was looking for a splash of colour of the regimental guidon, but the black and white stripes proved easier to pick up. I immediately flashed a sighting message, which was acknowledged instantly, so I waggled my wings to show I understood and then proceeded to fly low over the city defences. We were quick to establish that there were no concrete emplacements or tank traps to prevent access by tanks into the city, and the main line of defence was to block the major roads with barricades, light field guns and machine gunners. It was quite clear from the air that the defence force was too small and did not have enough men to throw a ring of steel around the city because they were stretched so thinly. There were many places where the infantry could outflank the defenders by infiltrating through the smaller roads and residential streets to circumvent the pockets of defence. I presumed that the town commander believed that these streets were too narrow for tanks to penetrate and felt confident in holding the major roads instead.

However, I drew on my map an approach through a small wood and across a small football field that would hide them from view because it was cut off from the defenders by a brick wall at least eight foot high. When the tanks were in position, they could easily push down the wall and fire directly at the defensive barriers manned by the Germans at the main road junction from a range of 500 yards. I flew back on a reverse course to pick up the leader's pennant again and relayed the message of all I had seen. He acknowledged and I saw him detach a cohort of about eight tanks to follow my suggestion. I flew above them to guide them towards the wood and to the football field. They slowly crossed the open space and lined up along the brick wall ready to move forward and knock the wall down in one move. To distract the defenders, A flight attacked the barriers with concerted machine-gun bursts to keep the defenders' heads down and just as our guns started to fire, I heard the roar of the tank engines as they pushed the wall down and opened fire on the German defences, which were burning furiously within a couple of minutes. By now, the first elements of the West Kents were following up behind the tanks and taking German prisoners. The road to the centre of the city now lay open and the main force of tanks with the Green Jackets in support marched to capture the city largely undamaged. It was getting dark when we landed back at Oudenburg and we were ready to eat and rest, in that order.

In the morning, I was summoned to the CO who showed me the signal confirming the award of the bar to my DFC, then said he had tried his best to get some leave for me to get married and had secured me eighteen days – he tried to get me twenty-one days, but he was not successful. Command said that as I had completed over eighty sorties without a break, I could take this leave anytime in the next month. I was ecstatic. I could not wait to write to Ruby and tell her to get Reverend Lewis to publish the banns this Sunday coming and fix the wedding for the first available date after the banns had been read and the licence granted. As soon as she had the date fixed, I would book my leave and get home as soon as I could. I wanted to be there to help with the wedding preparations and to spend a few days away with Ruby on our own, as a kind of honeymoon before I came back.

TWENTY-FIVE

Ruby

We continued a daily hectic round of sorties supporting the advancing Allied armies on the ground as Antwerp was taken and the Germans were withdrawing through southern Holland and Belgium to consolidate a last-ditch defensive line to prevent their national borders being overrun. Our location at Oudenburg was becoming less practical because even with the long-range fuel tanks fitted, we were expending so much fuel just getting to the patrol areas and back that we were not able to spend enough time over the enemy territory. A search was underway for a more strategic location somewhere to the east of Antwerp and Jamie Dalrymple was charged with finding us a new home. He eventually found an ideal location to the east of Antwerp, near the small town of Mortsel and the squadron was on the move again. This meant that we would be able to reach deep into southern Holland, northerly towards Breda and Rotterdam, easterly to Eindhoven and south-easterly towards Maastricht. Mortsel was also a large airfield with permanent accommodation like Oudenburg, suitable for housing large formations of aircraft, so it would become home to all of No. 2 Fighter Wing. We would be reunited with our fellow squadrons from La Coupole; it seemed like an age ago since we were all together. The move was planned for the end of the week, so everyone was busy packing, loading all our equipment and stores on to trucks to make the forty-five-mile journey to Mortsel on Friday morning. All 354 Squadron operations had been suspended for forty-eight hours to affect our move. After the fall of Antwerp, the Germans were holding a line stretching from Breda through Turnhout to Maastricht and we were sent to escort the bombers again as they attempted to destroy the railway communications and switchgear so

371

that reinforcements could not be brought in quickly from Germany for three raids at Breda, Tilburg and Hoogstraten, which went smoothly without an appearance from the German air force.

I must admit that for the pilots, our move was relatively simple because all we had to do was ensure that our batmen packed all our personal possessions and kit for transport, and then fly our aircraft to the new airfield after breakfast on Friday. Mortsel had been a main base and headquarters for the Belgian Army and used as a group headquarters by the German air force, so had a level of facilities that we were unused to. For the first time the whole of 354 Operation were in the same building with briefing rooms, offices and flight crew rooms all facing out on to the hard-standing area and the squadron hangar. This would be novel for us, who had been used to working in independent flight units but from now on we would become much more closely part of the squadron to which we belonged. I welcomed the opportunity to get to know the ground personnel who were in my flight because I had tended to delegate most routine matters to the flight sergeant and only dealt with defaulters personally. It would be easier to build a bond with everyone in the flight now that we were to be working in such proximity. All squadron personnel would now be accommodated in barracks and the officers' mess was in a lavish converted chateau. The airfield had been built across what was a vast country estate. My room in the chateau was a grand affair with a four-poster bed and a great view across the park towards the airfield, and the dining room was magnificent, equipped with high-quality porcelain dinner services mounted with the German air force crest, crystal glassware and copious amounts of silver plate for use at formal dinners. Squadron Leader Moss ordered that we should liberate all the crockery, glasses, and silverware for 354 Squadron, and they were all packed up and boxed for shipping back to the squadron home base after the war was over. We also liberated the German air force command colours which had been left behind when the base fell, as a souvenir for the squadron headquarters.

I had received a long reply from Ruby to my last letter and she was excited to tell me that the Reverend Lewis would publish the banns this Sunday, which meant that we could be married on any day after fifteen days had elapsed from the first reading in chapel. I said that I would travel so that I could be home for at least a week before the wedding day and be able to spend some time away together on honeymoon before I had to return to Belgium. I suggested that I would attempt to depart from Mortsel on Friday 26th April and that she should go ahead and book the wedding for Saturday 3rd May, the reception to be held at the rugby club afterwards. We would start to work on a guest list of our family members and friends so that we could write invitations together when I got home. I would have liked to invite my brother officers to my wedding, but I knew that this would not be possible so I had decided to ask my elder brother, Wesley, to be my best man and I wanted to invite Gwyn too, but assumed that we should have to invite Mair Davis to get him to come. Mum and Dad might be difficult about it, although I felt that they would have to get used to it because Gwyn seemed totally serious about this relationship, and I did not think he would give her up. I asked Ruby if she would like to go to Tenby for our honeymoon, for a week on our own by the seaside.

That evening in the anteroom before dinner I broke my news to Jamie, Terence, and Giles that I was getting married to Ruby on the 3rd of May in Bedwas. They were excited and wanted to celebrate there and then. I calmed them down and said perhaps, we could explore the local restaurants and bars tomorrow if we were not flying on Sunday, and this was agreed. I told them that I would have been delighted to have had a guard of honour of flying officers at my wedding, but the CO said that it was beyond his powers to arrange it at this time. Later that evening, Jamie got me to one side and said that it would be difficult to give me a present for my wedding being stuck here in Mortsel, he thought that he could loan me the Bentley for my leave period so that I could drive Ruby around and use it as the bride's car on my wedding day. I was taken aback and insisted he was too generous, and I couldn't accept but he said, "Of course, you will accept or lose my friendship as this is something I really want to do for you and your intended wife. I have told you before how much I look up to you and envy you your strong family values, and I would have loved to share part of it but this is a way that I can at least contribute to making your day happier." I was humbled by what he had said and thanked him profusely for his generosity. This changed everything because I would not have to rely on trains and connections to travel home; provided I was able to reserve a berth for the car on a cross-channel steamer I should be home by Friday evening. I was so grateful to Jamie and I knew that he and I would be life-long friends if we managed to survive the war.

My batman came to the rescue because he had a cousin who was in the Transport Corps and worked in the newly set up port marshal's office at Oostende, where he was responsible for allocating berths on steamers. This was a stroke of luck and he said if I would give him permission to use the telephone in the flight office, he would fix it up and all he needed was the travel warrant and leave pass numbers to make the booking. Two days later he handed me an envelope with the berth number for the SS *Rochester Castle*, Oostende to Ramsgate at 10:00 on Friday 26th April and return 06:00 Tuesday 13th May 1918. The ship should berth in Ramsgate by 13:00, which meant that I could be home by early Friday evening. I was extremely grateful for his efforts, tipped him an extra ten shillings this week and he was incredibly pleased.

The day before I was due to go on leave, Giles got all the boys together from A and B flights and after some ribald remarks impugning my fitness to be a husband and that Ruby was only choosing me because she hadn't met him, he finally got round to saying, "Congratulations on behalf of all your friends on your marriage and we have collected together to present you with a small token of our gratitude to Ruby in taking you on." He presented me with the wedding night medal, which had been fashioned in the workshop out of a piece of tin that was vaguely priapic in shape, with a brightly coloured striped ribbon and he concluded by saying, "You will notice that you have already have a bar to this medal because intelligence suggests that you have already had the first night's fun some time ago," to which there was a loud explosion of laughter and much slapping on the back. He pinned the medal on my tunic and then called on me to reply. I told them that during my studies at the Royal School of Military Engineering I was taught that once you have proposed a hypothesis, the careful scientist would embark on a series of experimentations to discover whether his hypothesis was true. I then went on to say that my Ruby was the most stunningly beautiful girl I had ever met who possessed a wonderful sense of humour, a great love of rugby and exquisite taste in men for choosing me for her husband, what more could I want?

"When we first met, I was a newly made corporal in the Royal Engineers in a siege company in the second battle of Ypres. She had lost her former fiancé, killed in the first battle of Ypres, and she hoped and prayed that history would not repeat itself. Then I saved the honourable Dalrymple from the jaws of certain death at the hands of the vengeful German infantry," there was much booing from the crowd, "and my life has taken a downward turn ever since. I was promoted to sergeant and persuaded by Messrs Dalrymple, Moss and Harcourt to transfer to the RFC and then to become a pilot and my Ruby approved because she thought I would be much safer than with the siege company. She was partially right, of course, but she is blissfully unaware of what a hardened crew of reprobates that I now had to spend my time with, involving me in so many things that the people at my chapel believe would condemn me to damnation for all eternity. I am glad that I still am able to get married in that chapel, safe in the knowledge that my reputation is pure and unsullied because none of you lot will be there to spill the beans on me." There was some cheering when I finished my little speech and Giles handed me an envelope, which he said contained the citation for the wedding night medal and a small token in lieu of a wedding present. He said, "We were thinking of buying you a polo pony but decided that you Welsh savages would probably eat it, so we have decided to let you choose for yourself." The champagne corks were popped, and they all raised their glasses to toast me and Ruby. I was touched and quite overwhelmed by the warmth of their best wishes and when I returned to my room and opened the envelope, I found it contained a cheque from the private bankers of Lord Eckington for the sum of £300 with a congratulations slip signed by all who had contributed. I was astounded but knew when added to my savings it would enable Ruby and I to pay for the wedding, the honeymoon and still have enough to purchase a house in preparation for the arrival of the baby.

Everything was packed into the trunk at the rear of the Bentley, and I set off for Oostende at 06:00 as I needed to be at the dockside for loading by 08:00. I found the SS *Rochester Castle* quite easily as she was identical to her sister ship, *Maid of Kent*, which I had crossed the channel on before. I parked up on the quayside to wait for loading. The loading master told me that the Bentley would be the last loaded and would be strapped down on the deck, but this was good for me because I would be the first to be offloaded in Ramsgate. Loading went on smoothly and at about 08:45 they slung the strops underneath the car, I climbed out, pulled the tonneau cover over and fixed it down to keep everything dry on the crossing. I watched the car being lifted and secured on the deck towards the stern and then sheeted over with a canvas tarpaulin.

I enjoyed a pleasant crossing sitting in the officers' saloon and reading the first British newspaper I had seen for some time. I was particularly interested in the editorials and leading articles commenting on the progress of the war and the prospects of a massive final battle to force Germany to surrender. Some newspapers believed that the Germans would never surrender but would fight to the end, whilst others thought there were signs that the war would be over before the end of this year because the tide had turned, convincingly, in favour of the Allies. The one thing that all the papers seemed to agree about was that the people at home were fed up with the war and really wanted it to end soon. The trench newspapers that circulated amongst the troops contained little of this kind of comment, so this was new and interesting for me to read about. By the time that I closed the newspaper I could see the English coast getting larger on the horizon and the steward asked if I wanted anything else, as we would be alongside in twenty minutes. I climbed up on deck and I could see that the deckhands were already taking the tarpaulin off the Bentley and loosening the restraints so it could be lifted on to the dockside as soon as we were alongside. I marvelled at the skills of the sailors as they brought the fully loaded steamer to a rest perfectly aligned with the quay, and the speed with which they made the ship secure and got the gangplank in place ready for disembarkation. There were few foot passengers, so I was able to stroll off the ship and was waiting on the quay when the Bentley was gently placed adjacent to the ship and the strops removed. The loading master wished me a safe onward journey and a good leave, and I set off heading for the harbour exit and the hill climb up Westcliff to join the main road to Canterbury. The clock tower opposite the harbour gates showed the time to be 13:10 and I guessed I could probably make it home within six hours if there were no hold-ups on the way.

I stopped for a light lunch at the roadhouse near Faversham, then headed for Maidstone and picked up the Guildford Road which then took me over the Hogs Back, north-west towards Reading, then on to the main road west via Cheltenham and on into Monmouthshire. By six o'clock I was approaching Abergavenny and knew that I would be at home by seven-ish. I drove down the Heads of the Valleys Road as fast as I could and watched the sun dropping down slowly to the west. It was a great feeling to see the familiar Welsh landscape and, of course, my excitement was growing as the thought of holding Ruby again swelled in my heart. It was still daylight when I pulled up outside the Station House, honked the horn and leapt out and up to the front door, which was pulled open and Ruby rushed out to meet me with a massive hug and many kisses. Eventually I managed to get her to go inside where I shook hands with Mr Thomas and hugged her mum. They had not seen a Royal Air Force uniform before, but they were approving of its fine cut and Mr Thomas wanted to know about the ranks and my new medals. I explained that the two thick blue rings were those of a flight lieutenant, which is the equivalent to the rank of captain in the army. I showed him that I had now been awarded the Distinguished Flying Cross twice which is marked by the bar added to the medal ribbon. He asked what they are given for, and I lowered my voice and said that they were awarded for shooting down enemy aircraft in combat and I got the first medal for shooting down five and the second award for ten. He said he would keep this quiet from the women, opened his little cupboard by his chair, brought out a bottle of whisky and poured two fingers into a couple of glasses and said, "Let's drink to you being home."

I said to Ruby to get her coat and hat on, and we would take a spin in the car to see my mum and dad. She was dressed and ready to go in double-quick time and we walked together to the Bentley sitting outside. She had never seen such a fine car and asked if it was mine, and I told her the story of the generosity of my friend Jamie who had loaned it to me to use for my leave. She climbed in and we drove up High Street past all the old familiar shops, the Railway Tavern, the gas office and turned into my parents' street. As soon as I pulled up, the front door was open, and they both came out beaming across their faces as they greeted their youngest son and his soon-to-be wife. I have never seen Mum so happy. The first thing I noticed was that she and Ruby were already so close, and I thought that Mum had brought up six sons in this small house, the three eldest were gone, one in a pit explosion and Cliff and Dylan killed in the first attack on the Somme in 1916; and this was the first of her surviving sons to get married. Mum said she had a light supper for us both in the parlour and there was the table groaning with sandwiches, small pies, jam sponge and Welsh cakes, enough to feed a whole army. I was quite hungry and tucked in heartily and so did Dad, but I noticed that Mum and Ruby ate extraordinarily little. This house felt so small and cosy after my grand accommodation at Chateau Mostrel but the warmth of the welcome somehow made it feel much superior. I took Ruby back home at ten-thirty and arranged to pick her up at ten in the morning because we had an important task to do tomorrow, to buy two wedding rings.

At eight in the morning there was a ferocious knocking on my parents' front door and Dad went to see who wanted us so urgently. A minute later he showed Joshua Andrews into the parlour and Mum poured him a cup of tea. I thought he had come to see Dad about something at the pit, but it soon became evident it was me he had come to see. He said he knew that I had only just got home and was busy with the wedding next week, but today was the last game of the season and they were short of a hooker, it was the return match with Cross Keys where we so narrowly lost earlier in the season.

"Are you able to play?" he asked.

"I need to go to Cardiff this morning with Ruby to buy our wedding rings which is more important to me at this moment, but what time is the kick-off?"

"A three o'clock start."

"If Ruby agrees I will be back by two-thirty and will play and you can check with Geraint Thomas after ten o'clock."

The last game I played was against Cross Keys away nearly a year ago, when we were narrowly beaten by a good side. It would be good to pay them back on home turf. When he left, I got out my boots and checked that they were in a good condition and thankfully I had cleaned and dubbined them before I put them away last time. I then shaved and got dressed in my best suit with a freshly laundered shirt and tie and was at Ruby's house at nine-thirty. She was ready to go, and it seemed that there had been some conspiracy between her father and Josh Andrews to get me to play in the game this afternoon. She was not happy that they had connived behind her back, but reluctantly agreed provided we were able to get our shopping done in time. Within ten minutes we were on the road down the valley via Caerphilly and on to Cardiff, and I was looking for somewhere to leave the car near to the jewellers where I had bought the engagement ring. It was fortunate that there was space to stop close to the front of the shop, so by eleven we were browsing the rings inside.

The old jeweller recognised me with a little smile and greeted Ruby as if she was his most special customer and brought her a seat, then laid out four trays of wedding rings, some for the bride and some for the groom. We explained that we wanted a pair of rings of similar design to exchange on our wedding day that were of good quality but not too ornate. He asked us to excuse him for a minute, he retreated into the back of the shop and after a couple of minutes he came back with a couple of boxes which he placed on the counter and opened before us. The boxes contained two thick solid-gold bands that were completely plain but shone so brightly on the counter. He measured the size of Ruby's finger and then measured the ring and then slipped it on to her finger. It was not a bad fit, but he said he needed to stretch it slightly to make it comfortable, and he said he would engrave our names and the date of our wedding on the inside of the ring at no extra charge. When I tried on the male ring it was too large, but he measured my finger and said he would shrink it to a good fit and engrave our names and wedding date on the inner rim also. He looked at me and said, "I remember that I made a deal with you when you bought that beautiful engagement ring your lovely fiancée is wearing that if you came back to me for your wedding rings, I would give you the best deal possible, do you remember?'" He went on that he seemed to remember that I was a sergeant training to be a pilot, and I confirmed that he was right. I told him that I was now a flight lieutenant in the Royal Air Force, serving with my squadron in Belgium. He asked if we liked these two rings and Ruby nodded her head furiously and I said we would take them and asked him how much. He said, "They will be thirty guineas for the pair, and I will have them ready for you to collect on Thursday next and you can pay me then.'"He then took Ruby by the hand and said, "My dear, I have a little gift for you to wear when your husband is flying to keep him safe and bring him back to you,"and he unwrapped a small silver brooch of the RAF pilot's wings and pinned it on the collar of her coat. Ruby was almost in tears as she thanked him for his kindness, but he modestly said it was his pleasure and he wished us a long and happy marriage. She said that she would never take it off but always wear it. It was after twelve when we left the shop, I had hoped to take Ruby for lunch somewhere nice and spend the afternoon together, but she said, "Come on, we need to back for kick-off so we can beat Cross Keys well and truly this time."

It was a fine spring day, but the sun was not yet too hot, so it would be perfect conditions for the game this afternoon. Ruby and I were so happy to have secured the wedding rings we wanted and that was something we could tick off the list. Tomorrow, we would need to finalise the guest list, write the invitations, and deliver them by hand or send by post on Monday morning. We were simply happy together riding up the valley road with the hood down and the wind blowing through our hair as the Bentley cruised at fifty miles an hour. I wondered whether Joe Powell would be playing for Cross Keys and whether he was still as fast as ever on the wing. We were back at the rugby club by two, which enabled me to become reacquainted with some of my team-mates who I had not seen for a while, except for Dai Rees and my brother, Gwyn, of course. Mr Thomas was there already, and Ruby said she would sit with him and Freda Rees. Dai and Freda were married on Easter Sunday, and I have to say that marriage suited her well because she looked radiant and healthy. I went to change into my kit and then dropped by the visitors' changing room to see if Joe Powell was in their team today. I knocked on the door and asked for Joe and they said he was over in the corner, so I came up behind him and said, "Sergeant Powell, can I have a lift back on your motorcycle?" He swung round and said, "Oh my God, Derfal Morgan. I heard that you have left the Corps and gone to the RFC." I told him that he had heard right and that I was now a flight lieutenant in the RAF. He was pleased to see me and was looking forward to a hard-fought match this afternoon.

We kicked off at three. A strong breeze had got up, Cross Keys won the toss and elected for us to play into the wind in the first half which actually turned out to be to our advantage because we chose not to kick too much but run with the ball in hand as much as possible. This enabled us to pin them back in their half for much of the time, for even with the wind advantage they were not finding touch. Gwyn had not lost any of his sleight of hand and was controlling the movement of the ball well from our set piece and Dai Rees on the wing was as fast as ever. We were forcing them to tackle fast and furiously within their own half, which meant any mistakes or infringements were punished by us and two penalty kicks put us in to the lead as we approached half-time. Just two minutes before the half-time whistle we were awarded an attacking scrum just inside the ten-yard line after they had knocked on, which I was able to gather and kick backwards easily, then Dai Rees gathered the ball and kicked it into the corner for a line-out just three yards from their line.

I knew this was a big throw for me, I pitched the ball up high and straight towards Euan Matthews, the big second row forward who took it cleanly, and the pack went for an eight-man shove to cross the line. The Cross Keys pack were strong and stopped our forward thrust just a yard short of their line, but the ball was filtered back and into my hands at the back of the rolling maul. I could see that the Cross Keys defence were expecting the ball to go to the right and quickly down the line of the backs to score in the opposite corner, so I broke left on the narrow side between the maul and the touchline, caught them by surprise and was over the line to touch the ball down before they realised what was happening. We were jubilant and went into a huddle for our half-time chat, happy with our first-half performance but Josh Andrews made it plain to us that leading by one try and two penalty kicks was too slim a margin to be confident of a win against a side as good as Cross Keys. He urged us to use the wind to advantage to kick long and deep to find touch and keep them pinned back in their own half. The minute we loosened our grip on the game they would open and release their fast men on either wing, who would prove to be very dangerous.

Josh was right in his assessment because immediately from the kick-off they chose to forgo the opportunity to kick and recycled the ball fast down the line, into the hands of Joe Powell who went off like the wind down the right wing. His pace was phenomenal but our full-back, Ashley Phillips, cleverly ran the angle and tackled Joe into touch, eight yards short of our line. This complete change of tactics by them had caught us on the hop and showed, yet again, the wise words of Josh at half-time were spot on. We were now on the back foot, and they won the attacking line-out, and tried to set up a strong rolling maul which we were just about able to hold up from charging at the line and the ball was sent left across the field to challenge us on the other side of the field. Fortunately for us the ball was knocked on and a scrum awarded to us, which we won comfortably and this time we used the wind to advantage as Dai hoofed the ball up high and long into their half and charged headlong to be first under it. The Cross Keys full back was unlucky as when the ball bounced, he was wrong-footed and had to change direction to secure the ball, Dai tackled him as he collected the ball into his arms, it sprang free from his grasp and popped up and into the arms of Gwyn, who caught it full on the burst and raced on to score between the posts. Luck was certainly on our side and we were now pulling ahead with the score, which was extended by an easy conversion kick from in front of the posts. Things were going much better than we expected but their latest foray into our half showed that we had no grounds for complacency with over half an hour still to play.

The home crowd was getting quite animated and excited at the prospect of a home win and were beginning to get more voluble and cheering everything we did. The smaller numbers who came with the visiting team were no match for the home supporters. I was sure that this was the largest crowd I had ever seen when I had played at home before. The next twenty minutes became rather slack as we tightened our grip on the game and deliberately kept the ball in hand, refusing to allow the Cross Keys players to move with the ball at all. I could see that the high rate of tackles they were engaging in defence was tiring them more quickly than us and we were looking to deliver the final blow of a try with just about ten minutes to go, so we decided to start kicking long and high to drop the ball closer to their line and take advantage of our apparent fitness to pressure them close to their line. Their defence was excellent and whatever we threw at them and however many phases of the ball we went through, there was no way through until we conceded a scrum ten yards out, the ball came out fast to the scrum half and quickly down the line to the centre, who attempted to kick for territory and the ball climbed away from his boot into the hands of Euan Matthews, who burst through and hurled himself over the line for the try. It seems that luck was still smiling on us. The conversion was kicked, and we ran back for the kick-off and straight from the restart we were pinned back by Cross Keys who assaulted our line with as much force as they could bring for the final ten minutes. We held them up the first time they crossed the line; they came again after winning the five-yard scrum and this time passed the ball swiftly down the back line and into the hands of Joe Powell, who weaved and jinked his way to score their first try. This was converted in just enough time before the final whistle went. We were pleased to have won convincingly by three tries to one but as we came off, I for one was certain that I had been tested hard by this Cross Keys team. It was honours even for the season with both teams winning at home, and everyone would look forward to next season's encounters.

After a bath, I was quick to rejoin Ruby and her father in the clubhouse and Geraint was congratulating me again on my try and I told him were lucky with all three of our tries. The rolling maul did all the work and all I did was sucker the Cross Keys defence into thinking I was going to the right when I was not. Gwyn backed up Dai and was able to capitalise when the ball popped up his way for the second try and Euan's interception was simply good luck for the third. Ruby was so excited, and she was positively glowing as she went round talking to everyone, showing off her engagement ring and discussing the wedding, of course. There was a little bit of speechifying, this being the final game of the season and both Josh and Geraint Thomas got up to speak, then the food was served, and the bar was open.

It was wonderful for me to speak with my brother Gwyn again, and I managed to get a few minutes quietly to talk the situation over with him. I was convinced that he was totally committed to marrying Mair Davis and nothing that any of us could do would prevent him. I resolved that I was glad for him and would not make things more difficult. I said that he had to, however, make things up with Mum and Dad who were struggling to come to terms with the situation and if he let it go, it would drive a wedge into the family that would be difficult for us all. I told him that both he and Mair were invited to our wedding and that Wesley was to be my best man. He told me that he had signed up for a course in electrical maintenance at the Mechanics Institute, he was hoping to gain qualifications as an electrician and break away from the colliery. I congratulated him on doing something positive and that now was the right time to start to study before the war ended and thousands of soldiers were discharged into civilian life. The beer was starting to flow freely, and I invited Gwyn to come and join with Ruby and I, Dai and Freda but he said he was not stopping long and would get home to Mair. I was glad that I had taken the time to speak with Gwyn privately and I hoped that he might be reconciled with Mum and Dad before the wedding next week. Ruby and I enjoyed our evening with Freda and Dai but did not stay late, because we needed to be up and alert for chapel tomorrow morning to hear the third reading of our banns of marriage read out by Reverend Lewis.

I drove Ruby and her father home and resisted the temptation to go in, for I was sure that Geraint would get his whisky bottle out and I wanted to keep a clear head for the chapel. Mum was just going to bed, but Dad was happy to sit and chat for half an hour before going up. He wanted to know about the game, and I think he was proud that his two sons both scored a try although he was reluctant to say too much about Gwyn. I pressed him a little and said that I had spoken with Gwyn, I had invited him to the wedding, and I believed that, whatever the rights and wrongs might be in the minds of the chapelgoers, he was my brother, and he was sincere in his love for Mair Davis.

"I want to have my whole family together for my wedding to Ruby and free from petty squabbles that will break us up as a family unit. I am proud to have Wesley as my best man and even prouder that he will shortly be a detective inspector, which is a great achievement for a man not yet thirty". Gwyn has signed up to study electrics at the Mechanics Institute, which he hopes will enable him to leave the pit for a more skilled job and I hope that my war record will help me get a good job in civilian life when the war is over." I sent him to bed with my final thought, that he and Mum should be proud that their three sons are all trying to make something of themselves and that was because the foundation of unshakeable family love that emanates from this home which is too great a prize to let go lightly. "Wherever I end up I want my children to always enjoy the kind of experience and upbringing that I enjoyed here in this house." Dad mumbled agreement and then took himself up to bed, and I hoped that my words had sunk in and that he would speak with Mum.

Dad did not come to chapel, preferring to spend a few quiet hours at the allotment and to dig up some fresh vegetables for the Sunday dinner, so I helped Mum into the rear seat of the Bentley, and we drove down to the Station House to collect Ruby and her mother. Geraint was on duty today and was looking smart in his station master's uniform, so with our two mothers ensconced in the back of the car Ruby and I made our way to the chapel in some style and in my mind, I could imagine her, and her father being driven here for the wedding in a week's time. I caused less of a stir this time in chapel because I was wearing a civilian suit so was able to slip in with Ruby and the two mums without anyone taking too much notice. I was saving my RAF uniform and regalia for the wedding day because it was markedly different from the sergeant's uniform, I wore the last time I attended the chapel. The service was as usual, with four or five hymns and much protracted praying and the Reverend Lewis excelled himself with a longer than usual sermon extoling the virtues of chastity and marital love, which I thought was probably for our benefit, before he came to reading the banns of marriage. My heart skipped a beat when he charged anyone who had just cause or good reason to object to this marriage to come forward and then settled back to normal when no one came forward to object. I squeezed Ruby's hand in relief, and I could see out of the corner of my eye that she was smiling too. As we came out of chapel, people greeted us and congratulated us and wished us all the best for next week, but we did not stay too long as Ruby and I wanted to get on with writing our invitations so they could be delivered tomorrow or Tuesday at the latest.

Most of our guests lived in the village or nearby, but Ruby's family were mostly from the area near Mountain Ash, so their invites needed to be in the post by tomorrow morning. We had counted roughly equal numbers on each side, plus a few friends and neighbours of both families giving us forty-six guests in total. It took us about three hours to write each invitation in our neatest handwriting and sort them into the different piles for posting or delivery by hand and I volunteered to walk around the village and deliver them this evening. Ruby had taken two weeks' leave from work so we could make all the arrangements together and I suggested that we paid an initial visit to the house agents in Caerphilly in the morning to have a look at what kind of houses were for sale, within our price range, and then drove down to Swansea to meet with Wesley to discuss his best man duties in the afternoon. We planned that we would arrange flowers and catering at the rugby club on Tuesday. Geraint interrupted me and said that he would pay for the catering and drinks served at the rugby club and he would arrange that tomorrow morning. With this all agreed, I left with the pile of invites for delivery and drove home for Sunday dinner with Mum and Dad. After dinner I took a stroll around the village, delivering the wedding invitations and then home for an early night.

By nine in the morning, I was ready to collect Ruby and our first job was to go to the post office in High Street to buy the stamps to send the rest of our invites, then we set off for Swansea. It was a bright morning, and I left the top down so we could enjoy the sunshine and the view. I chose to take a more scenic route via Brecon and drive down the valley to Ammanford, Caernarvon and then on to Swansea. Ruby had put on a light blue dress I had not seen before and a matching lightweight coat and hat and looked a real picture. I was pleased to see that she was wearing the RAF wings clasp on her left lapel. Before we set off for Swansea, I drove the few miles into the nearest small town of Caerphilly, and we went to visit the house agents to try to gather some information on the kind of houses that were available to buy that would suit our requirements. He was helpful and although there were not too many properties that we might be interested in, the ones he showed us looked promising. There were not too many properties for sale in our village, as most of the housing stock was owned by the colliery and rented out to the miners at low rent. We looked at the details of several promising houses within a couple of miles of the village that offered modern facilities and gardens at the front and back that we would look at later in the week.

We were happy and laughed together about all sorts of silly things as we sped along almost empty roads towards Swansea. I had a clear idea in my head what I wanted to discuss with Wesley about the wedding arrangements and his duties as best man. I knew he was a driver and I hoped that he would drive down on Friday evening so that he would join Dad, Gwyn, Dai, and I for a drink together for my stag night. It was not a particularly hot day, but pleasant enough if you were wearing a coat for an open-air drive. The forecast was good with no hint of rain expected and the visibility was good enough to offer us clear views of the Black Mountains as we drove down to the Swansea Valley. We had arranged to meet Wesley at the Ponterdawe Inn just a few miles inland from Swansea itself, away from the smoke and grime of the industrial side of the city. The inn was quite a large affair with several bars and a restaurant with ample spaces for customers' cars and looked quite upmarket from the outside. When we entered from the front door, I could see immediately that our initial assessment had been correct because it was a smart venue with a large reception hall, staffed by a bellboy and receptionist who directed us towards the restaurant for lunch. I could see from the key rack behind the desk that there were at least twenty letting rooms and could tell from the grand décor that it was an upmarket place.

We were greeted at the restaurant door by a smiling waitress in the restaurant livery who asked for my name. I said, "Flight Lieutenant Morgan and I am sure you will have a table booked in the name of Morgan?" She shepherded us into a large dining area and toward a table where my brother, Wesley, was already sitting accompanied by a smart young woman. Wesley jumped up to greet us both and was beaming all over his face as he introduced me and then Ruby to his friend, Alicia Bell. We sat down, ordered some drinks and I immediately chatted about the wedding arrangements and when all was easily settled, began interrogating him about his new friend, Alicia. He said that Alicia and he had been friends for quite a time but because of their jobs had to keep their relationship private for the time being as they worked in the same team of detectives in Swansea. He went on to tell us his good news, that he had passed the inspector's examination and was recommended for the next team leader role to become vacant in South Wales, which meant he would be leaving his present team and then they could make their relationship public. He was obviously immensely proud of Alicia because he went on to tell us that she was one of only three female detectives in the whole of Wales and had recently been promoted to detective sergeant. I asked if Alicia were able to attend our wedding on the following Saturday and he said that they were trying to rearrange the duty roster so that she could be there, but he said there was a problem about where she could stay as Mum and Dad have no spare room. Ruby immediately suggested that Freda and Dai would probably put them both up and that she would arrange it as soon as we got back this afternoon.

Our lunch was good and I thought of the lovely meals I had enjoyed in Madame Suzette's, washed down with copious amounts of champagne and red wine but resisted the temptation to have anything more than a cold beer as I was driving back this afternoon. It was good to be with Wesley again and I realised how much I loved my older brother. I was happy for him in his new-found love and wished him as much happiness as I had with Ruby. We parted about three-thirty as both Wesley and Alicia were going on duty for the late shift this evening and we looked forward to seeing them on Friday evening. Ruby told me in the car that as we boys were going out drinking together on Friday evening, Freda was hosting a little get-together at her house for some of the girls from the office, her mum and my mum, and Alicia was welcome to join them if she wished.

When we arrived back, Mrs Thomas had a high tea ready for us as soon as Geraint finished his shift at the station. We sat on the settee and read through the details of the houses that we had collected from the house agent, which were all priced within our budget. We were surprised that we could afford a much better house than I was expecting, and we picked out a large villa built in 1910 which had electricity laid on, hot and cold running water, an inside bathroom and three bedrooms upstairs and a garden at the front and back. We also liked an older property that was built around 1850, a double-fronted townhouse in Caerphilly town centre that only had a forecourt at the front but was very spacious inside with large drawing room, private sitting room, dining room and kitchen downstairs with four bedrooms upstairs. Electricity had been installed downstairs but not upstairs, which still had gas lamps and a bathroom had been created in the former scullery at the rear of the house, leading to a large garden and orchard. The first house was being sold by an under-manager at the South Wales Bank who was moving to take over the management of a bank in another town, and the second had been the home of a retired solicitor who had recently died. We all liked both and looked forward to seeing them tomorrow with Mr Evans the house agent.

We checked off our list the things we needed to do and apart from visiting potential new homes we still had flowers to order, and I needed to find a driver who could drive the Bentley to the chapel with Ruby and Geraint just before the service. Geraint said that one of his porters, Joseph Bennett, sometimes drove the village taxi to make some extra money and he said he would approach him and see whether he could do the honours on Saturday morning. This sounded good and I left it to Geraint to sort out with Joe. Ruby and I paid a quick visit to Freda and Dai so that the women could sort out the details of their females' get-together on Friday. I dropped Ruby home around nine-thirty and headed for home myself, but then changed my mind and drove to the Bedwas Hotel, went into the reception, and booked the honeymoon suite for our first married night together on Saturday. I decided to stop for one whisky in the bar before heading home, which became two before I forced myself into the car to drive back to Mum and Dad's.

With the flowers booked and paid for in the morning, we met Mr Evans at No. 8 Bryngwyn Street at eleven o'clock the next morning and he had a key to show us this house, which was empty, as the owner had already moved his family to his new location with the bank. This house was still quite new and had only been built about eight years ago. It stood at the end of a row of cottages on a plot that had once housed retired pit ponies but was acquired by a local firm of builders who divided the plot and put up two three-bedroomed houses standing in their own gardens. The house was spacious with a large drawing room and dining room, kitchen and scullery, morning room, bathroom and water closet and small study on the ground floor, and three large bedrooms and a nursery upstairs and a maid's room with wash handbasin and water closet in the attic. There was also a large outhouse, which was big enough to serve as a garage for a vehicle or a stable for a horse. The house was modern and light with electricity throughout and was heated by open fires with hot water via a back boiler behind the fireplace in the kitchen. Ruby liked this house immediately and I could see why, but I had a few misgivings because the house was situated at the top of a steep hill about a mile beyond our village on the way to Llanbradach, and I felt that this might prove quite an obstacle to getting to the shops and visiting her parents when the baby was born.

I much preferred the location of the second house because it was situated on level ground near the centre of the town at Caerphilly, which was less than two miles from our village and the next station down the line by train. This was an older house built seventy years before and part of an imposing terrace of large houses that were occupied by local business and professional people and their families. I felt it could prove to be an excellent family house, giving us plenty of room to expand our family in the years to come and although the actual number of rooms was quite like the modern property, they were on a grander scale. The front entrance was up four steps from the street to a wide front door, which opened into a large, tiled hallway from which doors opened to all parts of the ground floor and a wide flight of stairs led up to the first floor, where there were four bedrooms and a nursery. The kitchen was large with a solid fuel range that provided cooking, hot water, and heating, although there were fireplaces in all rooms. There were servants' quarters in the basement and a stable in the rear garden accessed from a back lane, which could easily accommodate a motor car should I acquire one in the future. There was work needed to modernise this house and to extend the electricity and water to the upper floors, but it might prove a better family home in the future. We certainly had much to think about in the next few days. I told Ruby that I had booked us into the Bedwas Hotel for our wedding night in the honeymoon suite, and then for seven days at the Grand Hotel in Tenby for our honeymoon itself from Sunday morning and she was delighted and excited with the prospect of spending a whole week together, doing what we wanted to do and sharing that special week without interference from friends and family.

When I got back to my parents' house, I was surprised to find an official telegram waiting for me and I had a sense of foreboding that I was being called back to active service and my leave was being cut short. Mum and Dad could see my reluctance to open the yellow envelope and tried to take the pressure off me, giving me some space by making a cup of tea. I could not wait any longer and I ripped open the envelope to read the news it contained. It was from OC 354 Squadron and I knew I was being called back but I forced myself to read on and it said:

> Sqn/Ldr Moss shot down and killed 26th April 1918 over Maastricht.
>
> Flt/Lt Morgan D DFC and bar, MM promoted Sqn/Ldr (acting) to be OC 354 Squadron RAF w/e 27th April 1918 (excerpt from the London Gazette)
>
> Flt/Lt the Hon J Dalrymple appointed acting OC 354 Sqn RAF until 18th May 1918.
>
> Fg.Off Lord Eckington promoted Flt/Lt to be flight Commander A flight
>
> Congratulations Boss on your promotion, appointment, and your marriage to Ruby. Holding the fort until you get back. Terence flying in my B flight slot.
>
> Jamie.

I could not believe that Sqn. Ldr. Moss was gone, nor could I understand why they had chosen me to replace him, but here I was promoted to squadron leader and appointed to command a squadron of fighter aircraft. I did not know why they had not chosen Jamie as he was an experienced pilot and a good leader but was pleased that he was the acting squadron commander until I returned from leave. I was extremely pleased for Giles Lacey and for Terence being given a chance to show what he could do. I could not contain my excitement and rushed to tell my parents in the back kitchen, and they were, of course, pleased but also a little bemused as to what it all meant. I knew what it meant for Ruby and I that I would earn even more as a squadron commander and be able to add to my savings significantly for after the war; it also meant that I would probably fly less in an operational sense which would please Ruby greatly and it would help me get a better position in civilian life when this war was all over.

It was fortuitous that I was going into Cardiff in the morning to collect our new wedding rings because now I needed to make a call to the military tailors to get my rank braid altered on my best uniform before Saturday. Ruby was not coming with me as she was having final fittings of the wedding dress and I would see her in the evening. I looked in my bag and found the card from the military tailors in London where I had my account and checked to see if they had a branch in Cardiff and was pleased to find that they did, near the Barracks at Pengam. I was not sure where that was, but I was sure that I should be able to navigate my way there without too much difficulty. I left early in the morning and drove fast to Cardiff, heading for the area of Pengam on the east side of the city centre. After a few minutes driving around I spotted the entrance of the barracks ahead of me and pulled in to speak with the guard corporal who advised me that the military tailors were inside the barracks within a cluster of military tailors' shops next to the officers' mess. I thanked him and he asked me to pull through the gate, stop at the guardroom and register my identification and car details, and then it was straight ahead, left at the main parade square and I would see the tailors' shops on my left. The tailors were immensely helpful and when I showed them my account card and number and they were happy to help. They examined my best uniform jacket, saying that they would have to remove one of the thick rings, insert the thinner pilot officer's ring between the two thick rings and that as they had the ranking braid in stock, they would be able to complete the job this morning. I said I would return after lunch at one o'clock after I had been to the jeweller's, and I left my uniform with them. I managed to park near to the jeweller's shop again, collected our new rings, paid his bill, and found it was still only eleven-thirty. I put the rings away safely to be passed to Wesley on Saturday and then looked for a suitable place to get some lunch to while away the hour or so before I could collect my uniform.

I found a seat in a small restaurant in a nearby street, ordered some lunch, picked up a copy of the *Times* newspaper from the rack and started to read about the progress of the war until my order of lamb chops with potatoes and spring vegetables came, and I realised that I was quite hungry. It was interesting to read about the progress of the offensive which seemed so far back in history, even though I had only been part of it just five days before. The fall of Antwerp had been a big triumph for the Allies and catapulted the British advance into southern Holland, whilst the Americans completely encircled Brussels and the French and Canadians were pushing into Luxembourg. The breakout from the stalemate of the Ypres Salient was complete and the speed of the advance had been rapid, but this time there seemed to be little appetite for delay or stopping the forward push amongst the high command. The opening up of Belgian ports, particularly Antwerp, had strengthened the Allies' supply lines and meant that we could sustain the forward momentum. The one thing that had not happened was the complete capitulation of the German resistance that had been widely talked about. Many rumours had circulated suggesting that one in three of the German front line troops were schoolboys, and another third of old men and wounded soldiers but this had not proved to be true. It was certain, the newspapers argued, that the Germans had been pushed back by the effectiveness of our offensive, but this was largely because we outnumbered their army by nearly two to one and the determination of our attack spearheaded by tanks caught them by surprise. The *Times'* war correspondent was sure that the German resolve was far from weakening but was getting firmer as they consolidated their defensive line to protect their homeland from attack. It was interesting to read the views of the war correspondents because they were there in the front lines, observing the war first-hand and reporting what they saw.

I drove back to the barracks and picked up my uniform suitably altered, now sporting the squadron leader rank badges, and set off for home. Ruby did not know my news yet and I looked forward to celebrating with her and her family this evening. I went to my parents' house first and was surprised when I walked in to find Gwyn and Mair sat in the parlour, talking with Mum. Dad had still not returned from his shift at the colliery, but Mum was at least talking with them both over a pot of tea. I could see that none of them looked particularly comfortable in each other's company, but I did not detect open hostility. I decided to risk going for broke and greeted Gwyn and Mair warmly, expressing pleasure that they would be at our wedding on Saturday. They smiled sheepishly and Gwyn said that he would be there, but Mair would only come to the reception at the rugby club afterwards, and I realised that this was the price Mum had exacted for saving her face at the marriage service. I smiled at Mum, then at Gwyn and Mair, and said to Mum that I was sorry but Ruby and I have decided who is to be invited to our wedding and we would very much like Mair, who is soon to be our sister-in-law, to accompany Gwyn to the wedding and the reception afterwards.

''I can also tell you that Wesley will be bringing his girlfriend Alicia as well. I do not care what the holier-than-thou brigade at the chapel may think or say because we Morgans have nothing to be ashamed of. We have given one son to the pit and two to the war but the youngest three will do you proud; Wesley is soon to be appointed police inspector; Gwyn is studying electrics so he can leave the pit and I am in command of an RAF squadron. Wesley and I have been decorated for our service in this war and we have nothing to hang our heads in shame for." As I said my piece, I noticed Dad hanging back by the kitchen door and as he came into the parlour, he said to all of us in the room that he agreed wholeheartedly with my feelings in this matter and that he was a proud father who could hold his head up amongst anyone in this village. He then shook my hand and Gwyn's, then embraced Mair and said he hoped to welcome her into this family soon. He sat down next to Mum and kissed her gently and said that this matter was settled once and for all, and we would all enjoy the occasion that weekend.

After tea I set off for Ruby's and broke the news of my promotion and appointment to Ruby and her mum and dad. They were excited and pleased for me and of course Geraint's whisky bottle came out and we had a few glasses in celebration. Mrs Thomas wanted to know more about the houses we had been to see and what we had decided, so we gave them the benefit of what we felt although neither of us had yet made up our mind on which we wished to purchase. They also wanted to know what being the squadron commander meant and I explained to them that I was now in command of a fighting unit of sixteen fighter aircraft, plus four in reserve with a complement of twenty-four officers and 260 airmen, and that we were a fighting unit equivalent to an army battalion. I said that I would probably fly less operations because many of my new duties were on the ground in planning and administration but hoped that I would still get to fly a little. When Ruby left the room for a few minutes I showed her mum and dad the lovely rings that we had made and they were extremely impressed when I showed them the inscription on the inside rim of the ring, which had our names and the date of our marriage. I put the rings away before Ruby came back into the room and she did not know that her mum and dad had seen them, but I showed them to her when we were alone so she could see the wonderful work that the old jeweller had put into this job. She was as impressed as I was and said she couldn't wait for me to slip it on her finger on Saturday in the chapel.

On Thursday, I was taking Ruby and her mother to Mountain Ash to visit old Mrs Williams. Ruby's grandmother was too old and infirm to make the journey down the valley to Bedwas for the wedding but wished to meet me and look me over before she gave her assent to Ruby on her choice. The journey was about twenty miles through Treharris towards Aberdare, through wooded country dotted with collieries and coal tips all the way, the heartland of industrial Wales. Granny Williams lived in a small farm cottage on the side of the mountain, a house that she had lived in for her whole married life and where she had brought up two daughters and two sons. Her husband had worked on the farm all his working life, which was why she was still living in this cottage. Grandsire had passed away three years before and was still remembered as one of the best shepherds in this area by the local farming people. However, she was a lively old lady but getting a little slow on her feet, her balance a bit unsteady but her wit and brain were as sharp as ever. She appraised me as if I were a prized exhibit at the farming show.

In the end, I guessed I must have passed muster because she began chatting easily to me whilst she directed Ruby and her mother to set the table and bring out the scones and cream, Welsh cakes, and fruitcake she had made to go with our tea. I found her a delightful old lady who looked at life with a twinkle in her eye and was optimistic and forward-looking, even though she was well over seventy years of age. She had been the one who had taught Mrs Thomas to use the needle, although she was happy to admit that she had become far better at sewing and dressmaking than she ever was. She wanted to know about my family, and I told her about losing my three eldest brothers, one in a pit explosion when the roof fell in when I was ten and two serving on the Somme in 1916 with the South Wales Borderers. I told her that my eldest surviving brother was a police detective inspector with the special investigation branch in Swansea and I was a pilot in the Royal Air Force. She asked me straight, "But what are you going to do after the war is over as there won't be much call for flying planes around here." I was honest with her and said that I did not know yet but that I had acquired some qualifications in engineering that I hoped would help me to find a secure job when I returned to civilian life.

By mid-afternoon I could sense that Ruby and her mother were anxious to get away and the old lady seemed to be tiring and drifting off slightly into little naps, so we decided to make a move to leave for home. She was reluctant to see us go but at the same time she wanted to close her eyes for a good afternoon nap to recharge her batteries after a busy day. She took hold of my arm before we left and said, "Derfal, you must promise that you will come and visit me again as soon as you're able and there is no need to bother about bringing my daughter but make sure you bring Ruby and your new baby to see me." None of us had mentioned the expected baby but Granny Williams knew that there was one on the way. She hugged us all but stayed seated in her armchair when we went out to get into the car and set off back down the Cardiff Road. I was extremely glad that we had made the effort to come and see Granny Williams today, who I thought was an interesting old lady who would have lots of stories to tell about her life stretching back into the middle of the last century.

It was a lovely drive back in the late afternoon spring sunshine. I remember thinking that it was May Day, hopefully the good weather would be here to stay for a while, and it would be fine for Saturday. There was only one more day to go before our wedding and I began to have fleeting notions that perhaps I was not doing the right thing, but these were only passing fancies. Very quickly my resolve and excitement for the future returned and any second thoughts evaporated as quickly as they came. Mrs Thomas told me that I was to stay for supper with them this evening because I was banned from seeing Ruby tomorrow, as this would be bad luck according to local marriage traditions. I wondered what I was going to do with myself all day tomorrow without Ruby, but then realised that I had so much to do to get myself ready and pack my cases for our honeymoon that I would have a full day ahead of me.

TWENTY-SIX

Our Wedding

Wesley arrived with Alicia mid-afternoon on Friday and came straight to Mum and Dad's house, where introductions were made all round. Alicia was rather shy and nervous meeting Wesley's family, but was happy to see me again for I was someone she had met before. Dad, as always, was quick to welcome her in his usual manner because he was always happy in the company of younger women. He and Alicia chatted happily, and he did not seem fazed at all by her professional manner and role in the police force. Mum was less comfortable because they seemed to have little in common, for Mum was a housewife and was born into a society where there was little opportunity for a professional woman, especially when they were working in what was predominantly a man's world. It was not that Mum was hostile in any way, but just did not know how to communicate with a woman who chose to work as a police detective rather than be bringing up a family or be a housewife. Wesley gave us his good news when we were all enjoying our tea and told us that he was being transferred to Newport Docks, where he was to be inspector in charge of the special investigation team. We were all so happy for him and could see the real pride that he and Alicia felt about his appointment. I was thinking of my own meteoric rise in the army, but that was because of the war – in Wesley's case it was his true merit and determined ambition which took him from constable to detective inspector in just over four years. I was sure that he was glad he had made the decision to leave the pit and join the police force, I hoped that this would encourage Gwyn to leave the pit also when he had gained his electrical qualifications. Wesley brought in his bag from the car. He was carrying a canvas suit carrier over his arm, and he stopped and opened it up to reveal a police inspector's dress frock coat and cap, which he said he would wear tomorrow in honour of my wedding as I would be wearing my uniform.

Around four, I drove Alicia and Wesley down to the Station House but waited outside as Alicia went in to join Ruby and go to Freda's for the party tonight. Wesley and I went back home to get ready for our night out this evening. Dad had arranged for us to celebrate in the Miners' Welfare Club, which suited me as I knew a lot of the regular customers and Dad had invited a couple of his pals to join us. We had agreed to meet at seven, so we left the house around six-thirty and strolled slowly up to the club. Mum had already gone to Freda's for the hen party, which was only two streets from us, so we were not surprised to find Gwyn, Dai, and Geraint already in the bar when we arrived. I got a round in, we all managed to get around one table and the first pint went down smoothly, as the chat began to flow. I thought that this was quite different from nights out at Suzette's but in other ways it was remarkably similar; the camaraderie, bonhomie and ribald chatter sprinkled with swear words seemed the same and I surmised that it would be ever thus when groups of men were together. I wondered what Jamie, Giles and Terence would make of this evening but realised that they would have fitted right in, exchanging their champagne for local beer but quaffing it down just the same.

Josh Andrews arrived just as we were finishing our first pint and immediately got in the second round. When he sat down the conversation inevitably turned to rugby, especially when there were three active players and two ex-players around the table. Soon we were extolling the virtues of the great tries we had scored and the famous victories we had been part of, and I could not help thinking if we were half as good on the field as we said we were around this table, we would be the Welsh champions. Geraint told me that Ruby was busy all day making herself beautiful for tomorrow. She had taken her mother and Alicia to Freda's tonight for their female celebration, and they were all in good spirits. He went on to say that he was proud that I was marrying his daughter, he knew we would be happy together and make him a proud grandfather soon. I was quite touched but Geraint and I had always hit it off right from the first time we had met at the rugby club, two years before. Our evening went well as the beer flowed freely, everyone was in good spirits, and I was pleased to see Gwyn looking far happier than I had seen him of late. He reassured me that he and Mair would be at the chapel and the rugby club afterwards, and he thanked me for my support with Mum and Dad. He hoped everything would be alright with Mum, we would know soon enough if tonight's hen party went off without sparks because Ruby had invited Mair to join them at Freda's.

I enjoyed myself immensely with my family and friends. I was thankful for the many congratulations and good wishes from local people who had known me from when I was a schoolboy, and this was much appreciated. Although I had been away from the village for over two years and now moved in different circles to the one, I was brought up in, I still felt part of this place and that I belonged here. I was glad of this because the war was likely to end soon and I would be returning here, attempting to pick up civilian life again in this village or nearby. I gradually slowed down on my drinking as the time went on, as I knew tomorrow morning would come soon enough and I had quite a lot to do before the marriage service at twelve-thirty.

So, when closing time was called at the bar, I was ready for home and Wesley, Dad and I made our way back in a happy and contented mood, reminiscent of the feeling on Christmas Eve when I was a child. I slept well apart from a couple of calls of nature during the night but awoke clear-headed and ready for the day. Our first task after breakfast was to deliver the wedding cake that Mum had made to the rugby club, then to drop the car off at the station for the driver to use later in the day. I had agreed to pay him twenty shillings and he said he would clean and polish the car and bedeck it with white ribbons and flowers. He would collect Wesley and I at twelve and deliver us to the chapel, then collect Ruby and her father at twelve-twenty to make the same journey and be waiting outside the chapel to drive Ruby and I to the reception at the rugby club.

Geraint had hired a charabanc to transport all the guests from the chapel to the rugby club after the photographer had taken some wedding pictures. The cake was on a silver plinth and had two tiers. I carried it gently out to the car, placed it gingerly on the seat and drove very carefully to the rugby club. The caterers were already hard at work preparing the room and making the food, and were happy to take the cake from me, placing it in the middle of the top table. I dropped the car off at the station, strolled back up High Street and as it was not yet nine o'clock, the shops were beginning to open their shutters and blinds in preparation for the day's business, and there were few people about. I was home inside ten minutes and was pleased to see that Wesley was up and dressed and did not seem to be hungover either. I gave him the wedding rings, making sure that I showed them to Mum and Dad first so they could see the inscription on the inner rim of the ring. He said that he would keep them safe until they were required, and he would keep them with his speech so he would be sure not to forget them.

I had polished my boots, ironed my shirt, and brushed my uniform at least thirty times yesterday so there was not much for me to do this morning. I decided to shave again to ensure that I looked fresh and smooth. I fixed my medals to the ribbons on my left breast of my best uniform jacket, double-checking my sword and ceremonial belt about three times. We were barred from the kitchen because Mum was bathing but I was finding it difficult to sit still as my nerves were rising. What if she changed her mind and did not turn up at the chapel? What would I say to all the guests? What if someone objected to the marriage in the chapel? I was never this nervous when I was in combat in the air, but this was all going round in my head like a whirlpool until Wesley poured out a cup of tea and then poured a good measure of brandy from his hip flask into the cup to cure my nerves. He made me settle down in the armchair and we just chatted for a few minutes. He asked me what I thought of Alicia, I was unable to give him a definitive answer on such a short acquaintance but felt that they had much in common and there was an obvious connection between them. I said I liked her and felt that if she had met me first, he would not have stood a chance remembering that these were the words that Gwyn had used when I first spoke to him about Ruby. We both laughed and he agreed that what I said was probably true, "but now you're spoken for I have a good chance!"

I asked him about his future in the police and he said that he was comfortable working as a detective, he enjoyed bringing enemies of our country to justice and hoped to continue doing this for the rest of his life. He said he was ambitious and was not afraid to work hard to achieve his ambitions; if he could prove himself capable of leading a team of detectives in his new job then he would try to become a chief inspector in a few years. He felt that there was security in the force with good wages and a decent pension in retirement, which was a much better deal than many other jobs available at this time. He said that the role of the police would become vital in maintaining law and order in peacetime, for when the war was over and large numbers of men returned to find that there were not as many opportunities as they had been promised by the politicians, there would be trouble. The men were fighting for a better life for their families and when they found nothing had changed, they would not like it much and many would want to take actions that may be outside of the law. I disagreed and said that I thought it would be legitimate for returning soldiers to expect that jobs and homes would be waiting for them, and if they were not there, to protest and take action to bring about change. Wesley said that it is not the job of the police to stop people protesting but he knew that there would be agitators and anarchists who would try to stir up violence and unrest where they could.

Mum appeared from the kitchen fully dressed in her finery, wearing a new dress that she had commissioned from Ruby's mum which was smart and appropriate for a wedding. I went through and shaved again, being extremely careful not to nick my neck and cause a bleed, which could mark my collar. I dressed in my uniform and then came down to check myself in the mirror in the hallway to ensure that everything was straight and in place. I took particular care to ensure that the sword belt was secure in the retaining hooks each side of my jacket where the cloth belt would usually be, so when the weight of the sword was added, it would not sag to one side. The sword belt was blue leather with gold facing which exactly matched the rank braid on each sleeve very well. I went through to the parlour carrying my cap, leather gloves and the sword in its scabbard and found Mum and Dad already to go. Dad was wearing his best suit with waistcoat and watch chain, looking smart, and Mum was a picture in her new dress, summer coat and hat. They both said how smart I looked in my RAF uniform and we sat and waited for Wesley. When he appeared, he looked great in his police inspector's dress uniform which was dark navy, almost black, with silver buttons, two pips on each sleeve and South Wales Police crests on his collar. The frock coat came to just above his knees and was buttoned up to his neck. I noticed the police medal ribbon on his chest, and he asked me if I would pin the medal in place for him, which I was proud to do. His ensemble was finished off with a smart cap and a tall ebony cane with a silver crest on the top, his badge of office. We then pinned white carnations to our buttonholes, and we were ready to go.

Mum and Dad were going to walk to the chapel, but I said that I would rather they rode in the Bentley and Wesley, and I would be happy to walk instead. I was glad to have decided to do this because they looked so proud sat in the back of the Bentley decked out in flowers and white ribbons, and I noticed that the driver was also wearing a chauffeur's peaked cap to complete the picture. With my sword clipped onto the sword belt, wearing my cap and gloves Wesley and I stepped out into the street and set off for the chapel. We must have looked an unusual sight because I am sure that they had seen no one in an RAF uniform in the village nor a police inspector in full dress regalia either, for we drew some stares, and a few congratulations were called out by passers-by. In fifteen minutes, we were at the chapel steps, quite a few guests had already arrived and were taking their places in the chapel pews. I was rather surprised that there were quite a few members of the chapel congregation who had come along to see us married, in addition to our personal guests. Wesley and I entered the chapel, and I felt a lump in my throat as I made my last steps down the aisle as a bachelor, and we took up our positions to the right in the front pew. I looked around to see if I recognised any faces and I saw Mrs Thomas sat in the second pew on the left side. She was accompanied by people I did not know, who I presumed were her brothers and sister from Mountain Ash. I smiled and waved, and then panning around I could see Dai Rees sitting with Josh Andrews, Gwyn and Mair. I got up, walked back down the aisle, and said to Gwyn and Mair to come and sit in the pew immediately behind me as part of my immediate family, then I went in search of Alicia who I found sat at the back of the chapel and brought her forward to sit in the same pew.

I now sat in silent contemplation waiting for the cue from the organ that Ruby had arrived. This seemed interminable, I must have looked at my watch two or three times until I was certain that she was nearly five minutes late. Just as I was beginning to get worried, the organ music changed, the strains of Wagner's 'Bridal Chorus' struck up and I knew that she hadn't backed out and was actually here. The Reverend Lewis appeared miraculously from nowhere in front of the altar as Ruby and her father processed sedately down the aisle slowly in time to the music. I stood up in front of the altar rail with Wesley beside me and kept looking forward until Ruby was in her place on my left shoulder. I turned and smiled and could not believe how beautiful she looked in her wedding dress and when she lifted her veil, I could see she was smiling, and her eyes were glistening.

The Reverend Lewis proceeded with the service. When we passed the bit where he asked if there were any objectors without incident and Mr Thomas gave Ruby to be married to me, I felt the pressure lifting. We repeated our vows out loud, I was impressed how strong and confident Ruby sounded, and exchanged our wedding rings, which were blessed and put on our fingers. We then withdrew to the vestry with our witnesses to sign the register and receive our marriage certificate whilst the congregation sang 'Cwm Rhondda' with some gusto. Within ten minutes we came back into the main chapel and the Reverend Lewis said a few words, but this time he was remarkably brief and then led the final prayers blessing our marriage with children, then we sang the final hymn, 'Love Divine, All Loves Excelling' and the service was over. The Reverend Lewis led Ruby and I out of the chapel and into the bright sunshine.

I was smiling from ear to ear as we moved slowly through the congregation and out of the front doors with the powerful organ playing the Wedding March very loud. As soon as we were out of the chapel, I took Ruby in my arms, kissed her deeply and said, 'Good afternoon, Mrs Morgan.' Within a few seconds we were surrounded by the well-wishers piling out of the chapel to wish us all the best and congratulations and then the photographer started taking his posed pictures – the bride and groom, the bride and groom plus the best man and maid of honour, with both sets of parents and with all the family members and finally with all the wedding guests. Ruby was busy trying to introduce me to her family members who I had not met, but with all the melee it was difficult to remember their names after a few minutes had passed.

Eventually the car arrived, and Ruby and I climbed into the back seat to be driven to the reception and as per tradition, before she sat down, she threw her posy of flowers into the crowd. It was caught cleanly by Alicia. The driver set off driving slowly through High Street, down the hill to the station and left to drop down the short incline to the rugby club, where he parked in front of the main doors. We went in to find the club room transformed with flowers and ribbons, the tables laid up beautifully and I felt proud of what had been achieved in just a few short hours by the catering staff. The food smelled wonderful, I hoped it tasted as good as the tantalising aroma coming from the kitchen. The barman brought a small brandy and a sweet sherry for Ruby whilst we were waiting for the bus to arrive and we chatted idly while we waited about the morning sickness which was becoming more regular and the little bump that was beginning to show, although the wedding dress had been engineered by her mum to hide the bulge. Mrs Thomas had built her successful dressmaking business on being able to flatten out her clients' tummies to make them look less noticeable in her dresses, so Ruby trusted her ability implicitly. If the wedding had been delayed a few more weeks I think it might have been too big a task for even her mum's skills. We both laughed together and realised that when the baby was born in September, our secret would be out.

The charabanc swung into the forecourt of the rugby club and we took up position at the entrance to welcome our guests to the reception. The two sets of parents came first, looking happy and relaxed. I noticed how smart Geraint looked in his station master's dress uniform, which he only reserved for wearing when the directors of the railway or the royal train passed through the station. My two brothers came next with Mair and Alicia, then Freda and Dai, then Ruby's family who I was introduced to again, but this time resolved to try to remember some of their names for a bit longer. The bar was open, people crowded around to get their drinks and Wesley and Gwyn were directing them to their seats at the table. I was looking around the room at our guests and I could see Mair and Alicia sitting together, chatting happily. I made my way over, joined them for a minute and brought them over to be with Ruby and me to wait for Wesley and Gwyn to sort out the guests and join us. I could see why Gwyn was so totally besotted with Mair as she was, certainly, exceptionally beautiful, and Alicia did not seem so serious now that she was more relaxed. Ruby joked with her that she would be the next to get married as she had caught the bride's posy today.

Eventually, everyone had drinks, the meal was ready, and we all took our places. Tongues were now loosened, everyone seemed to be enjoying themselves and the waiters started to serve the first course which was vegetable soup, to be followed by roasted Welsh lamb, roast potatoes, and vegetables, with apple tart and cream for dessert. I had ordered a case of champagne for the toasts so things should go well. Geraint was the first to speak and he amused us with stories about Ruby and her upbringing, how glad he was to be able to pass her on to a husband to look after her from now on which would be a great weight off his shoulders, and hopefully not too much of a burden on mine. He delivered this speech so good-humouredly that everyone knew he was joking and took it in good part, rising to drink the toast when he proposed it.

Then it was Wesley's turn, and I knew that he would have to deliver something special if he were going to match Geraint's witty speech. Wesley stood and looked across the room at the assembled company, then drew from his pocket what everyone immediately recognised as a policeman's notebook and proceeded to read from it as if he was giving evidence in court about the misdeeds of the accused, Derfal Ieuan Morgan, who in the summer of 1910 was caught scrumping apples from Farmer Evans' orchard in the bottom fields and was punished by his father; was punished at the village school for tying Amy Simmonds' pigtails to the back of her chair and caught again breaking wind in chapel just at a pause in the Reverend Lewis's sermon. At this point the old reverend stood up and said that he remembered the incident well but seem to recollect that it was Wesley and not me, which caused a real burst of laughter. Wesley continued reading from his notebook.

"… He poked his tongue out at Mrs Dixon in the butcher's shop and was cheeky to Mr Grigg the fishmonger, who was just closing the fish and chip shop one night when this wretch ran up and shouted in the door, "Have you got any chips left, mister?" and when Mr Grigg answered in the affirmative, the cheeky scallywag shouted, "Well you shouldn't have cooked so many", and ran off. Shall I go on? The list is very extensive, but I am sure that you can all see already what a hard job faces Ruby to keep this scoundrel on the straight and narrow. However, I am pleased to say that the former Miss Thomas has already had a positive effect on him, and he has managed to win some small promotions in the military and to convince her that he is worth saving.' With that he called everyone to fill their glasses and drink a toast to the bride and groom. Wesley now said he had received some telegrams from people who could not be with us today and he would read them out.

The first telegram came from 354 Squadron RAF, Belgium and simply said, "Congratulations Boss from all 354 personnel and good luck."

The second telegram came from Flight Lieutenant, the Lord Eckington and said, "Chocks away old boy, no more flying solo. Congratulations."

The third came from Flight Lieutenant, the Honourable Jamie Dalrymple and Flying Officer Terence Bradby and simply said, 'Wish we could be with you both but will raise a glass or two in your honour tonight. Cheers Jamie and Terence."

We then put both hands on to my sword and cut the cake ceremonially on the table in front of the applauding guests. The caterers took one tier away to slice into portions for the guests and Ruby and I walked around the table thanking everyone for coming and for their wedding presents. I noted that a quartet were setting up at one end of the room and I expected that they would provide some music for dancing a little later in the evening. By now men were crowding the bar to get a beer to wash down the meal and a sherry for their wives, and then the music started to play, and people began to relax. I went over to the bar to speak to some of the men I did not know, someone placed a pint in my hand and drew me into their conversation. He was Ruby's Uncle Herbert and said he was an old soldier, he fought in South Africa, and he said he needed me to settle an argument about my medals.

"We want to know why the Military Medal is not worn first before the Distinguished Flying Cross."

I was able to answer easily that both medals were of equal status, but because I was now serving in the RAF, the air force medal comes first as a matter of protocol. The only exception to this would be if I had earned a higher class of medal whilst serving in the Royal Engineers, that would take precedence. I could see that they had several opinions and I had settled the argument, so they all settled to amicable drinking again. Herbert asked if it were true that I was a rugby player and I said I played for this club when I could. The band was now getting into its stride, but no one seemed to be getting up to dance so I looked round for Ruby, grabbed her hand, and swung her on the floor as we moved into the waltz steps the band were playing. This seemed to be all that was needed, others got up and started to dance and soon there were plenty of couples on the floor. I encouraged Gwyn and Mair and Wesley and Alicia to start dancing, and reluctantly they joined in. We were most surprised to discover that Wesley was quite an accomplished ballroom dancer and had no idea where he had learned all the dance steps.

The reception was going well, both families seemed to be getting on and our friends on both sides were mixing well, so when everything was going smoothly Ruby, and I got ready to make our exit and set off for the short drive to the Bedwas Hotel where we were going to spend our wedding night before leaving for Tenby in the morning. Ruby slipped into the home team dressing room and changed from her wedding dress into another of her mother's lovely creations for going away, with matching shoes and handbag. She packed the wedding dress carefully into a dress bag and I slipped out and put the bag into the back of the car. When we were ready, we made our way slowly through the club room, thanking our guests and saying our farewells and made our way to the car. Everyone followed us out into the forecourt as Ruby and I boarded the Bentley, and they cheered and applauded as I drove slowly round the forecourt and through the gates with the clatter of tin cans tied to the back of the car ringing in our ears. I drove just around the corner and enough distance to be out of sight to remove the cans, then pulled up in front of the Station House to drop off the wedding dress safely before arriving at the Bedwas Hotel within two minutes.

I parked the car in front of the main door, the hall porter came out to collect our bags and carry them inside. I signed the register – it seemed unusual to sign as Mr and Mrs Morgan – and the hotel manager came to personally greet us and to invite us to enjoy a congratulatory glass of champagne with him in the bar before going to our room. Ruby and I went into the bar where the waiter had a bottle of champagne on ice, and the manager made a short speech of welcome, pouring three glasses of champagne and proposing our good health and congratulations for a long and happy marriage. This was a pleasant surprise; the champagne was remarkably good, and we sat at one of the tables to enjoy it for a few minutes. Several of the other guests came over to express their congratulations to us both. Ruby and I took a few minutes to relax in each other's company for the first time since the marriage service over eight hours ago, and to talk quietly together about the day and what we would remember most. We were just chatting so comfortably that we hardly noticed we had finished off the rest of the bottle. The waiter offered to bring us another bottle, but we decided not to take up his offer and went up to our room.

The honeymoon suite was a beautiful room decked out with flowers, with a large bed and a private bathroom. The room was spacious and comfortably furnished with a sofa and armchair and had good views towards Bedwas mountain in the distance. It was not until we got into our room did, we begin to feel the strain of all the activity of the day's events bearing down on us quite heavily. I ran a bath for Ruby but we both got in the hot water together and enjoyed soaping each other clean and soothing the aches out of our shoulders and backs. Within half an hour we were in the warmth and soft comfort of the big bed snuggled in together, and it was strange that we didn't have the great urgency to make love instantly but slowly, softly and with much sensuality we caressed each other all over and kissed and nibbled our necks and behind the ears before a slow build-up of foreplay leading to a glorious penetration which left us both spent and ready to sleep curled up in a tight embrace. We slept like this all night.

I was up first, bathed and shaved by seven-thirty whilst Ruby was still asleep. I clambered on to the bed and woke her up by gently rubbing my finger between her legs to which she let out a long, contented sigh, opened her eyes and kissed me deeply on the lips. I had already run the water for her so whilst she soaked herself in the bath, I packed away my uniform and medals, sword and sword belt into their case and selected a lighter weight suit to wear today.

We enjoyed a full Sunday breakfast in the dining room and after packing the car we were on our way to Tenby by ten-thirty. Ruby looked radiant in a light summer dress and jacket with matching hat, which was just about right for this fine spring morning, and I hoped that the clouds did not build too much to obscure the sun as the day wore on. I had heard that Mumbles Head was extremely beautiful, so had planned to stop for lunch in Oystermouth and then motor on via Llanelli down the Pembrokeshire coast to the seaside town of Tenby. I told Ruby that this was the first day of the start of our lives together and we could be, for this week at least, as carefree as we wanted to be without thinking about our baby or the war for a minute. It was just our time to enjoy ourselves without a care in the world. We laughed and sang songs as we drove and were as happy as a pair of larks as we motored through the lovely coastal villages, arriving at the Grand Hotel around four o'clock in the afternoon. With all the formalities completed we were in our room with an excellent view over the harbour and the beach by four-thirty. Our room was on the second floor, which meant a climb up two flights of stairs, but we were young and fit enough to do this with ease. It was good to unpack and know that we would be sleeping here for the next week. We were both a little tired after the journey, we laid on the bed and snoozed for an hour before we had to get ready for dinner at seven o'clock.

I slept soundly for an hour or so, woke quite well refreshed and found that Ruby had already bathed and was dressing and putting on some make-up. She had chosen a simple but elegant black evening dress and had pinned the RAF silver wings on the left-hand side, and I was glad that I had brought my dinner suit and black bow tie to dress for dinner. I knew I would also be welcome to wear my uniform in the dining room instead of evening dress if I wished but the hotel rules did not permit lounge suits after seven o'clock in the evening. The dinner was three courses and passably good, there was sufficient choice to satisfy all tastes and the wine list had a good selection of house wines that proved enjoyable. After dinner we went into the bar where there was a palm court trio playing quietly in the corner and a few couples sitting at tables around the room.

We chose a vacant table between two occupied tables. The waiter took our drinks order and we sat and relaxed. As I looked around, I caught the eye of the middle-aged couple sat to our left. I said good evening and they replied warmly with what sounded like a Manchester accent, and then said to the couple on our right, "These must be the newly-weds, don't you think?" I thought it strange to be talked about in our presence without being spoken to but immediately interjected that we were indeed the newly-wed couple, I was Derfal and this was my wife Ruby – Squadron Leader D. Morgan RAF and Mrs Morgan who were married yesterday. Introductions were then made, and we learned that one couple were Mr and Mrs Alfred Roberts, a cotton mill owner from Rochdale and the other were a family doctor and his wife, Dr. and Mrs Macmillan, from Edinburgh. They turned out to be good company and although friendly, did not try to push themselves too much on to us but were happy if we wanted to chat. Alfred and John were going to play golf in the morning and asked if I wanted to join them. Although I have never picked up a club before in my life, I thought I might give it a try whilst the women were going to visit the local market and stroll on the beach before lunch with us at the golf club.

Golfing turned out to be an unusual game where each shot you made was different, and it was difficult to see with so little experience how one could practice and improve. I found I could hit the ball a fair distance with the woods and drivers but had little control over the direction the ball went in so I was reaching the greens by the most indirect routes and often with a few more shots than my companions. However, they were good sports and encouraged me as best they could. Although I finished in third place some twenty-four shots more than them, they said that for a first time on the course that was very encouraging, and I should think about taking up the game seriously. I was not so sure whether I could persevere enough to become a good golfer, but Alfred and John were pleasant companions, we all enjoyed the fresh air of the links course and finished eighteen holes in time to join the ladies for lunch in the clubhouse.

Ruby said she enjoyed perusing the market stalls and the beach was lovely with soft sand, beautifully shaded by the harbour walls to make it a suntrap but told me afterwards that Barbara Roberts and Morag Macmillan were roughly the same age as her mother and she found them difficult to make small talk with. The concerns of middle-aged women seemed vastly different from those of a newlywed twenty-year-old and I supposed if Ruby had confided that she was pregnant they would have talked about babies, but she kept that information to herself. After lunch, Ruby and I broke away from the other two couples to take a drive to the beach at Saundersfoot where we found a long stretch of smooth sandy beach with hardly a person on it. We walked off our lunch, launching stones into the water to see how many times we could skim them over the tops of the waves. I was mortified to find that Ruby was better at skimming stones than I was; however hard I tried she always managed one or two more skims than I could. When we came to the end of the beach we sat on some rocks and watched a seal swimming close to the shore, trying to guess where his head would pop up each time he dived under the water. This was a difficult game to win at because there seemed no rhyme nor reason to the direction the seal would take once he was under the water or for how long he would stay under, for it seemed he would pop up several hundred yards away from where he dived in a totally different direction from where you thought he had gone.

We sat on those rocks for fifteen minutes or so watching the gulls circling above and occasionally diving into the sea to catch fish, when we were joined by a red and white Springer spaniel who came out of nowhere but was happy to join us sitting on the rocks. He took a shine to Ruby, who was stroking his head and ruffling his ears, until I found a stick lying amongst the flotsam on the tide line, threw it into the water and the spaniel leapt up and dived into the water to retrieve it. We did this a few times and the dog seemed to be enjoying this game with much delight until we heard a voice calling him shrilly from the house perched on the hill to the side of the beach. He pricked his ears up and ran off in the direction of his mistress, who waved a friendly thanks to us for exercising her dog for her. As we walked slowly back along the beach arm in arm, we wondered what the spaniel's name was and amused ourselves with thinking up suitable suggestions for the most appropriate name. Perhaps he was a Buster or a Towser, but we rejected them as unsuitable names for a Welsh Springer, so maybe he was a Caradoc or a Glendower, named after great princes, but in the end, we decided to call him Henry.

We were tired after our day in the fresh air and drove back to the hotel to have some afternoon tea and retire to our room for an afternoon nap before dinner. I took off my trousers and shoes, slipped my shirt over my head, hung my clothes in the wardrobe and we snuggled down on the top of the bed. We kissed and cuddled for a little while but soon we were both asleep in each other's embrace for the next hour. I was awake at five-thirty and crept out of bed so as not to disturb Ruby who was still asleep soundly and went into the bathroom to run the bathwater for Ruby's bath. I woke her up gently by nibbling at her left nipple, which was just visible at the side of her shift, and she slowly and luxuriously came back to full consciousness from her deep sleep.

Her bath was ready, so I lifted her gently in my arms, carried her through to the bathroom, slipped the shift over her head and lifted her into the bathwater. I sat on the edge of the bath watching her washing herself all over and marvelling at her expanse of soft skin, glistening and shiny with the bathwater. When she had finished washing, I took off my underwear and jumped in the bath with her and we rolled about in the water finally coupling in a watery embrace that splashed water and soap all over the sides of the bath as we both reached satisfaction and lay back spent. I thought to myself that if Ruby were not pregnant, she surely would be after the end of this week and smiled. I realised that we had spent nearly an hour in the bathroom and that we needed to hurry ourselves if we were to dress in time for dinner. I chose to wear my uniform tonight as a change from the dinner jacket and Ruby had yet another evening gown, this time in pale blue, that she would wear this evening. We dressed as quickly as we could, but it was nearly seven-thirty before we were ready to go down to the dining room for dinner.

The Roberts and the Macmillans were already eating when we entered but both couples looked up and smiled when we entered the room. The waiter had reserved a table for us in one of the bay windows, which commanded an excellent view over the sea and would allow us to enjoy the sunset towards the west. We ordered some dressed crab followed by excellent pork chops in apple cider sauce and locally grown vegetables with steamed pudding and custard for dessert. I ordered a bottle of red wine for the table and I felt ready to enjoy my dinner as all the fresh sea air today had given me a hearty appetite. The food was again very well cooked and both of us enjoyed it very much. In between the mouthfuls we began imagining what Henry would be having in his bowl for dinner and would his master take him down to the beach for an evening walk before the sun went down. Ruby said we should not be thinking of dog names but thinking of what we intended to call our first child. We must make a short list of favourite boys' and girls' names otherwise we would be caught out when the time came. We both laughed and said we would think about it over the next couple of days and see what names came to the fore. After dinner we took a stroll along the clifftop in the moonlight and tried out some of the baby names in our heads as we walked along, and surprisingly the girls' names were easier to think of than the boy's names. There were lots of individual names we liked but when combined with second name choices they did not work too well. We came up with a couple of favourites nevertheless – Alice for a girl and Alwyn Glyndr for a boy and decided that was settled for now. It was bridge night at the hotel and as neither of us were players, we slipped into the bar and enjoyed a nightcap before bed.

Tuesday, we drove to the western tip of Wales and visited the ancient capital of Wales at St David's, toured round the cathedral and the Bishop's Palace which were not generally open for large parties, but small groups could ask to be shown round by request. Wednesday we returned to Saundersfoot and swam in Carmarthen Bay, and enjoyed lazing on the beach in the warm sunshine all the time waiting for our old canine friend, Henry, to make an appearance but with no luck. On Thursday we took a boat trip to Caldey Island about a mile offshore, where there was an old priory and an abbey church, and an opportunity to get a view of many types of sea birds at close quarters. In the evening we went to see a performance of *Midsummer Night's Dream* at the Tenby Repertory Theatre. We linked up with the Roberts and Macmillan's on Friday and went to the weekly market in Pembroke and by opening the two rumble seats at the rear of the Bentley, we got all six of us in at once. The market proved to be busy and was a mixture of a typical weekly farmers' market selling fresh local produce, combined with some arts and crafts stalls selling trinkets and small antiques. Ruby was so excited that she searched most of the arty stalls, buying some presents for Freda and her mother to take back home with her. I invested in a small silver hip flask like the one that Wesley carried – I thought it might prove a useful accessory for me when flying on a cold day. Both of our sets of companions were leaving the hotel tomorrow to return home at the end of their holiday so we decided that we would have a final dinner together that night. We reserved a special table for six in the dining room and this turned out to be a happy and convivial conclusion to our short acquaintance this week. We said farewell after our dinner together, wished them well and the ladies exchanged addresses. That was the last we saw of them as they both had long journeys to make to get home and were leaving early in the morning.

Saturday was our last day. Ruby and I relished our last whole day alone together, as almost as soon as we got home, I would have to pack and be ready for the off on Monday, to drive to Ramsgate to catch the MV *Rochester Castle* back to Oostende. I could see that Ruby was getting a little moony and I guessed that after a week-long period in our company together she did not relish being separated again for an indefinite period. I tried to cheer her up by saying that the war was entering its final phase and just one concerted push would bring about our victory, but she was not really convinced. However, our ennui was shattered when we walked into the town from the hotel to find that there was regatta being held around the harbour by the local fishermen, which proved to be a happy and joyous affair with marching bands and singing accompanied by much tasting of local foods and beer with trawler and gig racing in the bay. The town was crowded with visitors from the local area and everywhere was brightly decorated with coloured bunting and lights, with folk dancers performing on every street corner. Ruby's mood lifted straightaway, and we enjoyed ourselves, fully joining in with the fun and games and spending a few coppers in the sideshows and arcades to win a small stuffed monkey toy, which we thought would be our child's first plaything. There was to be a grand firework display to mark the end of the regatta at sunset, but we decided that we would better be able to view the spectacle from the terrace at our hotel than amongst the crowd in the town.

After dinner we took our coffee and brandy on to the terrace where we had a grandstand view of the fireworks display out in the bay. Everyone was remarking on how good it was to see such a display again, as this was the first one since 1914. People hoped that this was a further sign that the war was nearly over. When the noise of the flashes and bangs had subsided, we could still hear sounds of revelry in the town as the local people enjoyed themselves, which I am sure they deserved after four long years without the annual regatta. We took ourselves off to bed and made slow, passionate love in the big hotel bed for the last time before returning to Bedwas. I knew tomorrow we would be squashed into Ruby's small bed at the Station House, frightened to make too much noise in case her mum and dad overheard us and disapproved of what we were doing under their roof.

I vowed that we should make an offer on one of the houses we had seen as soon as possible so we had somewhere to live after the baby was born. I favoured the town house in Caerphilly, but Ruby preferred the modern villa at the top of the hill, so we needed to think hard together about which one we would choose. Sunday morning came quickly enough, and we packed our bags and then enjoyed our last full Welsh breakfast before setting off for home. Ruby was happy to be going home and seeing her family again, in an ebullient mood after such a good week at Tenby alone together as the start of our married life. She also felt some trepidation as I was returning to the front and although I had always played down the dangers involved, she was aware that combat flying was not a safe occupation even though I stressed that as the squadron commander I would not be flying so much as before. She kind of half believed me, but also knew that I enjoyed flying so much that I would not settle myself to be an armchair warrior easily.

The drive back was enjoyable, and the views of the Black Mountains and the Beacons were glorious in the spring sunshine as we took the road through Carmarthen, Ammanford and Brecon back to the valley. We called in to Mum and Dad's on the way into the village to say hello and they were so happy to see us both, before going on to the Station House to my new in-laws. Geraint was so glad to see me and took it as an excuse to get out his whisky bottle, and Ruby was fully engaged in delivering a full account of our week in Tenby and everything we had done. Her mum kept saying that all she and Geraint had managed was three days in a boarding house in Porthcawl and how lovely it would have been to have stayed in the best hotel. Mr and Mrs Thomas were so kind, and I think they were truly glad to see their daughter so happy after such great sadness she experienced two years before. They kept saying she was a new woman and that was because she met me, and this gave me a great sense of confidence that Ruby would survive our parting and be well supported until the baby was born.

We discussed the houses again and although I preferred the town house in Caerphilly, I was persuaded that we should buy the modern villa in Bryngwyn Street. We decided that we would make an offer for the property in the morning I would instruct my bank manager to pay a ten per cent deposit and release the balance on completion of the contract at the price of £175.00. This would mean that the transaction could all go through whilst I was away, and we would be ready to move in when I came home at the end of the war or my next leave, whichever came first. I spoke with Geraint privately and told him that I had written a will that I would deposit with the solicitor for safekeeping, which if anything happened to me would bequeath everything to Ruby so the house and residual capital would be hers so she and the baby would be secure. I had not told Ruby this because she was worried enough about my safety as it was, but in the event of my death in action he would know what to do.

Monday was terribly busy as Ruby, and I were at the house agent's office as he opened and made our offer for 9 Bryngwyn Street of £175 cash and made arrangements for the payment of a deposit and completion cheque when the contract was completed. We then visited the bank and I arranged to put Ruby as a signatory on my bank account so she could issue cheques for the house purchase when required. While Ruby went into the dress shop, I quickly went into Gittings and Edwards, my solicitors, to ask them to act for me in the house purchase and look after my will until I returned from the war. We had managed to complete all this by eleven, for I knew that I had to leave by midday if I was to catch my sailing early in the morning. I had just enough time to change out of civilian clothes, put my uniform on and spend fifteen minutes or so quiet time with Ruby before setting off back to the war in Belgium.

TWENTY-SEVEN

Commanding 354 Squadron RAF

I was sad to be leaving my lovely wife behind after only a handful of days alone together, but by the time I was driving through Belgian territory that just a few weeks ago was German occupied I could sense a certain change in atmosphere amongst the townspeople and villagers, who now seemed to be picking up the reins of their old pre-war life quite easily. I was missing Bedwas already but looking forward immensely to being with the boys in the squadron again soon, although I realised that my promotion and appointment as the squadron commander may make it more difficult to enjoy such easy relationships as before. There was certainly a mood of optimism at home, expressed through the national newspapers, that the war would be coming to an end quite soon and the rapid progress of all the Allied forces in pushing through Belgium into Luxembourg and southern Holland meant that the Germans were going to be defeated in one final big battle on their borders. I was mystified as to why the press believed that the Germans would capitulate so easily, because even faced with superior Allied forces they managed to fight with determination and only gave ground after hard fighting had taken place. So far, the RAF had enjoyed total command of the skies, but as the battle front moved closer to the German border a great many more of their airfields became within range for their fighters and bombers and we expected the final battles in the air to be more difficult and bloodier than before. We had never been complacent about the bravery and skill of German pilots and we knew they would fight fiercely to protect their homeland. I was confident that 354 would continue to fight bravely and achieve what was asked of us, but I was also sure that we might lose more pilots as the air war intensified.

I drove through the main gate and immediately saw that at least three flights were airborne, so I did not expect a huge welcome home. I parked outside of the squadron headquarters, went into the general office and the duty clerks jumped up to attention and welcomed me back. Then Jamie stepped out of the CO's office, clasped me in a bear hug and said he was so glad I was back.

"A, B and D flights were on patrol over Eindhoven and were expected back within the hour," he told me. "C flight are being held in reserve but will fly tomorrow's sorties and D flight will be in the reserve slot. We have lost two pilots since you have been away, Flying Officer James Reader was shot down near Tilburg last Wednesday and is posted missing in action, and Flight Sergeant Knowles was shot down yesterday over Eindhoven but managed to crash land behind the German lines, so we presume he is a prisoner of war. We will try to get further information about whether he is alive or wounded and whether he is a prisoner or not."

Jamie was desperate to hear all my news from home and about the wedding, but I made him brief me fully on operations first. He brought me up to date with how the campaign had moved on since I had been away and although our momentum had been slowed down significantly by the enemy consolidation of their positions along a line from Utrecht to Eindhoven and Maastricht, they were able to halt our advance because of the easier access to reinforcements and supplies from Germany. "The High Command do not seem to be too worried," he explained, 'they see this as only a temporary setback as intelligence suggests that the reserve of men and supplies available in Germany is strictly limited and represents their last resources. 354 has been supporting the bomber wings in their attacks on the many factories around the Eindhoven area and challenging the German scouts as they vector in on the bomber formations. We have noticed an increase in the numbers of German scouts in the air and all our pilots have suffered greater stress and fatigue because every sortie involves close contact with the enemy air force. However, our strike rate is much better than theirs and our total number of kills continues to rise. Terence Bradby has been awarded the DFC and so has Giles Lacey, and I have been awarded a bar to mine."

Finally, he showed me my new quarters, which were quite comfortable and situated on the top floor of the officers' mess where I had a small suite of rooms and had been allocated a new batman, Cpl Steward Carlton, who said to leave my bags and he would sort my uniforms and other kit immediately.

I thanked Jamie for the loan of his lovely car, which certainly made a colossal difference to my leave, wedding and honeymoon and he modestly said that it was nothing and then brightly said that he had managed to organise a small car for the use of the squadron CO to get about, which was parked outside the squadron HQ. Later that afternoon I was in the squadron HQ for the debriefing of the returning flights from today's sortie and then met with the flight commanders to lay out my strategies for the smooth running of the squadron.

Around five, I met with the squadron adjutant Flt Lt Roland Holmes and the newly appointed squadron warrant officer, Mr Ronald Skinner, who had joined during my leave period and was the real new boy. These two appointments were vital for the maintenance of proper order and discipline. To look after the welfare of the men and without having confidence in their ability to do their jobs, I would find it hard to command the squadron effectively. The lion's share of my time would be spent liaising with 2 Wing and then planning the squadron sorties in support of Wing and Second Army strategy. Roly Holmes was a tried and tested officer with a distinguished record in the Royal Artillery before the RFC, where he was one of the first pilots to be trained in 1914 and had been fully operational for nearly four years. This was his first ground-based tour, but he exuded confidence and had a pilot's common understanding of the combat situation, which made him fit right into the fighter squadron mentality, as well as experience as a battery commander in the RA, where he learnt to command men effectively.

Mr Skinner was totally unknown to me, but he was tall, ramrod-straight, and extremely correct in his military etiquette when he entered the office. He was immaculately presented, his boots were sparkling as were his belts and buckles, and the creases in his trousers and sleeves were needle sharp. I commended him on his appearance but made it clear to him that the discipline of a fighting squadron was as much about getting the job done and being flexible in our approach to efficiency than always being parade-ground ready. Pilots who had spent up to eight hours in the cockpit in a day sometimes looked a bit dishevelled and air mechanics sometimes needed to work long hours into the night or even all night to get an aircraft ready or repair battle damage, so I did not care if their creases were not straight or the boots needed cleaning, providing their task was completed effectively and on time. However, tardiness, drunkenness and carelessness must be stamped on, but if an airman or, indeed, an officer turned out in a poor state for an official parade or function then he would be severely dealt with by me. As my two senior disciplinary officers, I relied on them to do their jobs while I was leading the squadron in the air. I found that I liked both very much and hoped that my trust was well placed.

I could see that my diary was already getting full for the following day, starting with a briefing for the day's sorties at 07:00 given by Jamie for the last time before I would take over the briefing duties for the next day. I was summoned to 2 Wing headquarters to meet with the wing commander at ten-thirty and in the afternoon was scheduled to meet with the squadron engineering officer to discuss operational readiness, serviceability and spare parts issues, followed by an opportunity to take my aircraft up for a short familiarisation flight in the vicinity of the airfield, just to get myself back in tune with it since it was over a month since I had last flown operationally. At four-thirty the padre was booked in to talk about pastoral matters and a social welfare issue in one of the flights. I was almost fearful to turn over the page to see what was already in the diary for the day after this, for I suspected that in my new role I would spend much more time flying my desk than in the cockpit of the SE5. I thought ruefully that ten hours a day in the office would not suit me well and resolved to find as much opportunity to fly sorties as I could get away with.

Jamie's briefing was thorough but succinct, and every pilot collected their briefing notes and maps of the target areas, signalling protocols and pre-determined courses to rendezvous with the bomber formations before the approach to the targets. 354 was again assigned to the high-level screen and would operate at 3,000ft above the bombers, to prevent the German fighters from penetrating through to the inner screen and onto the bombers themselves whilst engaged in attacking the targets. The bombers were to attack the canal network, docks, and storage warehouses at Hertogenbosch about twenty miles north of Eindhoven, where the Germans were bringing in fresh supplies of motor fuel for their tanks and ammunition by barge directly from Germany to resupply their new defensive line. The objective of the raid was to sink and destroy as many barges as they could, blocking access to the barge unloading docks with as many sunken wrecks as possible. It was well understood that this would only slow down, not prevent, the continued supply of these essentials for the German army but it would take some valuable time to clear the wreckage and debris before the docking areas became usable again.

A, B and C flights took off to join the bombing armada at around eight-fifteen, I retired to my office and Roly Holmes brought in two new replacement pilots who had arrived yesterday to join the squadron. When he ushered them in, I was struck by how young they looked, just a couple of schoolboys in uniform. They were Pilot Officer Gerald Graham, who we were to christen GG for short and Pilot Officer Digby Southern, who had recently graduated from the advanced flying school, but both had barely forty hours in their logbooks. They had both joined the OCTU straight from school and transferred to the pilot training programme after basic training. I was overcome by the huge responsibility to try to keep these two young fresh-faced lads alive long enough to see out the end of the war. They listened to me with great respect as if I was their schoolmaster. I remembered that Jamie always called me 'the housemaster' and I wondered what these boys thought when they looked into my face, as I was barely a couple of years older than them.

I asked Roly if he would inform the engineering flight to prepare two aircraft for them for this afternoon and they could accompany me on my sortie at 15:00. I told Graham and Southern to be in the briefing room at two forty-five in flying clothing and we would fly a familiarisation sortie for about an hour after my briefing. They seemed excited and grateful to be getting into the air so quickly and started thanking me, but I cut them off short.

"It's imperative I get a quick idea of how good your flying skills are'" I explained, "so that I can plan how we can train you to cope in the skies over the front line. The German pilots are skilled and brave, you will need to have your wits about you just to survive aerial combat for more than a few weeks and it is my job to ensure that you do survive and make it to the end of the war in one piece. You are replacing two men who were more experienced than you who we lost last week in action over the battlefield."

At ten-fifteen, I drove around the peri-track towards the No. 2 Fighter Wing headquarters and was looking forward to meeting Wing Commander Harcourt again. However, I was disappointed to find out he was no longer OC 2 Wing but had been promoted to group captain, posted to Second Army HQ and the new Wing commander was William Wells. He was accompanied by the group captain, who was delighted to see me, enquired about my wedding, and leave and then quickly got down to business. He told me that I was his first appointment and he had selected me personally to take command of the squadron.

"Jamie Dalrymple was senior in line for the job but although he is an excellent combat pilot, he does not have the same inner strength of character to lead the squadron as you do," he explained. "You have shown yourself to have exceptional ability to lead your flight in combat and to develop your men as excellent pilots too, but the thing that marks you out as superior is your commitment to get a job done thoroughly and to achieve the outcomes you desire, whatever the odds. The way you defended the infantry lieutenant in that recent court martial impressed me so much that I realised that you were the man with the determination to win and to win well. You will be pleased to know that Jamie was mightily relieved when I told him that I was going to appoint you to command 354 and he confided in me that he had been dreading that I might appoint him to the post instead."

Wing Commander Wells then gave me an overview of operations in theatre more generally before concentrating on the specific roles for 354 Squadron in particular. He shared with me intelligence that the Germans had moved ten squadrons of fighters from deep inside Germany to airfields at Zeist, Doorn and Culemborg, east of Utrecht and then Oss, Hertogenbosch and Veghel north of Eindhoven and at Geldrop, Hamont, Overpelt and Genk towards the south. He pointed them out on the big map on the wall and whilst he was talking the Wing intelligence officer joined us who was a fellow Welshman, Squadron Leader Gwyn Edwards, and the wing commander asked him to take over the briefing on what was known about these reinforcements. Gwyn explained in much more detail, and I was writing furiously on my note pad the key points.

"Some of the squadrons are reserve squadrons committed to the defence of the homeland and we suspect that they are less experienced in combat flying than front-line squadrons. I am disappointed that we are unable to find out too much about the personnel assigned to these squadrons, although the common feeling is that their pilots are very newly trained and have not yet been assigned to front line squadrons. However, four of the squadrons were much more experienced and had impressive records of operations over the Western Front but had been withdrawn after the abortive Allied offensive at Ypres in 1917 and committed to the defence of the German capital city. We do know that there has been some watering down of the strength of these squadrons to reinforce those still at the front, but we believe that most of their pilots are battle-hardened and ready for action."

I took down their squadron numbers and he pointed out where they were now based. He went on to explain that the main push would be centred on the line between Utrecht and Eindhoven, as it was believed that if this line collapsed the Germans would run to defend their borders from invasion and the whole front would implode. "Currently, the Wing is engaged in bombing escort duties but soon we will switch to attacking the German airfields starting with the ones where the more experienced squadrons were located. The objective is to severely reduce German capacity to challenge for air superiority over the battlefield and to assist your squadron in this task, four Sopwith one and a half Strutter fighter bomber aircraft are to be detached to 354 and placed under your command. This will enable your squadron to mount regular and mixed fighter and fighter bomber raids to cause maximum disruption to German air operations in the run-up to the next offensive, the date of which will remain a secret for the time being but is imminent within a fortnight. The detachment will begin from tomorrow afternoon and will include five officer pilots, five air gunners, SNCOs, twelve engineering flight crew – full details will be sent to your adjutant today so he can attend to victualing and accommodation before they arrive."

There was plenty of news to impart to the flight commanders and I now had my work cut out to plan the series of intense airfield raids jointly with fighter and bombers to destroy ground handling facilities, hangars, fuel dumps and as many aircraft as possible on the ground. I was busy as soon as I reached my desk and summoned the adjutant and SWO to brief them on the fighter bomber detachment arriving tomorrow, and to leave those arrangements in their capable hands. The engineering officer was briefed to find space for the four Sopwith aircraft and a bay for their engineering team to work, as well as space on the flight line so they could be easily refuelled and rearmed between sorties. I estimated that we would need to accommodate the detachment for approximately fourteen days so transit accommodation or tentage could be used if available.

I just had time to grab a hot drink and a sandwich before getting my flying gear and meeting the two young pilots in the briefing room, where we pored over the aerial chart for the airfield and outlined what we were going to do this afternoon. We would take off together in-flight formation and keep in echelon until we had climbed to 3,000ft. I would start to fly as if I were the flight commander and they would follow, in echelon formation, every move that I made keeping in close formation. I told them that I would simulate as far as possible the flying conditions on actual operations. 'When I'm happy that you can fly together and act as a member of flight,' I explained, "I will break off and you will try to track me and protect yourself from a surprise attack. I will try my best to out-fox your surveillance and jump you with a mock attack if I can." I stressed that they were not to fly straight and level but were to manoeuvre around in the sky, sticking together, although vigilance was the key word and that they were to look above, below, in front and behind to detect the presence of enemy aircraft.

"The attacking aircraft will make use of the sun or the cloud base and will come at you fast and firing from the direction that is the least expected by you'" I added. "Stay alert and keep looking for trouble all the time and even this afternoon, when we will be flying towards the coast between Antwerp and Ghent which is controlled by us, there may well be enemy aircraft in the vicinity." My last words to them before we went out to the waiting aircraft was that this was not a test which they would pass or fail, but an indicator of what they most urgently needed to learn before flying combat sorties with the squadron. They both nodded like eager young pups anxious to begin the game, but I hoped that when they were strapped in alone in their cockpit at 3,000ft, they would remember my words of caution."

I felt a sweet sense of homecoming as the engine of my aircraft sprang into life and I felt the familiar vibration tingling through my body and the pungent smells of the oil and exhaust gas which welcomed me back. I taxied out and we lined up at the runway threshold ready for the signal to take off. As the flare went up, I opened the throttle and roared across the grass to climb into the sky about 200 yards short of the perimeter fence and was pleased to note that the two boy pilots were in good formation behind me. Climbing steadily, we had achieved our operational altitude in under ten minutes, and I started a series of twists and turns, changing altitude, diving, and climbing and they seemed to keep with me well. So far so good, and I thought now we would go for the acid test so I signalled them that I was going to break formation, broke left and dived into the nearest cloud so that they would have to concentrate hard to see where I was going. This was a large cumulonimbus cloud and afforded me incredibly good camouflage to quickly change direction and to get into a position behind them and undetected. As I guessed they were much less confident flying on their own and their formation was much looser, and they were flying pretty much straight and level for too long. They had forgotten that just a few minutes before they were jinking about the sky, following my every move whereas now they were presenting a perfect target for any stalking German intruder to jump them with complete surprise. So, this is exactly what I did, and I watched their surprise as I simulated my first attack, which would have shot down at least one of them if I had fired my machine guns at them.

I flew off at speed to regain the safety of the cloud cover although this time I did not turn back, but sought altitude, climbed to 4,000ft and then came about and dived down through cloud to break out of the base about 200ft above them, about half a mile distant, still flying in a loose formation when I hit them from the front slightly offset but well-placed for a passing shot as I passed them at high speed. I circled back, signalled PO Graham to take the lead and take us in the direction of Vlaanderen, and I joined on the back of the formation. PO Graham didn't do too badly, and it was obvious that he was able to recognise symbols on the map and relate them to features on the ground, so then I signalled Southern to lead us back to base but after a few minutes I realised that he had no idea where he was and could not seem to orientate the map with the features, he could see below him. This was disastrous and meant that he was nowhere near ready to fly combat missions where the chance of becoming detached from his leader was high and the risk of him being lost over the battlefield was even higher. I took the lead again and led them back to Mortsel, then debriefed them before getting ready for the visit from the padre.

I had encouraging words for both as they had shown a good grasp of basic pilot skills and were able to fly the SE5 efficiently without any major mishaps, but they lacked a combat-ready awareness and the alertness required to keep safe in the air. I had demonstrated twice how easy it would be for an enemy to stalk them and catch them unawares. PO Graham showed more promise at this early stage, and I would be assigning him to replace Flight Sergeant Knowles in B flight, but PO Southern needed some further training and I decided to allocate a further five hours of combat preparation flying with me and Flt Lt Dalrymple to try to hone his navigation skills and combat awareness before allocating him to combat operations. I could tell he was disappointed so I called him back alone and explained to him that he should realise that I was taking this course of action not in any way as a judgement of his worth as a pilot, but simply to improve his value to the squadron by ensuring that he stays alive long enough to become a good fighter pilot. I recommended that he sought out Flying Officer Terence Bradby DFC and chatted to him about his experiences as a new pilot, who after a slow start had turned into one of the most successful pilots on the squadron.

"The last duty I ever want to perform is to write to your parents to tell them you have been shot down and killed in action. It is my mission to return all my pilots safe and well to their home and family when this war is all over. You will hear in tomorrow's briefing about our future missions as fighter bombers in waging a fast and furious campaign against the airfields where the reinforcement German squadrons were located to reduce their capacity to challenge us in the air. I need you to be confident and capable of flying in these missions and to be able to defend yourself and contribute to the effectiveness of the squadron." I could see he was still disappointed, but I thought he was beginning to comprehend what I was saying to him.

I certainly hoped so and was thinking about him as I changed out of my flying gear to meet the padre, Flt.Lt. the Reverend Tobias Wilcox who arrived five minutes early for his meeting. He was typical of an English country parson but in uniform; tall, thin, and rather gaunt looking but nevertheless he had a kind face and a soft way of speaking. When he took off his cap, I could see that his hair was receding. I guessed he was probably nearly forty years of age, and I could see from the campaign ribbons on his chest that he had served in the army during the South African War. I ordered a pot of tea to be brought and we sat together to chat about his concerns, but I asked him about his previous army service to put him at ease and get him talking freely. He had been a lieutenant in the infantry and had fought in the second Boer War, where his experience of warfare had helped him find his vocation – he had left the army to study Theology and was ordained in 1905. He explained that his family were of modest means so he was unable to purchase a comfortable living and had been forced to serve as curate in two parishes, hoping that he might be able to become the vicar of a less wealthy parish in time. In 1916 the bishop of his diocese approached him to become a military padre because of his previous army experience and he agreed and chose to come to the RFC thinking that a clergyman with military service would stand a better chance of become vicar or rector of a parish than an aging curate.

We then discussed the welfare of the men and his intention to hold regular services. Matins, evensong, and holy communion every day in the base chapel but he would like to request a church parade on Sunday mornings at 08:00 on the parade ground in front of the headquarters building. I agreed that this might be a good thing for the morale and spiritual well-being of the men but as we were entering the final phase of the war when the number of air operations each day would be much more intense, I would be reluctant to commit to such a regular event fixed on the calendar. He put up a strong argument that at the time of heightened pressure and greater activity it was just the right time to increase the religious expression for all men, so we compromised and agreed to a monthly service to be held on the main parade square subject to operational constraints. He was delighted and I got the distinct impression that this was what he had intended all along, then he went on to discuss half a dozen cases of airmen who were experiencing hardship through problems at home with children or bereavement etc. and sought to get approval for some compassionate leave requests and in two cases, some additional cash grants from squadron welfare funds which I was happy to approve. I found that I had quite warmed to the padre and realised that he was quite a character. I now knew that he was a skilled negotiator and that I would have to be on my mettle when he came with requests in the future. However, I liked him considerably and I felt that with his engaging personality he would be doing a good job among the squadron personnel. I asked if he had ever been up in an aircraft and he said he had not, so I offered to rectify this situation and to take him for a short flight in the two-seater trainer to give him a taste of what the pilots do when they take off on a sortie. He readily agreed and I said I would arrange a sortie for us sometime later in the week or next week, and our meeting was over.

I had completed all the tasks listed in my diary for the day but now spent an hour writing up the notes for tomorrow morning's squadron briefing, the arrival of the four Sopwith fighter bombers and their crews on detachment. I wrote memos to Jamie requesting his help with PO Southern and to Terence to ask him to have an encouraging chat with Southern too. I drafted the order attaching PO Graham to B flight with immediate effect to be promulgated in daily routine orders in the morning and a request to the engineering flight to prepare the two-seater trainer for a sortie for the padre within the next seven days. At six-thirty I left the office to return to the mess and realised that it was twelve hours since I had left for work this morning. Being a squadron commander was much harder than leading a flight in combat but perhaps a little less dangerous. After a passably good dinner I played snooker with Jamie, Giles and Terence in a foursome and passed a happy and contented hour before bedtime, for I needed to be fresh for the squadron briefing at 07:00.

The room was three-quarters full for my briefing next morning and I was pleased to see that the adjutant had rounded up the key ground officers to join the pilots to hear what I had to say. I gave them a full account of the intelligence briefing I had received about the location of the squadron reinforcements coming in from Germany to strengthen the aerial defence over the new battle front. I gave as many details as I could about the squadron numbers, strengths and their locations and requested that the intelligence section researched as much detail as they could for the more detailed sortie briefings that would follow in subsequent days. I then told them that I was about to impart to them top-secret information, which would mean that all leave would be stopped for the next fourteen days.

"The big offensive to break the German line between Utrecht and Eindhoven will begin within the same time scale. 354 Squadron has been specially selected to conduct an intense campaign against the airfields where the reinforcement squadrons are based to reduce the enemy capacity to resist in the air. With effect from tomorrow morning, we will conduct a series of intense fighter bomber raids on these airfields to crater the runway tracks and destroy aircraft and bunkering facilities on the ground. To assist us in this task a flight of Sopwith fighter bombers from 95 Squadron are being attached to this squadron until the job is complete. Each flight will have a fighter bomber attached to provide the bombing capacity. Our objective is to put these airfields out of action or seriously reduce their ability to operate, and to achieve this we will mount consecutive flight strength attacks in recurring waves of fifteen-minute intervals repeated two or three times each day as we have daylight extending well into the evening. Our targets are the airfields at Genk, Overpelt and Hamont, which are within easy range of Mortsel and are only twenty minutes flying time to reach the target from base. Each of the squadrons in No. 2 Wing will have a fighter bomber detachment and be allocated specific airfield targets and it is hoped our combined efforts will negate the potency of the German air defences. We do not yet know what kind of anti-air defences are in position around these airfields, but the Belgian Army are sending undercover soldiers to reconnoitre each airfield today and report back the defensive arrangements before the first raids begin. The 95 Squadron detachment will begin this afternoon, and we will reconvene at 16:00 here to plan tomorrow's raid on the airfield at Overpelt. In the meantime, flight commanders may begin initial preparations with their flights.'

Mr Skinner called the room to attention as I left, and I was comforted to hear an excited buzz of anticipation amongst them as I walked back down the corridor to my office. The pilots sounded excited and happy to be involved crucially in preparing for the final push. I knew this was going to be a frenetic and dangerous couple of weeks and I hoped that we did not pay too high a price in lost comrades and friends to secure air superiority.

I factored in a session with PO Southern at 11:00 to work on his navigation skills and we made a flight plan by marking off a series of waypoints to fly over the Scheldt estuary and into southern Holland, then returning to Mortsel over the city of Antwerp. Southern would fly as the formation leader and I would be his wingman, I would not interfere but follow his directions throughout. I warned him that once we were in Holland and returning towards Antwerp, we could be vulnerable as we were in range of enemy fighters so would need to keep a close look-out. I had ordered that our machine guns were fully loaded so we could defend ourselves, if necessary, when I would take over the lead to fight off any attackers. PO Southern did much better today and managed to lead me successfully through each waypoint, which made me think that it was probably nerves that had caused his poor performance yesterday. I was still a little concerned whether he would be quite so good if we were involved in wild manoeuvring all over the sky in dogfights, but thankfully our sortie passed off quietly without any appearance by the enemy and we landed back at Mortsel in time for a quick lunch.

Mr Skinner had requested that I deal with two persistent offenders who were currently in the cells behind the guard room. Both airmen had been punished by their flight commanders twice before, but this was a third occasion of being drunk and disorderly. Apparently when sober, these two were great friends and trusted mechanics but as soon as they started drinking together, they quickly fell out and started arguing, which usually resulted in angry brawling. Mr Skinner was sure that these two men needed a short but sharp shock to bring them to their senses to alter their behaviour. He marched them in together accompanied by Giles Lacey, who was their flight commander, the summary of evidence was read out and it was clear to me that there was something outwith the squadron that was causing this tension between them. Senior Air Mechanic Connelly and Senior Air Mechanic Faherty were both from Liverpool and had grown up together in a small village on Merseyside. I asked them was this why they were friends? They both agreed that they were the best of pals and were glad to be serving together.

"So why are you always fighting each other when you have been drinking?" I asked them. "You never seem to be violent or aggressive towards anyone else, drunk or sober, and when the military police are called to break you apart you are never violent towards them, but always submit to arrest quietly." I challenged them to come out with the truth and if their explanation was convincing it might reduce the seriousness of their punishment. They both hung their heads sheepishly but then Faherty blurted out that Connolly was trying to steal his girl, to which Connolly reacted that he was a liar because it was the other way round and that Faherty was stealing his girl. The truth was out and there was no way that I would be able to deliver a judgement that would resolve this case categorically. I was reminded of the biblical judgement of Solomon when the baby was cut in half, which would probably be the only solution. This was, of course, totally impractical and when I told them that I found the charge proven against them I knew we had to find a solution that would keep them apart in the future. They were marched out by the escort and Jamie. Mr Skinner and I had a brief chat about what we could do. I was determined that the charge was serious enough that they should be committed to the military detention centre for twenty-eight days with loss of pay and that whilst they were away, we would arrange to post one of them to another squadron in the Wing to separate them and prevent a recurrence of the brawling in the future.

This was agreed and they marched back in to hear their punishments. This nonsense took up nearly two hours of our time and whilst we were deliberating, I thought I heard unfamiliar engines, which I assumed was the arrival of the aircraft for the start of the fighter bombers detachment. Almost within a few minutes, Flt Lt Gerry Hamilton came to the office to report that his flight was joining 354 Squadron on temporary detachment. I took an immediate liking to Hamilton who had the build of a rugby prop forward, a broad Scots accent and hailed from Ayrshire. I called for Roly Holmes who had arranged their accommodation, I looked forward to working with them and would get to know them better at the briefing at 16:00 where he would get a chance to meet the four flight commanders and the pilots they would be working with.

The atmosphere in the briefing room was almost party-like, with an inquisitive interest in the new guests joining us for a few weeks and a buzz of excitement as everyone knew that this was a big operation. The sense of occasion was enhanced somewhat by the arrival of Group Captain Harcourt for HQ Second Army to give a short speech underlining the importance of this operation, which was to be called Operation Wildfire. He stressed the importance of our raids in reducing the effectiveness of the German air force responses to our ground offensive. The high command would be monitoring the effectiveness of the outcomes of the No. 2 Wing attacks on all ten airfields; this would be a major factor in determining the date for the start of the ground offensive. He went on praising the successes of 354 Squadron in aerial combat but now required us to put our great talents to the ground attack.

"I was proud to have commanded this squadron in the past and when I was No. 2 Wing commander, I remember your present squadron commander successfully destroying trains and ships and barges as well as shooting down many enemy aircraft. So, follow his lead and wreak as much mischief on your targets as you can. I know you will work well with the 95 Squadron boys but a word of warning to them, do not let the 354 boys lead you astray as they have been known to frequent some choice establishments in their off-duty time."

After this short pep talk the group captain shook hands with me and was out of the door to travel to the next briefing room, to deliver his pep talk again. We now settled down to discuss the business of our first raid tomorrow. The intelligence officer uncovered the large display maps of the layout of the target airfield at Overpelt and some smaller section maps of likely approaches for maximum surprise and effectiveness. This airfield was home to the 113th Staffel Berliner, a battle-hardened squadron with service on the Western and Eastern Fronts led by Major Otto Bohringer, who was a fighter ace with a tally of seventeen Allied pilots shot down. The squadron was assigned to the defence of the western approaches to Berlin but some of the strength of the squadron had been dissipated because of the attrition of pilots to reinforce squadrons still active on the Western Front. Nevertheless, the intelligence assessment was that they would prove to be formidable opponents, in the skies over the battle front, and their effectiveness needed to be reduced as far as possible.

The first sortie would commence at 06:00 when A flight would begin the squadron attack followed at fifteen-minute intervals by each subsequent flight, and the squadron would return to refuel and rearm by 07:15. The bombing and strafing targets were marked out on smaller maps given to each of the pilots, but it was clear that the bombers were to destroy the main hangar whilst the fighters were to strafe as many aircraft that were static on the ground and vehicles parked in view as possible. The second raid was to commence 09:00 with each flight coming in at fifteen-minute intervals again, but this time the bombing target would be to put as many craters as possible into the runway tracks to render them difficult for take-off and landing, whilst the fighters concentrated on the control tower and fuel supplies. The third raid was to be mounted at a time to be confirmed in the mid-afternoon after intelligence assessment of the damage caused by the first two raids.

The ground reconnaissance reports from the Belgian Army scouts showed that there were four batteries of high-angle anti-aircraft guns in the process of setting up but as of 00:00 this morning only one was complete, situated in the south-eastern sector of the airfield. It was estimated that the second battery would be in place on the north-west of the hangar by midday today and the other two by tomorrow. It was imperative to mount our attacks today before they were fully ready to defend the airfield properly and to approach the targets from easterly or westerly sides of the airfield if possible. If significant damage could be inflicted in raids one and two, the bombers could target the anti-aircraft defences in the third raid. Finally, it was made clear that while the fighter bombers had high-speed capability, they were less manoeuvrable than the SE5 so if we became engaged with enemy aircraft, the Sopwiths were to be protected at all costs. I explained that without them our attacks on the airfields would be finished, so to make sure they got home safely after every raid.

"Of course, each flight has four aircraft, and one section can escort the Sopwith fighter bomber whilst the other section fights off the enemy challenges if they come. Flight Lieutenant Holmes and I are available, in reserve, to fly if necessary and PO Southern will be assisting the intelligence officer in collating the incoming debrief reports but may be available to fly in later raids. Be vigilant and stay alert, as I need to see you all back home safely tomorrow evening. The camp is on lockdown, so I recommend an early dinner and straight to bed as aircrew breakfast is at 04:00 and take-off for A flight at 05:15, B flight 05:30, C flight 05:45 and D flight at 06:00. I wish you all good fortune and a safe return.'

I invited Gerry Holmes and his pilots to dine with me and my flight commanders at 18:00 and we had a pleasant opportunity to get to know them a little better before we set off on the venture tomorrow. After dinner I wrote a long letter to Ruby, cataloguing all the busy days since I had returned but kept quiet about the series of raids we were about to begin. I would be expecting some mail from home soon but wanted to keep Ruby abreast of what was going on here and emphasise that although I was being kept remarkably busy in my new job, I was at least safe.

I joined the aircrews for breakfast at 04:00, talked over last-minute issues that had come up overnight and ensured every flight commander was clear of his specific mission for the first raid. I took a little time to encourage PO Graham, who was setting out on his first combat mission and looked a little apprehensive. I told him that Jamie Dalrymple was one of the best pilots in the RFC, an exemplary flight commander, that he should stick to him like glue, and I looked forward to hearing all about his first sortie at debriefing. PO Southern had been told to stay in bed a little later for he would be working hard with the intelligence section to analyse the data brought back by the pilots after each raid and to collate the reports to be passed to Wing headquarters. I felt this was good that he would not be here to see Graham go off on his first mission and harbour any resentment that he was not involved in the actual attacks. I wanted him to understand that the intelligence analysts as well as the mechanics, the electricians, the wirers, the cooks, and the clerks were all essential to the fighting efficiency of this squadron, not just the pilots.

Right on time A flight were lined up in formation like mother hens around the larger two-seater fighter bomber placed at the centre of the formation, so that they would fly in a five rather than the usual two sections. Each wingman was now responsible for watching the back of his flight leader plus a joint responsibility for the fighter bomber. As A flight opened their throttles and roared down the runway, I could see B flight taxiing out from the dispersal towards the runway and taking up their position, waiting for the flare to go up to signal their take-off. I watched each flight take off from the command hut and then retired to my office to wait for the first aircraft to start returning. It was a strange experience being part of an operation but not actually being up there with the pilots facing the enemy alone in their cockpits. I hoped that I had done enough in briefing and preparing my pilots to complete the mission and return to base safely.

We all knew the risks and that every flight could be your last from enemy action, mechanical failure, or pilot error so, as a result, airmen were philosophical about their mortality otherwise why would they strap into their cockpits time after time to face this danger? I had never given much thought to the dangers we faced until very recently but my marriage to Ruby and our expected child had changed my mind considerably. Every one of the fine young men in 354 Squadron deserved to live and survive this war, to be returned home to their families when the war was over. I had now taken on the task, regardless of the imperative to defeat the enemy, to do my utmost to bring them all through this safely. I looked at the signals on my desk and was gladdened by the one laying on the top of the pile which informed me that Flt Sgt Knowles, who was shot down four days before, was alive and a prisoner of war in Germany. This was good news as this meant that he would survive the war and be returned home safely after the German surrender. I knew this news would cheer up the boys in his flight no end and I drafted a short letter to Knowles' family imparting the good news that he was alive and well.

At just after 06:40 the first flight returned and were rearmed, refuelled, and parked on dispersal ready for the second raid at 08:15. The pilots had a chance to stretch their legs and get a hot drink in the crew room for an hour before the off for the second time. I resisted the temptation to go into the pilot debriefing because I was anxious not to impede the work of the intelligence section, I was confident that they would report back anything of significance to me immediately. B flight landed at 06:50 and I was perturbed as I saw out of my window that only three SE5s and one Sopwith had landed together. Again, I hoped that we had not lost one of the B flight aircraft and immediately began to reproach myself for sending PO Graham out too soon. This time I could not stay away from the debriefing as I needed to know for sure and raced down the corridor to the debriefing area. The first person I saw in the doorway was PO Graham, so I was glad that he had made it safely back, but I was agonised to know who was missing. It soon became clear that it was Jamie Dalrymple who was missing but the accounts of the other pilots suggested that he was not shot down but had successfully fought off a challenge from two Storch fighters as we climbed away from the airfield, downing one in a ball of flames, and chasing after the second one at high speed towards southern Holland.

C flight had already begun to land and this time we counted six aircraft in the formation and realised that here was Jamie back safely from his jaunt over southern Holland. D flight came in just fifteen minutes later and went to the flight line to refuel and rearm. The overall debrief assessment was that the first raid had set the hangar on fire as three bombs had hit the structure but had not yet destroyed the building. It is not known how many aircraft were destroyed or damaged inside the hangar, but two Storch fighters parked on the hard standing were severely damaged by machine-gun fire. A and B flights reported little resistance from the ground defences, but C and D reported that machine-gun fire from the ground was more intense as the defenders got more organised. The anti-aircraft gun emplacement was not able to be brought to bear on us as we were attacking from the other side of the airfield, but they expected anti-aircraft resistance to stiffen as the day wore on. However, the Germans had a combat patrol airborne, and Flt Lt Dalrymple had shot down one Storch fighter over the airfield itself and one which crashed in a meadow about six miles south of Breda. There were no squadron casualties, several aircraft had been hit by machine-gun fire from the ground but were not put out of action.

The second raid was ready to go at 08:15 and was a straight repetition of before, meant to catch the Overpelt airfield in confusion and still reeling from the dawn raid this morning. However, the German air force had recovered well and were quickly on full alert, expecting a second raid to come shortly. The second anti-aircraft gun was now operational and provided some effective high angle shooting that coupled with the concerted machine-gun fire made the second wave more difficult to press home. The hangar was still standing, and the fire crews were still damping it down although the flames seemed to be out. There would be a need for further attacks on the hangar if we were to put it out of action permanently but that would have to wait until the raid later today as our target for this raid was the fuel and ammunition dumps on the far side of the airfield, and to try to crater the runway.

The first bombing run was at the aircraft fuel tanks on the eastern perimeter of the airfield and resulted in a direct hit on one of the large fuel tanks, which burst open, igniting the petrol inside which spread quickly to destroy the tanks nearest to it. However, there were two other fuel tanks situated a little further away that had escaped damage and would need to be attacked by the next wave. The fighters strafed a line of trucks parked in the transport compound but there were no aircraft on the hard-standing dispersals to be attacked. As A flight climbed away, they could see B flight were already homing in their bombing attack on the remaining undamaged fuel tanks but that they had not seemed to notice two Messerschmitts and a Storch fighter stalking them from the western side of the airfield. Giles Lacey did not hesitate but broke off with his wingman, signalling to his second section to escort the Sopwith back to base, whilst he fought off the surprise attack against B flight. Both Jamie's flight and the German attackers were so intent on what they were doing they were unaware of the threat to them, and this worked well in the favour of Giles and his wingman, who manoeuvred themselves into an ideal position for a surprise attack on the enemy fighters. Giles had opted for a side attack bringing the full force of their guns to bear in the hope that they may take down two of the German attackers in one pass.

They were closing in fast and still the German pilots seemed unaware of their presence. At one hundred yards, Giles squeezed the firing button, let rip a full four-second burst and could hear that his wingman was doing the same. The Storch fighter at the rear of the enemy formation took the full force of Giles' barrage and immediately bits were seen breaking off the airframe, the pilot lost control and it crashed to the ground almost immediately, whilst his wingman seemed to have caused severe damage to the tail of the second Messerschmitt which also crash-landed on the western grass, almost on top of the anti-aircraft battery. The first enemy aircraft tried to press home his attack, but by now B flight were aware they were under attack and broke formation to repel it. Jamie and his wingman rose to meet the challenge by diverting the attention of the German attacker away from the fighter bomber escorted by the second section. Jamie pretended to falter slightly to finesse the Messerschmitt into thinking he was experiencing problems, attracting his enemy onto him so that Southern would get a clear shot from behind. He hoped that his wingman would understand the ploy, for if not he might be dead meat. Jamie pulled back his throttle, lost speed and he pulled the nose up slightly as if he were going to stall which seemed to convince the German that he was going to be easy pickings. As he hurtled in with his whole attention on Jamie's aircraft, he failed to take account of the second SE5, which swung neatly in behind him about sixty yards back and opened fire with a full spread. The pilot kept his finger on the switch for as long as he could and told the debriefing officer that he was shouting at the top of his voice as he saw the enemy aircraft disintegrate before his eyes.

C and D flights encountered little resistance over the airfield and successfully put two craters in the middle of the main runway track, which would hold up flying operations for a few days whilst they were repaired. One of the D flight aircraft had to make an emergency landing in a field about halfway back from Overpelt, but behind our lines. Before he went down, he signalled his flight commander that he had a fuel leak and would not make it back to base. His section leader followed him down and marked on the map where he had landed so the recovery team could go out with the trailer and recover the aircraft and pilots safely. I was delighted with the results of the first two raids, we had only suffered minor battle damage and had one aircraft disabled. I decided that I would fly in D flight for the third raid to make up the numbers. PO Graham was shaking and in shock after shooting down his first enemy aircraft and although he was being congratulated and slapped on the back by his comrades, he seemed muted and perplexed at what he had done. However, Jamie took him to one side and thanked him quietly for saving his life and said that they would certainly go out to celebrate together when we got stood down from these raids. This seemed to calm him and enable him to see the shooting down with some perspective, and he brightened up. I congratulated him and asked if he wish to stand down from the third raid today and he told me firmly that he did not. The third raid went smoothly later that afternoon, the ammunition dump and supply store were hit successfully, and two more bombs were dropped on the hangar structure, which had now collapsed at one end and would have to be demolished because it was beyond repair.

I flew in D flight to replace the disabled aircraft, not as the squadron commander this time but as a wingman. It felt good to be back in the seat of my aircraft for combat flying and I was excited like a new pilot on his first operation. However, by two minutes into the mission all my trepidation slipped away to be replaced by professional attention to the job in hand. This was to be our third raid over the Overpelt airfield today and although we were certain that we had destroyed a fair number of the Berliner squadron aircraft on the ground and in the air over the airfield, we were not certain how many remained operational. The fuel tanks had been hit hard but the ammunition dump was still untouched, so this was our priority this afternoon. Some ground defences had been eradicated in earlier raids, but we were sure that the remaining anti-aircraft batteries would be in operation by this hour and would be expecting us. We were sure that they would have learned from the tactics we had employed in the two earlier raids and were hoping that we would employ them again, as they had seemed a winning formula. If the ground defence commander knew his stuff, he would guess that we would be going for the destruction of the ammunition dumps in these final raids and adjust his defences accordingly. The loss of both of his fuel and ammunition reserves put Overpelt out of action as a fighting airfield until further supplies could be brought in from Germany, whereas the craters in the runway were easily filled in within a day or two. D flight were the last to take off and would be the last to attack the airfield. We had been briefed to be prepared to adjust our target if we found the ammunition dump destroyed by the time we were in position, but we also felt that we might meet some stronger resistance from enemy fighters who would have had ample time to get airborne from neighbouring airfields to aid the defence of Overpelt.

Our forebodings proved uncannily accurate because as we neared Overpelt, still at 3,000ft, we could see below us a melee of SE5s mixing it with some Storch and Messerschmitt fighters in the vicinity of the target. We guessed that this was C flight and we wondered whether they had already attacked the target and were returning to base or had been jumped before they had attacked the target. The D flight commander signalled that he and his wingman would join the dogfight and assist C flight, and that our section would escort the fighter bomber on to the target as planned. I was a little disappointed because there was nothing that thrilled me more than engaging the enemy in aerial combat, but I had to obey the orders of the commander in the air. My section leader was a New Zealander, James Loveridge, who I knew to be a brave and resolute pilot and I was happy to follow his lead. We broke off from the flight formation and started our slow dive towards the target, which we estimated to be about four miles distant. As it was moving towards late afternoon, the clouds were beginning to form behind us. James wanted to use the clouds to mask our approach so the gunners would not be aware of us until the last moment. He took us right down to under fifty feet so that we merged in below the tree line, as there was a considerable stretch of trees behind our line of approach. This was a clever approach as he had reduced the effectiveness of the high-angle guns, which could not be brought to bear until we started to climb again but at the price of an increased vulnerability to small-arms and machine-gun fire.

He aimed straight for the ammunition dump, which we could see had been hit hard but was not fully destroyed and as we got closer, we saw that one of our Sopwith fighter bombers had been brought down. It had crashed through the perimeter fence but had not exploded, as the aircraft fuselage was largely intact. The crew were not still in the aircraft as both the front and rear cockpits were empty, and it looked as though the bomb was still attached to the underneath of the aircraft. Our fighter bomber pilot began his bombing approach, and I could see immediately that he intended to drop his bomb directly on to the downed aircraft, attempting to detonate the unexploded bomb with his bomb. We did our best to provide covering fire at the machine gunners defending the ammunition, but I kept one eye on the brave bomber crew who were in great danger of being caught up in the blast being at such a low altitude. At the last moment, the bomber pilot climbed and dropped the bomb from about 200ft feet with maximum power, in the hope that this would carry him clear of the blast in time. I saw his bomb glide straight and true and hit the stricken Bristol as he had planned. There was an immediate explosion as his bomb detonated, followed ten seconds later by a second explosion that was the unexploded bomb, and then a third massive blast as the ammunition dump erupted. There was so much smoke and debris we could not see whether our brave crew had survived, and it was a clear thirty seconds before we could see they were still just about airborne and climbing away to safety. We quickly reformed our protective formation and headed away from Overpelt to the east, before circling round to head for Mortsel. My personal instincts would have been to climb and engage the enemy fighters we had seen as we made our approach to the target, but the priority now was to escort our fighter bomber safely back to base.

Debriefing showed that our three raids against Overpelt airfield had been successful and it was out of action as an operational airfield for at least two to three weeks. The Staffel Berliner had lost eighty per cent of their aircraft, but only two pilots so had not been eradicated as a fighting force and would soon be back in the air with replacement aircraft. Our losses were light; two SE5s were shot down, one pilot and his aircraft were recovered whilst the other pilot was posted as missing in action. We lost one fighter bomber from C flight who was shot down on final approach to the target, but the fate of the crew was unknown and have been posted missing in action. On the plus side we destroyed seven Storch fighters on the ground, four in aerial combat and three Messerschmitt fighters from other units of the German air force in the air over Overpelt. Flt/Lt McDowell and Sergeant Air Gunner Davies are to be cited for the award of the DFC and DFM for their exceptional bravery in pressing home their low-level attack to destroy the ammunition dump completely. There was great relief that this raid was over, and I heard plans being made for groups to go to Antwerp and let their hair down in cafés and bars in the city. I received several invites to join with some of the parties, but I still had much to do, to write the reports for the raids and then liaise with the engineers about battle damage and serviceability and prepare the briefs for the second set of raids for later in the week.

The planning for the next raid on the Genk airfield began immediately and Gerry Hamilton brought into service his reserve aircraft and crew to bring our fighter bomber force back to four. There was lengthy debate about whether the single bomb raid was as effective as a combined raid, which could deliver a greater payload and destroy targets more effectively the first-time round. We decided that we would change tactics for the raids on

Genk, send in all four bombers against one target and use the SE5s for close protection and offensive action against the German air force. We had little detailed intelligence to work on about the layout and defence of the airfield itself, again the Belgian Army were reconnoitring the target for us and would report back to us on the enemy dispositions before the raid. The high-spirited intentions of painting the town red fell a little flat as many of the pilots were too overcome with fatigue after three gruelling two-hour sorties in one day. When I left my office and returned to the mess around seven, I found most of the squadron pilots gathered in the bar in more sombre mood, holding a wake for our lost comrades. I joined them a for a single drink and then knew that I needed to eat some dinner as I would be working all day tomorrow, so I made my apologies and took my leave to the dining room and early to bed. I had promised to take the Rev Wilcox for a flight in the morning in the two-seater followed by detailed analysis of battle damage assessments in the engineering hangar and a planning meeting with Glyn Edwards at No. 2 Wing about the forthcoming raids.

Towards the end of the day, I was going to take PO Southern up for another assessment sortie to see what he had taken on board during the past week. I had several letters from home to reply to, including legal papers to sign for the purchase of the Bedwas villa, which was likely to complete by mid-July. I was glad that the house would be ours before the baby was born and hopefully, we would be able to move in and get settled before the birth. My family appeared to be well and there was good news that Wesley had proposed to Alicia and she had accepted him, and they were hoping to marry next spring. Gwyn was still studying hard at the Mechanics Institute and had passed Part 1 of the Electrical Mechanician Certificate, which would qualify him to work under the supervision of an electrical technician who had passed the Part 2 examination. He was actively looking for a job where he could work with an electrical technician whilst studying for his Part 2 qualification. I was proud of him because he did not have the educational opportunities that were afforded to me and was forced into the mine when he was fifteen years of age. He would not give his notice at the pit until he had secured an electrical job. I was happy for him and respected how hard he had worked to commit himself to making life better for him and Mair.

TWENTY-EIGHT

Morgan's Orchard

Our raids on Genk with the four bombers making a concerted attack succeeded in destroying the hangars in the three attacks that day and creating a large trench in the middle of the runway, which would be a major task to fill in and level before flying could resume and the subsequent raid on Hamont was almost unopposed as the airfield appeared to be deserted. The success of the No. 2 Wing joint operations with 95 Squadron fighter bombers had denied to the enemy significant resources in the air and forced them to operate from airfields further behind their defensive line, which was restricting the length of time they could spend over the battlefield. HQ Second Army were pleased with the outcomes and judged that we had tipped the odds in favour of our ground forces by providing superiority in the air. Major tank reinforcements had been transported through Oostende and Antwerp to spearhead the push, which was to come at Eindhoven and pivot the attack towards the German border. There was a general air of confidence that this might prove to be the last big battle of the war, although there was little complacency that this would be an easy task to accomplish.

There was a clear understanding that the Germans would fight with everything at their disposal and even though they were outnumbered considerably by the Allied forces, they would defend their homeland vigorously. Heavy bombers continued to fly sorties daily, attacking communication hubs, major roads and railway junctions between the enemy defensive line and Germany to restrict their resupply operation. Belgian Army intelligence was carrying out undercover surveillance of the German lines and were reporting back numbers, equipment, and resources available for this last-ditch stand. The Belgian Army had reformed some units so they could participate in the battle to free their country from German occupation after four years of foreign rule. Our fighter bombing role was at an end, the squadron returned to flying combat patrols along the German lines and beyond, into the still-occupied territory. Our brief was to engage German aircraft and deter them from operating close to the battlefield but also to engage ground targets of opportunity when we observed significant enemy movements on the ground.

Jamie Dalrymple was promoted to squadron leader and posted to the advanced flying achool at Kenley as senior flying instructor. I was pleased to recommend Terence Bradby to take over as B flight commander instead, welcoming his promotion to flight lieutenant at the same time. I was glad that Jamie was being moved to a vital training job, which he very much deserved given his three years of active combat flying and sixteen victories in aerial combat. I am not a fatalist but perhaps a pilot's luck can run out with time. I was now certain that Jamie would survive the war and I hoped to continue our friendship in civilian life. The squadron officers managed a farewell dinner in honour of Jamie the night before he was due to depart for Kenley, which was an enjoyable and rumbustious affair as all the outrageous stories about Jamie's exploits were revealed. The following morning, I shook Jamie's hand and hugged him before he jumped into the Bentley with all his kit piled into the rear seats and drove off, out of the camp gates hooting his horn constantly on his way to Oostende and the ferry to England.

Digby Southern had learned fast under the tutelage from Jamie and me and had overcome his nerves. He was beginning to develop into a competent pilot, and I was pleased to assign him to C flight as section 2 wingman. PO Graham had been blooded a few days earlier, he had overcome the shock of realisation of the enormity of his first kill in action and was accepted by everyone in his flight as a brave and useful comrade to have around in action, christened GG affectionately by the whole squadron. I took the padre up in the two-seater trainer and gave him an hour of stooging around the sky, including some aerobatics that I thought might make him feel a little airsick. I had no such luck for when we landed, I could see from his beaming smile and florid complexion that he had enjoyed every minute of the flight and was looking for more. He could not stop thanking me for the opportunity to have experienced flight in such a small aircraft, which was an experience he would never forget. I was glad to have been able to give our padre the opportunity and knew that it would increase his empathy and understanding of the pressures on our aircrew, taking on the enemy in aerial combat.

The night before the offensive was due to open, I received a letter from Ruby who was a little anxious because she was entering the last six weeks before her due date and the doctor was concerned because her blood pressure was too high. The weather at home had been hot and humid with thunderstorms in the evening, and this oppressive atmosphere was awfully hard to cope with when nearing the end of pregnancy. The doctor wanted to book Ruby into the cottage hospital at Caerphilly for the birth to be on the safe side, but Ruby was determined to have the baby at home, attended by her mother who had enlisted the support of my mother also. I thought she was very brave to contemplate having the baby at home, but she said barring last-minute complications this is what she was determined to do. I expressed my love for her and how proud of her bravery to go into the unknown of the birth of her first child so confidently. I was not sure whether I could get a short leave to be there for the birth, but I expected that the progress or not of the offensive would determine whether this was possible or not nearer the time.

The whole of the Allied ground and air forces in Belgium and southern Holland were on stand to at 04:00 the following morning for the commencement of the attacks. The artillery barrage was to commence at 04:00 and was scheduled for thirty minutes, during which time over 200 tanks were moved into position immediately behind our lines, ready for the initial push forward to break through the enemy positions along a three-mile stretch of their front. These were not the deep and well-fortified emplacements of the Western Front in Northern France, but much more hastily erected positions, in some places little more than sandbagged shallow trenches which would not stop the advance of tanks, whilst in other sectors firmer defences had been erected. Behind the tank formation we had committed four brigades of infantry from twelve regiments to spearhead the push forward with a similar number held in reserve. 354 and all our aircraft were primed and ready to go as soon as it was light enough for us to operate safely. Breakfast was served to all personnel at 04:00 and we could hear the guns firing as we ate. Briefings were at 04:45, take-off was expected to be around 05:15 and we expected to be present over the front lines by 05:35 or so. Our endurance on the standard fuel tanks would give us about an hour over the battlefield on each sortie and enable us to refuel and rearm as often as was necessary, and to rejoin the patrol in flight formation throughout the day until our positions were consolidated or the advance was halted.

This was going to be an active day for us over the battlefield, as for those fighting for every yard advanced on the ground, and we would all be tired out by the end of this day. I led the squadron into action today and as we approached the battlefield in flight formation, spread out across a far acreage of sky, I could see that the tanks had done their job effectively and had broken through in many places along the German defences. Enemy troops could be seen retreating before their advance, whilst other sections of the enemy line had remained firm and already large numbers of British infantry were surrounding them to cut them off from the opportunity to retreat. My attention was caught by the flashing of a signal lamp, sending me a Morse message from the ground asking for the squadron to mount strafing attacks on the small village town hall from where it appeared that the German command centre was situated. I acknowledged with my light and led the squadron on a broad turn to starboard, at the same time detaching Terence Bradby's flight to fly aerial cover whilst the rest of the squadron dived on the German strongpoint.

I led the first wave of the attack and dived steeply at high speed directly over the town hall, firing a five-second burst of machine-gun fire. I could not hear the firing of my comrades over the noise of my guns, the screaming engine, and the wind through the struts as I pushed the aircraft to its limits; however, I could see from the damage being inflicted on this building that we were hitting the target hard. Tiles from the roof, the fabric of the exterior facings and broken glass were flying everywhere, and the German defenders had their heads well down under the hail of our bullets. There appeared no end for them as the next two flights repeated more of the same, and I circled around to assess the damage we were causing whilst A flight manoeuvred into position for another attack if this proved necessary. By now I could see that sections of the roof of the building were alight and smoke and flames could clearly be seen billowing out. Enemy soldiers were evacuating at great speed when the third flight roared in to attack the building, catching many of them out in the open. I could see that the defenders could not take much more of this and even as I led A flight back into position for a fourth pass, we could see that they had had enough and were surrendering, throwing down their weapons and putting their hands up in the air. The battalion commander flashed me a quick message of thanks as his troops moved in to secure this section of the former German line.

We had spent thirty-three minutes over the battlefield and only expended twenty per cent of our ammunition so could afford to look for other business. I swept the squadron eastwards towards Germany, keeping a close look at what was moving on the ground as well as in the air when Terence spotted a long column of men and vehicles heading eastward from Eindhoven. I signalled him to lead the attack on the column with the intention of destroying as many vehicles as possible. We came in low, two abreast so that we could sweep the column with the widest arc of fire as possible from behind so that we were not spotted until the very last minute, when the men began to break for cover. Sadly, for them, they were too late; many were caught exposed to the machine-gun fire, half a dozen vehicles were set on fire and the road was blocked. The second and third wave attacks concentrated on the stationery vehicles abandoned in the centre of the road and left them on fire with a pyre of black smoke curling into the sky. I recalled the fourth wave to rejoin the squadron and we climbed to gain sufficient altitude to make our return to Mortsel to rearm and refuel.

After thirty minutes on the ground to rearm and refuel and for the pilots to get a drink, we were back in the air to rejoin the battle and I vectored on to our sector just to the north-west of Eindhoven. It was amazing to see by just how far the Allied advance had moved in just a few short hours, and to acknowledge that the whole complexion of the battlefield had changed since our last visit here just over an hour ago. I could see the ruins of the town hall that we had attacked, and where the defenders surrendered was now several miles behind our lines – the column of marching Germans was moving again, but this time back the way they had come, into captivity. We kept flying towards the retreating Germans when a flashlight message caught my attention and we were directed to the area around the village of Veghel, approximately ten or twelve kilometres north of Eindhoven where our most advanced tank formations and following infantry had been held up by heavy attacks from German bomber aircraft.

I led the squadron around in a sweeping turn to port and climbed to 3,000ft to get a good look over the battlefield from a distance. From this vantage point we could see that the initial attacks were over and that there were no German bombers in sight. I studied my maps and tried to guess from which airfield they were operating and made a guestimate as to which direction the second wave of attacks would come from. I was taking a bit of a risk, but I felt I was making educated guesses about the German approach and placed the squadron at 4,000ft to wait for them to reappear. We had plenty of endurance and could afford to be stealthy in our approach. In ten minutes or so, our patience was rewarded when a large formation of German heavy bombers came into sight. I was amazed that the Germans had assembled such a large force within range of our tanks so quickly. We were unable to see any close escort fighters, but I ordered Giles Lacey and his flight to fly cover for us and to stop the enemy fighters coming down on to us whilst we attempted to knock down as many bombers as we could bag.

We roared down on to the bomber formation from above, catching them completely unawares. This was their second visit to this target, there were no fighters present before and they did not expect any now. It was like a duck shoot and I had signalled my pilots to pick their targets and we did just that. Thirteen of us screamed down on the first rows of bombers; ten enemy aircraft were hit and falling out of formation a long way short of the target. There were not enough of us to follow them down to destruction as we were immediately turning to engage the next rows of attacking bombers – six more were severely damaged and some were on fire. The bomber attack was breaking up and some of the rear-most bombers were turning and running for home, although some still persevered to press home their attack against the tanks but found themselves prey to our guns too and I saw several jettison their bombs and run for safety. We had managed to turn back a raid by thirty or more bombers and I was sure that we had destroyed or seriously damaged over half of them. The tank commander signalled that only four bombers had made it past us to drop their payload anywhere near their positions. We climbed away from this location, glad that we had stopped the raid in its tracks, but now looking for Giles Lacey and his flight was our priority.

It did not take long to find Giles and his flight, as they were heavily engaged and outnumbered by some enemy fighters although it seemed that they were putting up a sterling fight to even up the numbers. I led A flight into the melee, and we picked off two of the Storch fighters at the rear of the skirmish leaving Giles and his flight to settle with the other three. I did not expect to raise my tally, but now I had one more to add. The rest of this day passed without further incident although the squadron was able to account for the destruction of sixteen German tanks and five Storch fighters from one raid alone.

As the summer days drew on, the pace of the war slowed a little as the enemy seemed to hold back from too much offensive action, pulling back and consolidating their defensive lines almost in line with their borders running from Turhout to München Gladbach to Heerien in our sector. We were poised to begin raids inside Germany itself if the war lasted that long, although we would probably want to look for another base a little closer to the border to increase the range of our penetration if it was to continue much longer. Many on the front line of all ranks began to suggest that this was a job well done, although the Germans had not yet sued for peace. We were aware that the political situation in Germany was not stable and there were rumours that a revolution was brewing amongst the ordinary people that could take place sometime in the autumn, which would lead to an end to the war. The military forces were still doing their duty but were so hamstrung by the lack of resources that their ability to play an offensive role was seriously depleted. The Kaiser had lost the confidence of the army and many thought it was only a matter of time before he was replaced. These rumours were widespread, but it was difficult to know how truthful a picture they provided of the actual situation in Germany at this time. There was also an outbreak of inter-service jostling between the War Office and the Admiralty as to which of them would gobble up the fledgling new service and redirect the funding to the maintenance of our peacetime forces. They were already spreading much chatter that air power offered little to the Allies' success on the ground, whereas without the air superiority and bombing strategy of the RAF, the ability of the army to move forward without facing heavy resistance would have been greatly reduced.

However, I had greater worries on my mind than the political ramifications of ending the war for I had the imminent birth of my first child due around the 8th of September and I was desperate to be with Ruby when the child was born. This was becoming the most important thing in my life, and I badgered my new wing commander for a few days' leave around the birth. I had not been turned down, which meant that there was a hope that I might get a few days away from the squadron to be at Ruby's side nearer the time. If the lack of action continued into September, I was optimistic it would be approved. The summer rolled on and we were still flying combat patrols every day but with hardly any contact with enemy aircraft at all. It was as if they had withdrawn all their remaining aircraft for a last-ditch defence of the homeland itself. It was difficult to keep the men motivated and we organised cricket matches, football, and entertainments to keep them happy in the growing boredom. I was remembering the terrible unruly behaviour in St Omer by large groups of bored soldiers before the Ypres breakout six months before, and I was anxious to avoid any such behaviour within our squadron. One of the airframe corporals requested permission to open a sweepstake book on the weight of my baby at birth if I would approve at two pence a guess, which would raise enough money to give three prizes of £30, £20, and £10 pounds to the three closest guesses. I could see no harm in it provided it was restricted to members of the squadron only and it proved immensely popular, selling so many tickets that they were able to give a further £40 to the padre's welfare fund when it was all over.

I was summoned by Wing Commander Wells on the 3rd of September who told me that he had selected me to represent No. 2 Wing at an important conference at RAF Halton, the headquarters of the RAF, where Lord Trenchard wished to consult about a peacetime role for the RAF. 'The conference is scheduled for the 5th and 6th September,' he explained, "and I thought it would place you more strategically for your new arrival if you were already in Hertfordshire." I was ecstatic and had begun to work out how I was going to get across the channel and to the conference in time when he suggested that I take the two-seater trainer and fly to Halton directly, then I could leave the aircraft there pending my flight back after our baby was born. I was so grateful, and he handed to me a briefing paper from Lord Trenchard that was for discussion at the conference.

I wrote to Ruby immediately that evening and told her I would with her when the baby was born, although I knew that she would not have time to write back before I left for RAF Halton. I appointed Giles Lacey as temporary squadron commander in my absence and in the late afternoon of the next day, I took off in the Bristol two-seater with my kit secured in the front cockpit. I knew I had four hours' daylight but estimated that I could make it easily within three hours. The weather forecast was good, and the Bristol trainer had enough fuel to make the flight in one hop. By seven o'clock I was on final approach to Halton airfield, about thirty miles north-west of London. I taxied into the visiting aircraft flight, who took charge of my Bristol and would look after it until I was ready to fly back to Mortsel in a few days. A car took me across the main road to Halton House, the grand Palladian mansion that was used as the officers' mess, also housing Lord Trenchard and his staff. I was tired after my long flight and after a simple dinner, I went to my room and had an early night as I wanted to be fresh for the discussions tomorrow.

Lord Trenchard looked splendid in his Royal Air Force Marshal's uniform and after a few words of introduction, was quickly down to business. It was clear that the rumours that had been circulating through the squadrons were in the most part correct. The War Office wished to kill off the Royal Air Force and recoup the funds it believed it lost on the foundation of the separate air service and had managed to get the support of the navy in this quest. Their prime argument was that there was no peacetime role for air power, and the navy agreed because they believed that warships were not vulnerable to damage from aerial attack. He tasked us, in our discussions, to come up with a strong counter argument that highlighted possible roles for the air force after the war was over. He would leave us to discuss alternatives and would join us for dinner that evening, then all day tomorrow to hammer out our strategy. He thanked us all for our efforts and assured us that we were engaged in important work that would decide whether the Royal Air Force lived or died at the declaration of peace. He had set us a difficult task. We wrestled with this thorny question in small groups and all together before coming up with several suggestions. Our main suggestions were that air power could:

- speed up communications of mail and materials.
- bomb strategic targets effectively many miles ahead of the advance of ground troops
- carry out reconnaissance over larger distances.
- patrol over much larger distances than ground troops with fewer men and less equipment, more cost effective
- offer much greater fire power from one aircraft than the combined fire of infantry battalions.

These five suggestions could be fleshed out into compelling arguments for an effective air force in peacetime and all of us particularly stressed that when the peace came, who was going to police the peace? We all felt sure that peace would not mean a return to stability or an immediate end to fighting. We realised that the Allied governments would immediately want to release all the hostilities-only soldiers and officers back to civilian life, and pension off many older veterans who stayed on during wartime. The peacetime army and navy would be significantly smaller, and here we thought was a key point in our favour if we could convince the government that there were essential military roles that could be undertaken by the RAF more cheaply and effectively than by the army or navy.

Lord Trenchard was most convivial at dinner and made a point of talking with us all at pre-dinner drinks or after we had got up from the table. He came up to me and asked me, Tell me truthfully, which of those two beautiful girls did you marry? I hear on the grapevine that you are about to become a father for the first time'" I told him that I had chosen Ruby, the red-head, and he congratulated me on my choice although he said, "I seem to remember suggesting bigamy would be a better choice at the time. I told you, young man, that you would go far and the fact that you were the only young officer who brought two beautiful girls to his passing-out parade marked you out as different. You have proved that prediction to be right and I hope that you might consider a future in the RAF if it manages to still exist after peace is declared. I wish you all good luck and happiness with your baby," and he moved on to chat with someone else. I looked around the wing commanders and squadron leaders in this group and I thought that we were the cohort of officers that he hoped would help him build the peacetime air force.

The second conference day was just as intense as the first, as Lord Trenchard chaired each of the sessions as we built the detailed arguments around each suggestion that would be put to government ministers in due course. By mid-afternoon he thanked us for our hard work, said he hoped he would have the pleasure of working with us again, and the conference was over.

I had time to change into a civilian suit and hire a taxi to take me to Tring Station, where I could get a train to Reading to join the Red Dragon Express to Cardiff. Just after eight-thirty I was knocking on the Station House door and was admitted by Geraint, who was more than relieved to see me standing there. He said that Ruby was upstairs, and it appeared that the baby was going to come a couple of days early. I rushed up the stairs; Mrs Thomas and my mother were there in the doorway and said that her waters had broken, and labour would begin very soon, so they were so glad I was there on time. I wanted to push past them to see Ruby, but they stood firm and said that the birth was no place for the father, I should go and keep Geraint company before he drank himself into oblivion. Reluctantly, I went back downstairs and joined Geraint, but my mum called down the stairs that they would tell Ruby that I was there.

Geraint and I were like two cats sitting on the proverbial tin roof. We could not settle, and we couldn't keep tippling any more whisky or we might miss the birth altogether. Eventually, I dropped off to sleep on the sofa for about an hour and when I came round, I could hear from the heavy breathing that Geraint was also asleep. I went through to the kitchen and put the kettle on the range to boil water for tea for us all when I heard my mum calling me and I raced up the stairs two at a time. She calmed me down and said I was to be quiet, and she took me into the bedroom, and I could see Ruby sat up in bed clutching a small bundle and smiling with tears in her eyes. I went forward and Ruby said, "Here is our Alice," and then to Alice, "This is your father," and I was so full of emotion when I looked down at the small bundle in her arms. I know people always say they can see the likeness of fathers or mothers or grandparents in new-born babies, but I am afraid that I could not see any likenesses yet. She was just a tiny little bundle of flesh, still wrinkled and pink from her mother's womb but I knew that in the weeks, months, and years to come she would grow into one of the riches of Morgan's orchard of which I would be forever proud. Ruby was tired and the baby needed feeding, so I was banned again and went down to break the news to the first of the new grandfathers sleeping downstairs.

I was able to stay one more day before I needed to get back to the squadron, but in the morning, I looked over the deeds of the house Ruby and I now owned and took an early morning walk up the hill to view it again. It was a more imposing property than I had remembered and stood alone in a nice plot with gardens all around. The house was empty, and I was glad because it was a blank canvas for my new Morgan family to paint on. When I looked out of the kitchen window towards the back garden and I could see a small apple orchard of five or six trees, with fruit ripe for picking, I knew that this house would be known as Morgan's Orchard.